Old Loves Return

Old Loves Return

An Anthology of Hopes, Fun and Despair

by

Vice Admiral Sir Louis Le Bailly
K.B.E. C.B. D.L.
C.Eng., F.I.Mech.E., M.I.Mar.R.,
F.Inst.Pet.

The Pentland Press Limited
Edinburgh · Cambridge · Durham

First published in 1993 by
The Pentland Press Ltd.
1 Hutton Close
South Church
Bishop Auckland
Durham

ISBN 1 85821 071 2

Typeset by Elite Typesetting Techniques, Southampton.
Printed and bound by Antony Rowe Ltd., Chippenham.

Dedication

This book is dedicated to those leaders and workers in our once great shipping and shipbuilding industries. In the change from sail to steam and wood to iron and steel their innovative labour force provided the sinews of Empire. After the first, as after the second Great War, much of their handiwork and many of their people lay dead on the ocean floor. But after the second war as happened after the first, new ships were built and sailed again across the seas with 99% of the trade by which we live. The difference was that while, between the wars there had been neglect, after the second rebuilding phase there was deliberate destruction of both industries by statesmen who did not understand the importance of the sea to our Island race. So today only 2 of 115 Cruise Liners are British built and there seems no chance that the 300 super-tankers soon needing replacement will be born in our yards, while our fishermen are despised or spurned by Whitehall. Our pusillanimous rulers, hypnotised by a once uncertain ally and a vanquished enemy, apparently content to burden the nation with 3 million unemployed, oblivious of our maritime heritage, and just when conflict is imminent for the riches of the ocean and its floor needed for the world's exploding millions, seem bent on destroying the Royal Navy as they have already snuffed out our Merchant Fleet.

Contents

Contents

AN EARLY POEM BY RUDYARD KIPLING

The year wears by at last
The long days go
And pain is over past
And past is woe.
Oh friend, ill cannot last for aye!
Oh friend, the darkest night must fade away
Into dawn's glow

Old hopes are hard to kill,
Old passions burn,
Old strivings stir us still,
Old loves return.
Oh friend, ill cannot last through life!
Oh friend there is an ending to all strife
Whereto all yearn.

Peace for the aching brain,
Rest for the strained eyes,
When love returns again
And past joys rise.
When tired hearts are joined, true souls close knit
And Love is King, who changeth not a whit
When evil flies.

Oh friend the time is near
The dark is white
To sunrise – while the drear
Cold blank of night,
Kindles with dawn – have patience yet a space.
Ere God brings thy love to thee face to face
And all is right.

Published as an Appendix to *Early Verse by Rudyard Kipling, 1879-1889*.
Edited by Andrew Rutherford. Published by Clarendon Press, Oxford.
Reproduced here by kind permission of the Oxford University Press.

Acknowledgements

This Anthology would never have occurred if Mr Correlli Barnett, the famous historian and Keeper of the Churchill Archive, had not asked for my papers. I am grateful to him. And my wife, whose support I can never repay, is profoundly relieved that she's seen the last of them. My thanks also to Andrew Rutherford of the Clarendon Press for permitting me to use a line from one of Kipling's earliest poems as a title and to include the poem in my book. Mr Lyne, (late of the *Western Morning News*) kindly allowed me to use on the front dust cover the photograph he once took of me. It was Commander Sloan for the Director of Public Relations (Navy) and Mr Bishop, civil assistant to the Director General (Ships) in Bath who ploughed through and obtained approval for my original script which has given birth to *The Man Around the Engine, From Fisher to the Falklands* and now, much of *Old Loves Return*. Others in the MOD vetted my speeches at Leeds Castle and Chicago. To them all I extend my thanks and heartfelt sympathy in their ordeal.

My stint in the States under our then Ambassador Sir Patrick Dean gave me an abiding respect for the US Navy and the US Marine Corps. Louis Heren of *The Times*, Jeremy Campbell (*Evening Standard*), Ross Mark (*Daily Express*), Henry Brandon (*Sunday Times*) created for me a bond with their calling already initiated in the UK by Charles Douglas-Home, David Divine, Colin Welch, Clare Hollingworth, Harry Chapman Pincher and Nowell Hall. It is a pity for both professions that Service officers are now forbidden to speak to the Press.

It was in the States that I came into close contact with those clever men and women who run the 'Think Tanks'. Dr Chester Cooper and his wife Orah, David Abshire, Ed Feulner, Frank Barnett, Robert Pfaltzgraff, Jackie Davis, all helped me to appreciate on my return to the UK the wisdom of the late Professors Leonard Schapiro and Hugh Seton-Watson, Professor Laurence Martin of Chatham House and Professors Gutteridge and Wilkinson who, with the Chairman, Mr Frank Brenchley, contribute so much to the Research Institute for the Study of Conflict and Terrorism. The RUSI, its Director, Group-Captain Bolton, Editorial Staff and Librarian have been a constant source of help and advice. Lord Dulverton and Sir David Wills introduced me to the world of education.

This book would never have been produced if it had not been for Mr Daniel Russell of The Pentland Press whose patient responses to my often contradictory amendments earned my gratitude. Rosemary Rudd has the awful chore of trying to market it. As I do, my Bank Manager wishes her luck.

Unlike the other two Services naval officers never retire, but their duty done, remain in the inactive section of the Navy List until they depart this vale of tears. From the moment in 1928 when Captain T. H. Binney was rash enough to pass me into the Navy, unaware that I would come under his command in 1932 for my first year in HMS *Hood*, till forty-five years later when I worked successively, for the late Marshal of the RAF, Lord Elworthy, Admiral of the Fleet Lord Hill-Norton and Field Marshal Lord Carver, Lord Carrington (for the second time) and Lord Mason. I have had fun with all three Services, officers and others, together with those many humorous and normally brilliant civil servants, with whom or under whom, I have served. In this topsy turvy world where even loyalty to the Queen seems now to be questioned, Service life provides an anchor to example and leadership, which neither the Church nor the political establishment are able to do.

Foreword

by Air Chief Marshal Sir John Barraclough

Although I was complimented to be asked to write this Foreword it was not immediately clear why the author picked on me. His views are born of a long career in the Royal Navy, with the alarming dynamics of being bombed, torpedoed, and mined throughout much of the Second World War, finishing up in the highest reaches of the intelligence and administrative worlds some 30 years later; unsurprisingly this is a book with a strong naval colouring whereas I am an airman. However we do have an early, as well as a later, affinity in that I spent the war flying over the sea from the Arctic Circle to the Roaring Forties; frequently thanking God that with luck we would be home and dried before too many hours rather than struggling on interminably against the elements like the Navy below.

But it was in Whitehall that Admiral Le Bailly and I served together and also discovered mutual links with the West Country where he is now retired. It is from that fastness that he is still letting off cerebral fireworks about the ills of this world and the misgovernment of our country or, in calmer moments, just writing to The Times to lament the disappearance of sweetbreads from British menus.

In my time as Vice-Chief of Defence Staff my ever-tactful Military Assistant, when sensing that I was a little gloomy, would sometimes engineer a meeting with the Director-General (Intelligence.) In due course Admiral Le Bailly would appear on some trumped up agenda and ideas, thoughts, half-thoughts and strictures would come tumbling out of his head like sparks from a Wimshurst machine. If the rate of fire sometimes left the thoughts a little loosely connected that only heightened the stimulus of the encounters.

Readers may find that same ebullience, and sometimes its counter-vailing deflation, reflected in these essays and articles. Overall it is an anthology where the selection, so it seems, was somewhat of an after-thought while his papers were being consigned to Churchill College. So, not surprisingly, a continuous thread is somewhat elusive and Rimsky-Korsakov's Flight of the Bumblebee lodged itself obstinately in my head as I set about my task. But if I can impart to readers of this book some-thing of the flavour of this unusual Admiral, coupled perhaps with a mild health warning, then my duty and old friendship will both have been served.

But some themes – or old loves – do keep returning; the Royal Navy and its ships and engineering, defence and strategy, international affairs, the need for greater wisdom as man tries to manage his own output of new knowledge, seapower and world security, leadership and inspiration. Mr Kinnock gets guidance and Mr Major gets advice, while during his long naval career the higher reaches of the Royal Navy got a fair serving of both. The author makes good use of lateral support and his essays are embellished with many apt references so that this volume is also a quarry of engaging quotations and snatches of evocative verse. For my part, in addition to those articles of particular professional interest where some, with different backgrounds, may choose to go 'fast forward' until they hit the next nugget, I found the Remembrance Day Sermon at Rendcomb College especially moving.

On a different tack, I vehemently endorse the author's strictures on the need to prevent modern management techniques from stunting the devel-opment of leadership, and indeed of the whole person. I speak here with authority, as the only 4-star officer of the British Forces who is also a graduate of the Harvard Business School. While modern techniques are assuredly needed to manage modern technology and make the best use of costly assets; they are no more than the handmaidens of leadership in its paramount task of releasing the energies, and developing the loyalty and courage, of our fellow men and women. Pretentious jargon in Whitehall from those who know no better, and have perhaps never been frightened by anything worse than an opinion poll, must not be allowed to obscure that fact.

In pointing to so much that he sees needing to be done Sir Louis strikes a pessimistic note in his Epilogue. There is certainly plenty to be dis-turbed about in the governance of our country over the years. One can wonder, for instance, what has happened to the vast oil-wealth that has been flowing as an uncovenanted bounty in the last decade but finds us still with so much creaking infrastructure, or how it came about that we need to dispose of our brand new submarines and fighter aircraft to help pay pensions and defray other soaring welfare costs; to say nothing of our vanishing merchant marine and shrunken manufacturing industry. And so on, through the whole dismal litany of national decline, from the appalling failure of state education to the reorganisation of broadcasting which seems calculated to quicken the downhill slide of our once enviable television and radio services.

Depressing symptoms of these deeper ailments abound, as for example in the way our prelates of the Anglican Church seem unable to distinguish social deprivation from spiritual impoverishment; or, if they can, are content to ignore the latter. While, as a background to the flow of banalities from some of our politicians, we are treated to the unedifying sight of the Conservative and Unionist Party holding its annual cabaret against an emblem incorporating a mutilated national flag.

Those who share these sort of concerns will find much to admire and endorse in this anthology and probably plenty to provoke and annoy as well: but that is the way of the bumblebee. You have been warned.

July 1993

Author's Preface

Sir George Mallaby, under whom I worked when he was Secretary-General of the Brussels Treaty Organisation, then located in a half (bomb) destroyed 36, Whitehall, later published a book entitled, with typical modesty observing that he had been Assistant Secretary to the War Cabinet, *From My Level*.

After the surrender of the Japanese in Tokyo Bay, as a young lieutenant I found myself, greatly to my surprise, an acting commander in the engineering specialisation and 'Chief Engineer' of the Fleet Flagship. The Commander in Chief, Admiral Sir Bruce Fraser bade me give him a 'worm's eye' view as to why the mobility of the British Fleet was so much worse than that of the US Navy; and that story has been told in *The Man Around the Engine* (Kenneth Mason) and *From Fisher to the Falklands* (Marine Management (Holdings) Ltd.).

The report which the C. in C. despatched with his blessing was not at all well received by either the Engineer in Chief or the Director of Naval Construction. Indeed, had the former, who had worn himself out carrying a technologically backward navy through the war, not retired shortly after its end I might have received permanent excommunication. Happily his successor allowed me back into the fold.

Recently Mr Correlli Barnett, Keeper of the Archives at Churchill College, having read my two books asked me if I would leave my papers to his archive. To my wife's relief I agreed and the papers, such as they were, have gone to Cambridge. But in the sorting even I was surprised at the volume of unsought (and mostly unaccepted) advice I had seen fit to inflict on my elders and betters since Admiral Fraser set me on that perilous path.

Whether (to me) these gems of wisdom led ultimately to my exclusion from the Navy into the (civilian) post of Director General of Intelligence at the Ministry of Defence, I shall never know. Marshal of the Royal Air Force Lord Elworthy, in giving me my charge told me, 'Your job will be to tell those who won't listen all the things they don't want to know. It's something you seem to be pretty good at.' But of course I left all those pessimistic intelligence prognoses behind me when I finally left the MOD.

After a period on the Civil Service and Police selection boards and a further stint as Chairman of Governors of an Independent School, I had knocked all my papers together into a book I hoped to call *From Fisher to the Falklands*. I intended that it should contain some naval administrative and technical history of the last forty years in which I had been involved, together with a fairly lighthearted personal résumé of my activities during my fifty years of service. Over the many succeeding months I learnt patience as the MOD cleared my manuscript, and also that publishers, though always polite, clearly preferred spy thrillers or records of sexual delights to stories of war and peace. Kenneth Mason was the exception and his scrupulous editing restricted *The Man Around the Engine* to my personal biography. To my great surprise the Institute of Marine Engineers asked if they might publish the remainder and Kate Williams' gentle touch eventually produced *From Fisher to the Falklands*, albeit in a more technical mode than had both books been in one volume, as I had originally intended.

In sorting my chaotic filing system for Mr Barnett and in an excess of vanity I decided to publish an anthology of a small selection of those papers, memoranda, speeches and lectures which, at one time or another had been cleared by the MOD and had provided the bases for my books, together with those appendices which the Editors had excluded.

Then came the problem of what to call such an anthology. But fate, in the shape of Andrew Rutherford and the Clarendon Press brought to my attention an early poem by Rudyard Kipling whose works I have enjoyed all my life. One half verse particularly interested me:

> *Old hopes are hard to kill,*
> *Old passions burn,*
> *Old strivings stir us still,*
> *Old loves return.*

Those lines seemed to meet so well what I had unearthed. 'Old Hopes' that I might see a return to the maritime heritage that made this Nation great. 'Old Passions' roused, as they frequently still are when, as I believed, my views were cravenly disregarded. 'Old Strivings' on the dining room table, giving way ill-temperedly to my patient wife's need to lay the lunch before feeding our family. 'Old Loves' as particular items brought back happy memories of battles fought and sometimes won but generally lost. All these could have provided a title. But I've enjoyed it all so I chose the latter.

Only two pieces are frankly political. Mr Kinnock, when Leader of the Opposition, seemed to me to be either ignorant of, or badly briefed on, the reasoning behind our nuclear deterrent. And, in a letter, subsequently published and distributed widely by *Aims of Industry* I sought to put the facts clearly before him. Mr Major's government, like most Tory governments that I have supported in the past, seems totally blinkered as regards maritime affairs. And so, as too often happens under such administrations, shipping, shipbuilding, (just as cruise liners and 300 super tankers both need replacement) fishing and the Royal Navy (and with Mr Major's administration coal too) are thrown away. If the Maastricht Treaty is ratified then it seems that our Queen and our parliamentary democracy will likewise be discarded or marginalised.

The policies inflicted on to a stagnant Navy in the first decade of the century by Admiral Lord Fisher have been of absorbing interest to me for the last forty years. He tried, and was succeeding, in moving an unwilling and over conservative Service towards the industrial revolution. And had he not done so we would have lost World War 1. Nevertheless, an unwise Board of Admiralty, despite the efforts of Earl Beatty to find some compromise, abrogated the Fisher reforms in 1925 and consigned the Navy's engineering specialists to a position where they could no longer effectively influence their seamen colleagues in matters technological, thus rousing again the mutual antagonism between the two groups, which Fisher had sought to assuage. And these decisions ensured that lives and ships would be needlessly lost when Germany once more sought world hegemony.

By 1945 all officers from Vice-Admiral to senior Captain were products of the original Fisher scheme and, in Admiral of the Fleet Lord Fraser, Third Sea Lord and Controller (responsible for material) in the pre-war and early wartime era, C. in C. successively of the Home Fleet, the East Indies Fleet and the British Pacific Fleet, they found a leader who thought as they did.

The Noble, Nihill, Montague, Geddes, Mansergh and Murray Committees (amongst others), on three of which I served as assessor or secretary and the first of which allowed me to give evidence, clearly discerned and once more recommended the lessons which Fisher had taught, albeit in a modern context. The war experienced Boards of Admiralty, now with political backing, restored the Fisher philosophy that all officers should possess: 'Some community of knowledge and a lifelong community of sentiment.'

The phrase 'community of knowledge' was interpreted as a need for all naval officers to have technological education, on which the US and Soviet Navies, following the Fisher concept, had long insisted. 'A lifelong community of sentiment' was seen (by Mansergh and Murray) as 'Identical Training' to be followed by 'Common Training' (specialist training but in the same establishment) for as long as possible.

To move the small (RN capacity only 80 officers) Royal Naval Engineering College in Devonport to a new site capable of expansion at Manadon outside Plymouth was decided by Admiral Sir Reginald Henderson (who died from overwork and was succeeded by Admiral Fraser as Controller in the immediate pre-war years) as part of the answer to the technologically backward Navy they were trying to get ready for war. And through the war years both colleges were found to be essential to a vastly expanded Service.

After the war Mr Attlee's government saw an even wider role for the College, embracing the training for deck and engineer officers and designers for the shipping and shipbuilding industries. And Sir Stafford Cripps, as Chancellor, approved the project in principle. The funding was delayed due to expenditure on a British nuclear weapon and the Korean War, but just before Suez (1956) a Tory government released money for the building to commence in earnest, although the Treasury forbade its wider use for the shipping and shipbuilding industries, the latter then dying for want of graduates.

Although Admiral Sir William Fisher, a great leader of men, after the Invergordon Mutiny (1931) advocated the adoption by the Navy of a regimental system whereby the officers (after Dartmouth or Public school entry) and ratings would serve together and become (in Drake's words, enshrined by Mansergh), *all of one Company*, the Naval Staff jibbed and no action resulted. Thus, after Mansergh (1956), Manadon became the core establishment where deck and engineering officers could develop some community of knowledge and a lifelong community of sentiment, analagous to that an Army officer absorbs in his regiment or an RAF officer in his squadron.

So I have sub-titled this book AN ANTHOLOGY OF HOPES, FUN AND DESPAIR because the Government shows no sign of looking to the sea and every sign of entering an incestuous European Federation. While the Navy Board, weakened by the lack of any political spokesman, bullied by politicians (whose financial incompetence and a naive belief that world peace is round the corner, are cutting the Services to the bone) has agreed to abolish Manadon and, with it, all those lessons learnt at such a cost in blood and treasure between 1939 and the end of the Korean War; abandoning indeed the one Establishment and all the World War II lessons which made the Falklands victory possible.

RECENT ARTICLES

FUN, STYLE, EXCELLENCE

General de la Billière's book and David Gower's autobiography, the latter recalling the above inscription on the plaque he received when 'Batsman of the Year' in 1982/3, led me to some philosophical ruminations on how much these three qualities led to leadership; and how the absence of a sense of fun was the most important in these days to a sense of discipline.

I recalled that the young and older civil servants with whom I had served almost all had these three qualities in abundance, but that I found them often lacking in the candidates I interviewed when on the Civil Service selection board.

I went on to suggest that the current emphasis on 'Management' was just beginning to cause young naval officers to reduce their prime function of developing 'leadership' skills and, if pursued, however excellent the financial accounting, would lead to a dullness and a lack of fun and style such as I had found in the Civil Service candidates.

This led me to the idea that the abolition of National Service, however much it had helped to produce the superlative Services the Nation now possesses, was, by the lack of training and discipline it gave to a vast segment of the population, leading to a lack of cohesion in our society. I tried to sum up the problem by suggesting that the assault course was preferable to the racing of stolen motor cars – and with hindsight I might have suggested adventurous training was as well.

By coincidence our local lending library produced two books for me for Christmas whose stories could not, prima facie, be further apart, but which I came to believe, however unlikely, complemented each other. They were General de la Billière's *Storm Command* and David Gower's autobiography.

The former is in many parts a sombre document. It tells the tale of a continuing battle between the General in the field aided by the Operation Commander at High Wycombe on the one hand, and the civilian denizens of Whitehall (and in fairness political and service organs as well) who, once bitten financially by the Falklands, (and though it was fairly obvious that the Gulf States, as they have and more, would reimburse Britain) fought bitterly on cost grounds against every requirement of those facing a very fearsome battle.

Mrs Thatcher's diktat during the Falklands was, '*If we've got it, you can have it*'. No doubt if she had not been dismissed that would have been the case again. Certainly it was clearly the policy of General Sir Peter Inge who gave unstintingly from every resource at his disposal in BAOR, as did the RAF with Tornados, Jaguars, Phantoms, Hercules, tanker and reconnaissance aircraft. The Navy, from the General's account, was a bit more stingy in their provision of resources. The carrier which he felt was necessary as a flagship with superlative communications for the Commodore (who, to help in his dealings with the US Forces and certainly for his own responsibilities should surely have been personally uprated, even if temporarily) was denied the British tri-service commander. This failure was due in part perhaps to a lack of enthusiasm by Whitehall and, more than likely, because the US Navy department in Washington DC, has never been attracted to the Harrier to the same extent as the US Marine Corps. The less conservative US Admiral on the spot seems to have welcomed the idea of any such reinforcement. But the gap between General Schwarzkopf and his staff, already disturbed by the volume of US naval support, and the traditional gap between the US Army and Navy made liaison more difficult than that happily existing between General de la Billière and Commodore Craig.

Our successors will have to examine the relevant documents before a balanced judgement can be made as to whether the fault for all the arguments lay with the Secretary of State, the new and inexperienced Prime Minister (whose visits General de la Billière reports did so much for morale), the Commander of the Operation at High Wycombe (who had the benefit of frequent visits to the scene of action denied to Admiral Fieldhouse in the Falklands) or whether the CDS of the day failed to exert the extraordinary influence on possibly an equally petrified War Cabinet, as closely as his Falklands predecessor managed to do – or was it just the absence of Mrs Thatcher, whose dismissal, the General records, astounded and discouraged all those in the Gulf? These matters will have to await the judgement of future historians.

Anyway, in all elements of the Home Front there seems to have been, though on a far greater scale, the kind of shirty attitude which David Gower suffered at the hands of the selectors. In both cases rather grey and faceless men with a wholly unimaginative appreciation of what was needed or what could be accomplished, seem to have held the whip hand.

Discipline

On the first page of his book Gower recalls that his most prized possession, with words that he would like on his grave, was the plaque he received when 'Batsman of the Year' in 1982/83. The inscription read: 'FOR FUN, STYLE, EXCELLENCE.' Looking back over my 60 years since I first went to sea, *fun, style and excellence,* these three words, might well have been in the minds of Admirals Kelly, James, Fisher, Chatfield, D'Oyly Lyon when they restored discipline and prepared the Navy spiritually for war between the Invergordon Mutiny in 1931 and 1939. And how much more are they needed in the homogeneous services society of today. Indeed perhaps they can be expressed in one word: *Discipline.* So were they also in the mind of Admiral Sir William Fisher, where the discipline in his Mediterranean Fleet was a byword in the Navy of that era, when he wrote:

> Our best and indeed our only bulwark against any of the tendencies of today that go to undermine law and order is the fuller recognition by officers of *Noblesse Oblige*, and that, when a condition of mutual trust and respect between officers and men has been attained in a ship, administration shall make in possible for it to be carried on as far as is humanly possible.

Was such a philosophy also held by General de la Billière who, when with his own experience as a 'Battle Casualty Replacement' (BCR) in Korea, he spoke to the BCRs in Jubail, and charged the young officers with direct responsibility for the morale of that inevitably depressed group waiting to step into dead or wounded men's shoes?

Fun, style, excellence must be at the heart of the Army's performance in Ireland and in the desert. When I was the tri-services Director General of Intelligence I was asked to arrange for a newly joined European defence attaché, with much battle experience, to visit the army in Ireland. As the

RAF flew us back through a snowy night he predicted, 'No army can stand for long the sort of conditions you are asking your men to undergo'. Three years later (eighteen years ago), when he came to see me to say 'farewell' he recalled his words adding, 'None but the British Army could continue that battle and still maintain their morale which to me was so very obvious.'

In the desert, many elements of the army spent six months with no action, much hard work, acute discomfort, no alcohol, no bright lights, constant threat of chemical or biological attack. How, I wonder, did Brigadiers Cordingley and White (the latter in Jubail) and their officers (for both they and their commands were there for the full period) manage it? Or for that matter, Lieutenant-General Rupert Smith, the Divisional Commander and Brigadier Hammerbeck, both tossed in at the last moment, the latter with a Brigade whose units, or many of them, had to get to know each other, to be acclimatised, retrained and made ready for a quite novel form of battle, all within six weeks. Style and excellence have long been hallmarks of the British Army. But how, amidst all the labour and hard living, did they and their officers create some fun, without which good discipline and high morale will always wither? Surely it is the same, as I write, with the Cheshires and their CO in Bosnia. The dull grey men in the MOD, it is reported, have already reprimanded him for creating fun, which he knows full well is the basis of good discipline, so essential in the appalling conditions he and his soldiers face.

The basis for leadership

In that secret of *fun, style, excellence* as the basis for discipline, lies the answer to leadership in today's world. It is too often forgotten that the object of true discipline in all three Services (deriving from those three elements rather than intimidatory Acts of Parliament) is to inspire men with bravery, firmness and with a sentiment of honour. And what politicians and those with the purse strings too often forget is that Services so disciplined are less expensive to the State and, even more important in this increasingly anarchic and crime ridden age, provide the State with citizens who, on their return to civil life will be a much needed strength to the community. This is a factor in the cost of training the Services which is always grossly undervalued by politicians, the majority ignorant of the value of service training, anxious always to economise and gain votes; as well, of course, by the civil servants who have to answer to them.

It may well be that it is this lack of fun and, in particular, a sense of fun, (the one element in the three which is the factor whose absence negates the other two) which therefore contributes to the grey, budget dominated, and (in the case of the cricket selectors as well) hypnotic spell created by that buzz word of today: 'management'. This surely is the main, or one of the main causes of our national troubles. Yet certainly as regards the civil service that was not always the case.

I write only as a naval officer, but also, after leaving the active list, as a chairman for nearly five years of some of the Civil Service Selection Boards (CSSBs), founded on the War Office Selection Boards of fifty years ago and run (overrun I would say) entirely by the psychologists. Having also served closely with the Civil Service in Western Union, in the Admiralty, in various independent committees, in the United States and in the Ministry of Defence, I have worked under or closely with executive officers, young principals, intelligence research and scientific officers and indeed the whole gamut up to permanent secretaries and secretary of the cabinet. In such labouring I have rarely found those three essential elements *fun, style and excellence* altogether missing in any of them. Yet with one major exception I find it difficult to recall in the late 70s when I was on the CSSB any civil service candidate who possessed those essential qualities which many years acquaintanceship had convinced me made the best civil servants. Perhaps I was just unlucky. Some of my chairmen colleagues were happier – but by no means all.

Too much excellence

On looking back, brilliant as the psychologists and their selection procedures may be in theory, I can see that they often judged academic and intellectual *excellence* correctly, but for *style* and *fun* they seemed unable to produce any yardstick. In some cases they seemed positively to mistrust such qualities when the independent chairmen, such as I was, maintained that those qualities were present in such abundance that less than fully satisfactory marks in the rather artificial academic part of the tests should not always be the main deciding factor as to ultimate suitability. And when, by chance, a couple of years ago, I met the parents of the one exception referred to above, I learnt that after doing brilliantly in his early career for some years, he had left the Civil Service as he found his life so dull. It can't be, as another chairman replied to whom I spoke about a particular candidate, 'Well what can you expect of a Wykhamist and a tee-totaller?' There have been plenty of the ilk who resolutely pursue *fun, style and excellence*, though perhaps fewer are teetotal. The Admiralty was always reputed, with the exception of the Treasury, to have had the pick of the Home Civil Service. Most civil servants that I knew there had Balliol or 'Univ' backgrounds and some may have been Wykehamists though I met no teetotallers. But one and all, besides intellectual excellence had style and certainly a huge sense of fun. In the old Admiralty too, although all of them were outstanding, the few (compared I think to many in the other Services) became not only fast friends with the Admiralty uniformed staff, but also accomplished Whitehall warriors. This enabled them often, to take on and convince their cold, dilettante and allegedly more objective Treasury colleagues what in fact was the best possible course of action in the national interest. Perhaps the most terrible mistake is the constant movement of civil servants between the departments of State.

The story of the fly and the flea and the elephant also seems to me to be appropriate. As Mr Fly met Mr Flea on the elephant's tummy and gazed at the view, the former remarked, 'There you are Mr Flea, what did I tell you, the bigger the organisation the bigger the balls.' There is much to be said for the old civil service organisation and perhaps those I found so dull would have blossomed in a small group serving a particular department for life with a well ordered departmental promotion pyramid.

Management dullness

If I am correct what worries me is that the creeping paralysis resultant on the injection in the late 70s into the vast administrative civil service of so much, as I saw it, dullness, (for so many of the candidates were looking for a safe haven away from the stormy world) is spreading by means of the often misunderstood word 'management' into the three Services. This dullness could be accentuated in the Services by too much petty accounting, too much time spent on short term cost analysis, too much delegating to inexperienced officers who should be developing their leadership skills, a task more difficult than ever in the homogeneous society in which we live. It would not perhaps be putting it too strongly to say that this emphasis on management, even if it is served up as 'man management' (something entirely different to leadership) is what is afflicting not only our industrial but also our political leadership.

As regards industrial leadership, I have no doubt that any Army or RAF officer of my vintage could quote many similar cases to the following naval examples of brilliant industrial leadership derived from service training, which spring to mind of many naval officers when industrial success is mentioned. Commander Craven pulled Vickers up by its boot straps. Harvey Jones likewise with ICI and many other firms since. Donald Pepper of Rolls-Royce Nuclear, Platt of BP Tankers. I only know, personally, two of those four; but from what I have read of the other two, fun, style and a sense of excellence means a great deal to all of them.

Certainly the old ways did not always prevent cost over-runs. These are always bound to happen. Again I speak only of the Navy I know. But very very few, whether civilian or serviceman, attending a Controller's 3–day annual Finance meeting to look at the money needed for the design and building and maintenance of the Fleet could escape with unwarranted expenditure amongst the thousands of items scrutinised by the Admiral and his personal monitoring staff. What Stores Petty Officer in a ship could ever escape with an unapproved expenditure of cotton waste? What Chief Stoker (or his modern equivalent) responsible for fuel expenditure could not suspect the beginnings of a fuel allowance overrun without warning his superiors? What responsible senior officer in any Fleet could ever get away with expenditure unauthorised by the Command Secretary? Why, if not for reasons of strict financial control, did we, as midshipmen have to purchase Brasso for our picket boat funnels, rendered green from inevitable spray, out of our pay of 5/– a day? And what of the Polaris project completed to time and well within the estimated cost?

All that was *fun,* had *style* and produced *excellence.* But in those days strict financial control was well exercised without the bureaucrats who have erected the Department of Management and Budget, whose (I would allege) malign and time consuming influence seems bent on destroying the elements of good discipline, the maintenance of which in the Services, is an all absorbing occupation called 'leadership'; or in plain language: 'knowing how to motivate people by a mixture of fun, with style and an insistence on excellence, to fight or to lay down their lives for a cause.'

'Alas, alas for England'

The tri-Service pattern is here to stay and the means of confronting a threat to peace is all the better for it. But in the process of change, compounded by political 'I know bests' the decision making has got into the hands of men who will not have to do battle. Politicians and civil servants particularly should heed the words of John Stuart Mill when dealing with the Services:

A state which dwarfs its men, in order that they may be more docile instruments in its hands even for beneficial purposes . . . will find that with small men no great thing can really be accomplished.

Perhaps however G.K. Chesterton put it best:

> The men that worked for England
> They have their graves at home:
> And bees and birds of England
> About the cross can roam.
>
> But they that fought for England,
> Following a falling star,
> Alas, alas for England
> They have their graves afar.
>
> And they that rule in England,
> In stately conclave met,
> Alas, alas for England
> They have no graves as yet.

If one thing is certain in this world of a population increasing at a net rate of 200 per minute it is that there will never be peace. Looked at carefully, General Sir John Hackett in his 1962 Lees-Knowles Lectures at Cambridge, presented a complete analysis of David Gower's *Fun, Style, Excellence* as being the basis on which life in the Army should be founded (but applicable to all three Services) – to which naturally General Hackett referred. And perhaps the General's last words should be heeded by our elected leaders in the light of what John Stuart Mill and G K Chesterton wrote. This is how General Hackett concluded:

> The profession of arms is an essential social institution offering an orderly way of life, set a little apart, not without elegance. 'The performance of public duty is not the whole of what makes a good life' said Bertrand Russell in language which would have pleased Cicero; 'there is also the pursuit of private excellence'. Both are to be found in the military life. It gives much and takes more, enriching freely anyone prepared to give more than he gets. It will remain with us for as long as man continues to be what he is, too clever and not good enough. That looks like being a long time yet.

General de la Billière's book and David Gower's autobiography may not seem to have much in common. Yet both in their different ways proclaim the same message. Without a sense of fun, without style and without insistence on excellence, in a world where all three are so desperately needed, there can be no leadership. And without adequate leadership there is little hope for the moral cohesion of our society. I know and understand many of the difficulties of National Service. But in a Nation where the small and diminishing oases of service training still have so much to give, we are all at once brought face to face with the difficulty presented by the prevailing spirit of the times. It is called Democracy. Unfortunately to a large extent it means a disinclination to accept any form of restraint, and a desire for unrestricted freedom of life and action.

A lack of political direction

I have no doubt that officers in the other two Services have watched with delight, as I have, the passing out parades of young servicemen, attended also in their hundreds from far afield, by enthusiastic Mums and Dads and sisters and brothers. *Fun, style, excellence*, these rarely exist now except in the Services. Somehow the political will has to be found to cherish and replenish this service legacy. The legacy that kept the Royal Marines and Paras 'yomping', the young soldiers, after months in the barren desert still ready and able to fight, the pilots in their cockpits and the naval minehunters operating in horrendous conditions. The Churches have largely deserted the battlefield. The Church militant is no more. Overworked doctors are daily handed the priest's pastoral duties. Moral cohesion cannot be maintained by the coercive force of law alone as seems now to be the politician's only answer. Service training has always had a Christian background. The cry goes out from young men denied a job by political incompetence for *fun, style and excellence* and in the modern Services there is an abundance of all three.

As things are going the optimist views the future without nuclear weapons and a non-federal Europe, wherein each country looks to its own prime security interests. Yet without nuclear weapons, when that time comes, Britain will be virtually defenceless. Conscription or a universal system of reserves based on conscription will be required. The assault course must replace the stolen car race. Political will may be needed but the general public is deeply disturbed at the break up of our society and the inability of the present generation of politicians to deal with it. The extent of that necessary political will may well be not as great as politicians of all Parties fear.

THE EFFECT OF PEACE ON PEOPLE

In the decade after the Falklands and the Gulf War I was as shocked as many others at reports of quite highly paid people 'cracking' during or even before these two events had actually occurred. Such reports seemed to be confined to the Navy and Air Force although anyone who has read his history will know that the soldier too has a limit to his powers of endurance.

In a privately circulated naval periodical, there has been a series of articles entitled 'The Effect of War on People' to which I contributed. These articles discussed the issue of what is now called 'Post Traumatic Stress Disorder' (PTSD) and what was once called 'shell shock' or (mostly in the Navy) 'bomb happiness'.

In ruminating on this phenomenon I recalled that in nearly two years of fairly intensive bombing of my ship between 1940 and 1942, until we were finally sunk by torpedo, I had only come across two bad cases of PTSD – although many of us were mildly bomb happy and apt to jump at any sudden noise or laugh too often with an element of hysteria. Had the Welfare State somehow softened the younger generation I asked myself? Was there something wrong in our officer selection process and training for officers and ratings? Was 'fortitude', defined as 'grace under pressure', no longer the main requirement of a leader? Were we paying too much attention to academic prowess, so evidently needed to cope with the sophisticated weaponry of modern war, with the result that we were paying less attention than we should to the words of Lord Moran 'that the man of character in peace is the man of courage in war'?

Janowitz defines 'ascription' as meaning that an individual's position in the military depends on social characteristics and not on personal achievement and, until Kitchener's citizen's army took the field, the amazing resilience of the British Army in Flanders was largely due to 'ascription'. Today, increasingly, we live in a homogenised and almost classless society where quickly and easily acquired wealth, not character in the sense Lord Moran certainly used the word, seems to separate the elements in our society. This led me, after experience on civil service and police selection boards, to the thought that a more prolonged selection process was needed, especially for naval officers and perhaps pilots. I concluded that this could best be established by putting all those entering the Navy together, as sailors, for the maximum time possible within a tight training schedule. Then, having initially established their academic prowess, by means of a subsequently longer selection procedure it might be possible more surely to pick out those with character as defined by Lord Moran and try somehow to meld together the optimum mixture of brains and character, the two main qualities that the Navy needs for its leaders.

The following article explains my rather muddled thought processes in more detail.

In the last paragraph of his published 1962 Lees Knowles Lectures, delivered at Trinity College Cambridge, General Sir John Hackett ended thus:

> The profession of arms is an essential institution offering an orderly way of life, set a little apart, not without elegance. 'The performance of public duty is not all that makes a good life,' said Bertrand Russell in language that would have pleased Cicero, 'there is also pursuit of private excellence'. Both are to be found in the military life. It gives much and takes more, enriching freely anyone prepared to give more than he gets. It will remain with us for as long as man continues to be what he is, too clever and not good enough. This looks like being a long time yet.

The editor of the naval periodical, about a year ago, rightly drew to a close articles concerning The Effect of War on People so this article purports, in a military context, to discuss the effect of peace on people who may have to sustain the first shock of war. The article is triggered by three events: a considerable correspondence in the newspapers about the sacking from Headships of several innovative and indeed well known men and women due to parental pressure; consideration by the European Court of the infliction of three strokes of a gym shoe on the bottom of a 7 year old; the sentences in *Pablo's War* (Squadron Leader Mason, Bloomsbury Press) which read as follows:

We were all reluctant to carry on delivering these lethal weapons. A FEW CREWS AND INDIVIDUALS HAD ALREADY RE-FUSED TO GO TO WAR (This writer's capitals). Others were fast approaching breaking point. In the Second World War they would have been branded as lacking in moral fibre and would probably have lived a life of misery, shunned by their service comrades for the rest of their days. In the First World War they would simply have been taken out and shot.

In Chapter 10 of my book from *Fisher to the Falklands* I wrote about my year at Birmingham University:

Here I found myself one of a mob of (mostly) ex RAF officers studying for their degrees on Forces Educational Grants; young men with old faces from Bomber Command, whose record of courage has never been properly acknowledged but who, amongst the many kindnesses they showed me, gave me an abiding respect and admiration for their service.

That was 45 years ago and nothing I have seen or learnt since, including close friendship with a number of RAF officers, serving and retired, has caused me, in the slightest, to alter that opinion.

And who could forget that paragraph in a letter to his mother written by a young bomber pilot before a sortie and to be delivered to her only if he did not return, as he failed to do:

You must not grieve for me, for if you really believe in religion and all that it entails that would be hypocrisy. I have no fear of death, only a queer elation . . . I would have it no other way. The universe is so vast and so ageless that the life of one man could only be justified by the measure of his sacrifice. We are sent into this world to acquire a personality and a character to take with us that can never be taken from us. Those who just eat and sleep, prosper and procreate, are no better than animals if all their lives they are at peace.

Three times in my father's lifetime and twice in mine the Germans have brought down France or Europe in flames. I saw the assault on merchant ships bound for Spain in 1936–37, I was made aware almost before anyone of Gadhaffi's attempt to torpedo the *QE2* full of Jews on the way to Haifa. Littoral states are already purchasing ships of the Soviet Navy to give them restrictive power on their adjacent sea routes and choke points; China ferociously hates Japan, covets the oil in the South China Sea (as does Japan) and is buying an aircraft carrier to add to her fleet already building. The USA has supplied Japan with sufficient hardware to build six Aegis Class cruisers. Maritime war of the most difficult sort from many causes is likely in the near future. Intensive farming in Britain uses 10 joules of fossil fuel energy brought from overseas for every joule of edible energy produced. Under EC rules much land is going out of cultivation. If the supply of fossil fuel lapses for any period we should quickly starve. Even Europe, as a result of trying to swallow Eastern Europe at one gulp, is in trouble again. It took 28 Italian, 8 Rumanian and 11 crack German Divisions to oversee the Balkan Peninsula. War not peace is in the air.

Between the First and Second World Wars Germany carried out a virtual spring cleaning of the minds of her younger generation. There was a calculated (and largely successful) policy to inculcate the whole German nation with the prized qualities of a soldier. I met some of the *wandervogel* in the Thirties and the 'Strength through Joy' movement had much to impress anyone who had seen the squalor of Jarrow and read of Britain's mass unemployment. In different forms and under different guises the same process used by the Germans (and for the same reasons) is being carried out in a dozen countries today. No democracy can attempt anything like this, yet demonstrably as General Hackett asserts: 'war will remain with us for as long as man continues to be what he is, too clever and not good enough. This looks like being a long time yet.'

Today with our accelerating science applied to war we, in the industrialised world, face a dilemma, particularly in our small increasingly over-crowded island. Should our officers in the Services (as I have always held) be well above the intellectual median of the nation, innovative, imaginative, and deeply thoughtful? Have we, over the last 50 years in our preoccupation over a major conflict with a nation no less ideologically motivated towards war than was Germany, sought to avoid the difficulties of training democracies in peace to accept the trials of war as a natural feature of our national life, by turning too much towards the development of weapons operable only by the brainy? Crudely put, in our officer recruiting, have we gone too far for brains and not far enough for brawn?

Has our educational system, under the influence of parents, particularly single parents, started to become too soft. 'More life,' Thomas Hardy has written, 'may trickle out of men through thought than through a gaping wound'. And does this policy into which, in peacetime, we have quite necessarily been forced, affect the fighting qualities of men (and women) in the sea-going fleet? A fleet that can be said in general to be the most sophisticated battle apparatus yet devised, thus needing the highest academic calibre officers and ratings to operate it; and similarly has this 'softening' of our society affected also the almost incredibly skilled RAF pilot in his cockpit, alone with his highly complicated battle apparatus and the elements, in particular? 'The man of character in peace is the man of courage in war', so writes Lord Moran with his experience as a doctor in the trenches in World War 1 and as Churchill's shadow in World War II.

Admiral Woodward's book with its references to men who 'cracked' even *before* the Falklands were reached and Squadron Leader Mason's paragraph quoted above would seem, if Thomas Hardy was right, to suggest that the softening policy has gone too far and search for character, in the true sense of the word, not far enough.

Bartlett's *Psychology and the Soldier*, The Revd. Norman Copeland's book of the same name, MacCurdy's *The Structure of Morale* and, in the context of World War 1, Trotter's, *The Instincts of the Herd in Peace and War*, deal mainly with the soldier's morale and leadership problems. To some extent these are quite different as regards the detailed application of technological expertise in the crash and din of battle than, say, that of the young officer seeing a missile approaching on his screen, in an air conditioned operations room below the waterline, or a lonely pilot intent on a bombing run hearing the squawk indicating the same danger. But peacetime training has to ensure that all three possess equal courage however differently, as the crisis approaches, such courage has to be demonstrated.

Janowitz defines 'ascription' as meaning that an individual's position in the military depends on social characteristics and not on personal achievement. Until the beginning of this century, certainly in general, men were only born into the officer class or they were excluded. Now personnel records of both academic and leadership qualities have supplanted social pedigree. At the beginning of this century in the Army and Navy and since World War II particularly in the Navy and pilot/navigator element of the RAF, technical skills have inevitably undermined the impact of ascribed authority. And between 1914 and 1945 many of the genes which made the hereditary and almost feudal skills of leadership in the British Army so particularly effective on the field of battle, despite the benign drawbacks of peacetime democracy, have been left in the mud of Flanders, on the beaches of Italy, Normandy and Gallipoli, in Burma, in North Africa and the Middle East, never to return. Some too would hold that the Royal Navy's heavy casualties in World War II and those of the RAF also contributed to the lost-for-ever national gene bank.

In paragraph 2 of this article I mentioned the sacking of school 'Heads' and the extraordinary case of a small boy lightly 'slippered', now under advisement by the European Court. It has been my delight since retiring, to be for five years, until I was to be relieved by the late Admiral Sir Richard Clayton, the Chairman of Governors of a smallish Independent School founded some 70 years ago by a far-sighted and extremely rich man, who had been desperately unhappy at his Public School, but was still big enough to appreciate the benefits he had absorbed there. Consequently he devoted a large part of his fortune to instilling the best of these benefits into the sons of his estate workers by purchasing, initially, a large house with 200 acres and setting up a school which in a few years reached 90 pupils. There was to be no corporal punishment, no marks, a school parliament known as the General Meeting was to be largely responsible for good order and internal discipline without bullying, lovely playing fields, beautiful pictures and a musical tradition extending to this day were all provided for. His aim he enshrined in one short sentence: 'The true aristocracy is an aristocracy of brains and character.'

To someone who had undergone the sadistic discipline at Dartmouth, which I have described in *The Man Around the Engine* and who had accepted the post of Chairman of Governors rather reluctantly and only at the instigation of a childhood friend, the son of the Founder, the whole ambience was a revelation. There could be no doubt of the success of the experiment. From the original roll of 90 mostly from the estate, up to the war, 24 went to Oxbridge and the same number during the six years of war. In the twenty-five post-war years by which time the roll was rising to 150, there were over 100 scholarships to Oxbridge and with the roll now at about 270 a proportionate increase since has taken place, together with many going to other universities and polytechnics and a steady stream into the services. An editor of the *Financial Times*, a partner in one of the great PR firms, a highly placed Foreign Office official, the Keeper of the Bodleian, the Keeper of the British Collection at the Tate, a member of the Council of Lloyds, 15 authors with 42 books ranging from novels, through woodland ecology to Chinese Art, were only some of the achievements of a few of that early 'vintage'.

In the post-war era when even the very rich were feeling the pinch the arrangement was amended. 20 boys (and now girls) from Primary Schools largely paid for by the Founder's Trust, by 'Friends' of the school and, until Labour gained a majority, by the County Council, were merged in their third year with another 20 thirteen year-olds, the children of fully fee-paying parents from independent preparatory schools. And so, to quote just three rather different instances personally known to me, a pigman's son who, while at the school and paid for by the Trust, climbed the Eiger (the school had a great climbing tradition), became a brilliant pianist and gained a scholarship to Oxford; another wrote from the gun turret of a Challenger main battle tank on a quiet evening in the Arabian desert just before Operation Desert Storm, while another boy with 10 O-levels under his belt who chose to defy the Head and his parents and leave at sixteen, has become one of the two greatest National Hunt jockeys of the present era.

I came to believe in those five years that, desperate though the loss of natural leadership genes may have been in two world wars, there are still plenty about if we look for them and recognise them. Both abundantly difficult questions which we have to solve in peacetime if our Services are to give of their best in any conflict. I have been impressed too by the names on the gravestones in the churchyard by our home. Apart from Captain Bligh who was born here but buried in Lambeth, the same names appear century after century, as well as on the war memorial for the two wars, on the photographs of those who went to World War 1 and amongst the sterling yeomen farmers in the neighbourhood and on the Parish Council.

In the Navy of today it seems to me that the intellectual gap between the best of the artificer entry and the academically worst of the officer candidates is virtually non existent; this is born out by the fact that 40% of the engineering branch, weapons, propulsion and air, who graduate with an Honours degree are ex-apprentices. Quite often the two types of candidate were separated only by their immediately preceding social status, which initially or by chance tended to aim them at one type of entry or the other, by their maturity, or lack of it, at school and as seen by the recruiter and the success or otherwise of their school teachers in giving them the necessary numeracy, literacy and *savoir-faire* to pass one or other of the Selection Boards. I surmise that the same differences may well exist between some of the new entry rating recruits, those who might always remain a rating and those who might develop petty officer or even officer intellectual and leadership potential.

So where do we go from here now that the fee-paying preparatory schools and public schools have largely ceased to provide the officer corps of all three Services? And in particular, how in the case of the Royal

Navy should we solve the equation? How should we attempt, in our diminishing Navy, to select officer candidates, who will be accepted by those they have to lead, and who, in critical and dangerous moments will spread fortitude rather than put on their survival suits and curl up under a table as Admiral Woodward records? (The same, of course, would apply to those who Squadron Leader Mason alleged, refused to go to war.)

Would it be better to emulate the school I have mentioned where, during 5–7 years, regardless of social background, a factor during that period almost entirely forgotten and always discounted, the real aristocracy, the aristocracy of brains and character, is seen slowly to emerge and to be identified?

The Navy could not spare all that time of course for such a selection process and anyway the ages are greater and therefore perhaps the characters more recognisable; but should we perhaps revert to something on the lines of HMS *King Alfred* which, from an always young and sometimes rather motley crew entered as sailors, gave us that vast and, on the whole, outstanding supply of reserve officers without whose help the war would never have been won. My five years on the civil service and police selection boards convinced me that the two or three day War Office selection board procedures, effective though in some cases they might be, were really no substitute for a far longer observation and selection procedure.

I believe there is a lesson here which we should not neglect. I visualise an entry examination based, as at present, on about three broad levels of academic ability and whatever age ranges for each might be considered appropriate. The first academic standard would constitute the lowest level acceptable for the rating recruit and might have a wider age range than the other two; the second, the lowest level acceptable for the apprentice entry and the third and highest, to be of university standard preferably with some maths and physics, both the last two batches of candidates having fairly low ceiling age ranges. All candidates for service in the Royal Navy would have the choice of which of the three academic examinations they wished to opt for and, on passing at whichever grade, would be offered perhaps twelve weeks of what might be called 'pupillage' while dressed and living as sailors in HMS *Raleigh*. HMS *Raleigh* itself would contain, besides the necessary training staff, a greatly enlarged Selection Board watching for officer potential in all three entries. Clearly the third and second entries would need the closest observation; but the chase for academic potential, as opposed to achievement, should cover all three. Late developers are often the best in these fast moving times.

Prima facie such a change suggests the abandoning of Dartmouth and it well may ultimately come to that. But if, after selection, and a year's seatime still as sailors, there is obvious officer material in a candidate, then some additional academic 'cramming' may be needed provided the maximum age limits are not exceeded and, for a time this might be Dartmouth's role. All officer selectees would anyway finish at Manadon, now allied to Plymouth University, by taking courses, some leading to Honours degrees, all tailored to their ultimate specialisation.

Experience in the Fifties when the officer academic standard of entry was similar to that of a Post Office clerk, demonstrated that Manadon and Dartmouth were both hamstrung in their endeavours, by the need to 'cram' a small proportion of entrants to achieve minimal standards required of naval officers, sometimes to the neglect of the brightest. In many cases where even the 'cramming' failed with its accompanying drag on those not needing it, the officer concerned who failed his exams was discharged from the Navy with no hope of being downgraded perhaps to Special Duties Officer or Petty Officer, where their adequate leadership qualities would have served the Navy well. If such cramming could also be accomplished at Manadon or Raleigh rather than Dartmouth, then the latter would indeed have to be abandoned as a naval training establishment.

Such an arrangement, the writer holds, would greatly enhance the early and – by reason of the much longer period for the selection period, the full 12 weeks for officers – more certain choice of those with officer potential whatever their social background. It would also enhance the all of one company philosophy by making clear, at the earliest stage, and amongst their peers, who should lead and who, however clever, would be more likely fated only to follow; those who welcomed and overcame stress and those who succumbed.

The abandoning of Dartmouth with its chapel and books of Remembrance for the multitude of naval officers who gave their lives in two world wars would be an unbearable wrench. But in the last 25 years this country, despite the wonders of the North Sea oil exploration, has fallen far behind the United States in the exploration and development of the sea bed beyond the Continental Shelf. There needs to be one centre of applied scientific research. The 'undersea-men' trained at Dartmouth could well add lustre to the seamen who once made that little port so famous.

Sir Edward Heath, when joining the European Community, is said to have given away 80% of British Fish stocks to our continental rivals and once remarked to me that shipbuilding was a purely Third World Activity.

Pressure, constantly exerted on the government may one day restore to British fishermen what is rightly theirs; and as for shipbuilding being a 'Third World' activity tell that to the Finns, the Koreans, the Japanese, the Norwegians, the Germans, the Italians and they will surely dispose of such a gross misjudgement. If, as many hope, the UK distances itself from the more bizarre of the Brussels lawmakers, (what sailor requires a Delors approved standard sized condom?) then training in all types of construction of once more British seagoing merchant ships and those deck and engineer officers who will man them (the Treasury refused in 1956 to contemplate training merchant navy engineers at Manadon although no extra overheads would have been needed) could well also be concentrated at Dartmouth. There could be training too in more up to date fishing techniques, training in the properly organised harvesting of the oceans, training in sea bed exploration. In a world dying because of the 200 extra mouths to be fed and 200 extra aspirations (never to be satisfied) for every minute of every day, Dartmouth could become in time one of the most important centres by which our planet might be saved. For those who recall the Georgics: *Sed fugit interea, fugit inreparabile tempus*. For those who don't: 'Meanwhile time is flying – flying, never to return'.

THE ROYAL UNITED SERVICES
INSTITUTE

THE FUTURE OF THE ROYAL UNITED SERVICES INSTITUTE 1963

While I was at the Imperial Defence College Mr Alastair Buchan, then Director of the International Institute for Strategic Studies, wrote a challenging letter to 'The Times' on the need for the development of strategic studies in our universities.

Three of us, Group Captain Neil Cameron (later Marshal of the RAF Lord Cameron), Brigadier Kenneth Hunt and I decided that the Services themselves should have a say in all this and we spent much of a weekend, to the annoyance of our wives, composing the following, grossly overlong, letter. Having been given our Commandant's permission on the Monday we hired a taxi and naïvely delivered the letter to 'The Times' office.

By Thursday it had not appeared and we began to lose hope until that afternoon, when I was summoned to the office of the Chief of Defence Staff, Admiral of the Fleet the Earl Mountbatten to be given a blast by his Secretary, Vice-Admiral Sir Ronald Brockman who had been sent the letter by Lord Hayley the Editor of 'The Times', on the grounds that serving officers should not write to the press. However CDS had said the letter should, if possible, be published in the Journal of the RUSI and meanwhile he had circulated it to the Chiefs of Staff for future discussion: and with that perforce we had to be content.

Though the mills of God grind slowly, in due course and with the help of an increasingly dynamic staff, things started to move and today the Royal United Services Institute for Defence Studies is one of the foremost 'Think-Tanks' in the UK.

Sir, – Recently *The Times* published a challenging article by Mr Alastair Buchan, Director of the International Institute for Strategic Studies, on the need for the development of strategic thought in our universities. In it he also expressed the view that the Whitehall Ministries had a part to play in the future success or failure of the academic community in this field.

There is no doubt that a large part of the original thinking on contemporary strategic problems comes from America and France, from their universities and, in the case of America, from such organisations as the Rand Corporation. Many strategic thinkers active in American university seminars are among President Kennedy's closest advisers and the Service attitude to those resources of thought is perhaps more sympathetic in America than it is in the United Kingdom. At the same time it is difficult for defence planners in Whitehall to give strategic problems the intellectual analysis they deserve: the pressure of day to day work and sudden peaks and dips of the international barometer limit the opportunities for measured thinking.

We hope the universities of this country will respond to Mr Buchan's challenge and set up graduate studies, and we also hope that Whitehall will go some way to encouraging the universities with the assurance that there will be participation in such studies by those who work at policy making in Whitehall; and here security need not really be a limiting factor. In our view a meeting of minds is required at a forum where students of the subject from the universities, the Services, the Civil Service, industry, the economy, and politics can get together to debate strategic concepts within a practical framework.

The Institute for Strategic Studies does provide an important forum of discussion, but it is an international organisation partly funded from abroad, and for the function we have in mind it has certain limitations. There is still a requirement for essentially a national forum to meet the need outlined above, and we feel this might well be met by an enlargement of the function and membership of the Royal United Services Institute. That Institute is not receiving the support its efforts deserve, and members' subscriptions have to be subsidised by an annual grant from the three Services. The direction is admirable and vigorous: the lectures are of excellent standard and deserve better audiences than they get. We have an interesting and controversial quarterly Journal, our library is second to none and the recently organised information service is the admiration of all who use it. We have excellent premises specially designed for our needs, a sound organisation, and all the essentials for focusing service thought. Although our present members use the Institute's facilities far more than they did a few years ago, membership does not show that vigorous upward curve we need. There are several reasons for this including the run-down of our armed Forces and the stationing of so many units overseas.

We feel the time has now come for a new approach to the problem. It is likely the universities will answer the challenge posed by Mr Buchan and this, coupled with the creation of a new defence structure would seem an opportune moment for the establishment of a 'British Institute of Strategic Affairs'. This we suggest could be based on the present RUSI organisation and facilities, and we see it as a meeting place where the best brains amongst the civil and military defence planners from the new British 'Quadragon' could join in debate and study with the best brains from the universities, aided by the mature experience of the retired and serving officers who are already members. We should like to see the new organisation initiate studies into strategic concepts in conjunction with university Chairs, and run seminars at which the many disciplines essential to any realistic analysis could take part. The proceedings would normally be in confidence as is usual in discussions of this character.

We believe an organisation of this type is sorely needed in this country and the framework is already there in our Institute with its nucleus of the right type of staff and experience. The RUSI has a great and distinguished history of which it can be rightly proud, but present day defence matters have become so complex that they are no longer the preserve of the military. The scientist, the economist, the sociologist and the industrialist all have their part to play and it is essential that they should come together with the military when strategic concepts are being discussed. We feel our suggested organisation could achieve this admirably.

It would of course require money. It is not the purpose of this letter to suggest how this might be found, but the time may come for the formation of a suitable foundation helped by contributions from the many large companies concerned with defence. We would also hope that the Government might make a worthwhile grant. We are of the opinion that the present function at the RUSI is too narrow to fulfil the requirements of the missile age. There is a desperate need for enlightened strategic thinking from this country and this could be achieved by the new organisation we have in mind. It is really a national issue and the entrenched position of tradition and the likelihood of small organisational hazards should not be allowed to stand in the way of success.

> Neil Cameron.
> *Group Captain*
> Kenneth Hunt.
> *Brigadier*
> Louis Le Bailly.
> *Captain, Royal Navy*
> *July 13th 1963*

THE SOVIET MARITIME THREAT AND
SOVIET AFFAIRS GENERALLY

THE STRATEGIC INTENTIONS OF THE SOVIET UNION

Report by a Study Group of the Institute for the Study of Conflict, March 1978

Unlike the rest of the pieces in this anthology, what follows is far from being all my own work. However I was asked by Mr Crozier to chair this Study Group and I may have contributed in one or two directions which intensely interested me, namely to defining the maritime threat and to the possibility which I had found it difficult to sustain in the M.O.D. that, with the maritime threat went an acute threat to the swathe of airfields across England from Soviet airborne troops. But, apart from those two aspects, it would be difficult to put together a group who, between them, knew more about what was going on at that time on in the Soviet Union, than the following:

Dr Iain Elliot. Editor 'Soviet Analyst'.
Air Vice-Marshal S W B Menaul C.B., C.B.E., D.F.C., A.F.C. Lately Director-General of the RUSI.
*Sir Edward Peck, G.C.M.G. British permanent representative to North Atlantic Council 1970–1975.
Professor Otto Pick. Faculty of Human Studies. University of Surrey.
*Professor Leonard Schapiro, F.B.A., Chairman of ISC Council. Emeritus Professor of Political Science, with special reference to Russian Studies. London School of Economics.
*Brigadier W.F.K. Thompson, O.B.E. Military Correspondent of 'The Daily Telegraph' 1959–76.
*Brian Crozier. Director and Co-Founder of the ISC. A famous Soviet analyst.
David Rees (Rapporteur). Senior Research Fellow. ISC.

Dr Peter Janke. Senior Researcher, ISC.
Professor G.H.N. Seton-Watson, F.B.A., D. Litt, Professor of Russian History, School of Slavonic and East European Studies, acted as a wise Consultant.
Those starred, like me, were members of the ISC Council.

This wide ranging report, thanks in the main to those mentioned above, was considered a landmark of assessment at the time particularly in the United States. It is still on sale from the Institute. After the Introduction given below the following extracts cover only some of the naval aspects which particularly interested me and the ISC have kindly given me permission to record them.

Although it is now 15 years old it is my hope that by quoting extracts from this report others of a new generation may read and profit from it. Although there have been changes, much has remained unchanged.

Introduction

The Study Group believes that no analysis of Soviet strategic intentions is valid unless due weight is given to the ideological self-justification of the régime. To ignore or discount this factor and the closed and totalitarian nature of the Soviet system, can only lead to misjudgement and issues are of such importance that any misjudgement could be both costly and dangerous, or at the very least will lead to disappointed hopes and expectations unfulfilled.

Accordingly, this special report considers the ideological basis of Soviet military doctrine and examines the decision making process, as well as the actual state of weaponry on either side of the Strategic Arms Limitations Talks (SALT).

Although this paper principally involves consideration of SALT, for which the United States bears the burden of major responsibility, the gravamen of our report applies equally to other aspects of Western defence and affects every member country of the North Atlantic Alliance.

What then are the issues? The Study Group agrees that they include not only war and peace and the survival of mankind, but also the preservation of pluralist and representative societies in which a free inquiry, such as this one, is possible.

Military doctrine – the technology gap
. . . 'War is the continuation of political intercourse with the admixture of other means'. Clausewitz.

'War is a continuation of politics by other means'. Lenin (adapted from Clausewitz.)

One of the principal Soviet military theorists, the late Marshal Sokolovsky, specifically stated that this even applied to thermonuclear war which would result in victory for 'the world socialist system'.

. . . The conventional Western view that Soviet superiority in numbers is more than compensated for by the greater sophistication of Western technology no longer holds good. By 1978 the disparity in the quality of weapons systems between the NATO powers and the Soviet Union has largely vanished, with the possible exception of aircraft and their associated electronics, computers and guidance systems. Even in these critical fields, the apparent eagerness of Western countries to sell technology to the Soviet Union is narrowing what remains of the technological gap between East and West.

Soviet sea power

. . . Two points need emphasis. One is that the across-the-board development of Soviet sea power once again illustrates the 'all arms' doctrine. Secondly, although the Navy is out-numbered numerically by the aggregate of all NATO navies, it has the initiative and can be deployed when at the maximum state of material and training readiness; it is sufficient in any case to interdict critical Western trade routes, such as those in the North Atlantic or around the Cape.

It is difficult, if not impossible, for the West to determine quickly whether a sudden deployment of well maintained Soviet surface ships and submarines with fully trained crews is for the purpose of realistic war exercises or a precursor to an actual assault on the West, or to coincide with an attempt at nuclear blackmail of the West. With, in practical terms, very little possibility of much warning time, the Western maritime forces have therefore always to be on the alert, and to this extent the wear and tear on their ships and aircraft must offset much of the numerical advantage the West may possess.

Apart from 6 new Soviet Delta-class submarines which are launched every year, the Soviet Navy has about 390 general purpose submarines, of which about 250–270 are thought to be operational. (*Jane's Fighting Ships*, 1977–78). The latest missiles launched from these submarines have a range of 4,800 miles, or from the Barents Sea to San Francisco. In his recently published book, *The Sea Power of the State* (1976), The Soviet Navy's C-in-C, Fleet Admiral Sergei Gorshkov, gives surprisingly clear indications of Soviet naval intentions in case of war. He writes that the Soviet Navy must have a war winning potential on the high seas in order 'to counter the oceanic strategy of imperialism', i.e. the vital, historic trade routes that sustain the West.

. . . Marshal Grechko's logic is applied also to naval doctrine:

> 'Side by side with the traditional task of destroying the enemy's ships, the navies of the leading maritime powers have now been given a new task: to destroy the military-economic potential of the enemy by direct assault on his vital industrial centres by nuclear strikes from the sea'

The long range capability of the Soviet Navy was stressed in *Red Star* (7 February 1978) by Fleet Admiral Gorshkov, who has masterminded its enormous expansion in recent years. 'Besides its importance in paying friendly and 'business-like' calls to ports around the world, the fighting capabilities of its ships had been greatly changed by advances in science and technology, notably in submarines,' he said. 'Nuclear engineering, missiles and other arms, radio electronics and computer technology now make it possible to develop vessels fully responsive to the demands of modern warfare, able to operate in any of the world's oceans.'

It is this cool acceptance of the use of nuclear weapons which is so frightening, particularly in view of the Soviet tendency to regard all power as an entity and to reject escalation as a figment. If its armed forces are seriously considering this type of tactical doctrine, then at the strategic level their belief in Mutually Assured Destruction is obviously not as firm as is supposed in the West.

Air transport

A critical element would be the Soviet Air Transport Force numbering 1500 aircraft. Although the numbers of this force have changed little in the past decade, lift capacity has increased by more than 50%. The force has already the capability to provide a complete lift for two airborne assault divisions to areas in a 1000 mile radius from their bases, and freight in the form of support equipment to a radius of nearly 2000 miles . . . It will be remembered that the Air Transport Force played a central role in the occupation of Czecho-Slovakia in 1968 when AN–12s and AN–22s landed without warning the assault troops who then seized Prague airport and its vital communication facilities. Almost certainly this force is intensively trained to attempt similar offensive operations in Western Europe.

Chemical Warfare

... Nor is the Soviet threat confined to various forms of firepower. The Russians have always laid great emphasis on chemical warfare. Very large stocks of war chemicals are maintained and a wide variety of means for their delivery have been developed. Unlike NATO the Russian armed forces have large contingents of chemical warfare troops in every formation down to regimental level. It is generally accepted in NATO that the Warsaw Pact has about seven times NATO's capacity in chemical weapons, and that about one-sixth of the total Soviet stock of ammunition can, if necessary, be chemically charged. Precise figures are, however, unavailable.

The Soviet View

It is important to understand that the Soviet rulers view the States of Western Europe not only with hostility but with fear. They know well that as long as free institutions exist in Western Europe, knowledge of them cannot be kept from the peoples of Eastern Europe. They doubtless understand that resentment against themselves in Eastern Europe is due not only to Western influences but also to their own policies, which insist not only in the forcible maintenance of Soviet type political and economic structures, but also on a continuous interference with indigenous cultures, a continuous system of national humiliation, which inevitably and permanently creates anti-Russian feeling among these peoples, no less among working men in the fields and factories than among the intellectual élite.

But if they were to abandon this policy of national humiliation they would incur another deadly danger. If they allowed Poles to live like Poles, Czechs to live like Czechs, subject only to guarantee of subordination of their governments to Soviet interests in foreign policy – if, in short, they permitted a 'Finnish-type' relationship for the Poles, Czechs, and other Eastern European peoples, then very soon the Ukrainians, Moldavians, Tartars, Georgians, Uzbeks and all the other nations of the Soviet Union would be asking for the same liberties, and the Soviet Union would be in danger of breaking up.

... It may well be argued that the Soviet intentions towards the West have been consistently hostile in the post-1945 period. What is new is the growth in Soviet capability which has now reached a point, especially in nuclear missiles, where the threat to the West has dramatically increased.

What is also new is the growing confidence of the military machine at a time when the prestige of Soviet politicians is steadily declining. While the ultimate decisions on policy remain in the hands of these politicians, the West cannot ignore the increasing influence which the prestige of the military entails.

Conclusion

If all the sombre facts are looked at together the drive for quantitative and qualitative superiority in weapons on land, sea, in the air and in space, civil defence, military doctrine and morale – it is only sensible for the West to envisage the possibility that the Soviet Union may, in certain circumstances, contemplate a nuclear first strike. But, at the same time it is true that the countries of the Western Alliance, if they will the means, have it within their power greatly to reduce the risk of such a world catastrophe.

All experience shows, unhappily, that unilateral concessions never cause the Soviet leadership to change course; rather, such concessions increase the danger by tempting the Kremlin down the path of adventurism. This is also the lesson to be drawn from appeasement of other totalitarian regimes in the 1930s. Security will only come if the West exhibits determined resistance to Soviet chicanery in negotiations for arms limitation and at all times maintains its own strength and cohesion at a proper level. To these ends, the first essential is a realistic understanding of the true nature of the adversary. This report attempts a contribution to this understanding.

THE ONE OPEN HIGHWAY[1]
JOURNAL OF THE RUSI, 1962

This I think was one of my earliest forays into print. It was triggered by genuine anger at the absurdities enunciated whilst listening to a debate in the House of Commons on the British Shipping Industry.

Two years experience in the office of the Controller of the Navy, until quite recently the Admiralty official responsible for sponsoring that industry, had shown me how badly, in some cases, firms were managed and also how badly the industry as a whole had been treated by the government. Further, the shipyards built many years before had been so busy in the war and immediate post-war periods that no major modernisations had been possible.

In this article as in many others I put forward the idea of nuclear power not only for naval but also for merchant ship propulsion. The trouble then was lack of money and lack of nuclear engineers. The trouble today (1992) is the problem of disposing of radioactive machinery when hulls are no longer serviceable.

Had the government ever firmly adopted the idea of surface nuclear propulsion for surface warships and merchantmen the great new naval engineering college at Manadon in Plymouth could have trained the necessary numbers. But we were defeated by the Treasury even on the more modest proposal of training Merchant Navy engineers there, which could have been done with the barest minimum increase in overheads as no extra staff would have been needed. The Treasury assessed the per capita cost of training the then output of foreign naval engineer

---

[1] 'The ability to assure free movement by sea at the right time and place remains of fundamental importance to these islands; indeed the sea may in certain circumstances by the one open highway for strategic movement free of international political hindrance.' (Cmd. 1639. Statement on Defence, 1962, para. 26)

*officers and demanded that shipping firms should pay the same per
student, a totally unrealistic but sadly typical attitude which still muffles
the nation's great industrial potential today.*

*As for the disposal of radioactive machinery, the ingenuity of our
scientists and engineers has never been properly harnessed in the hunt for
the most safe and satisfactory methods. By a technically illiterate Parliament nuclear power is still regarded as a form of witchcraft; although in
the early 1980s a Secretary of State actually discovered, only after some
time in the post, that steam was involved. A true example of the prevailing
parliamentary ignorance of matters technical, which has led this country
towards penury.*

THE ONE OPEN HIGHWAY

Some thoughts on British sea power in the next 40 years – engendered
whilst listening to an exceptionally gloomy and ill-informed debate on the
British shipping industry in the House of Commons.

> Nausea fills me, and the only essence
> Is in my tangible illegal presence.
> I start from here. But where then did I learn
> The terms that pose the choices I discern?
> *Thom Gunn.*

Mr. Speaker, Sir.
When Mr. Jenks delivers my manure he brings it by horse and cart
because, in spite of space ships, jet aircraft, and gas-turbine motorcars,
Mr. Jenks finds that with his horse and cart he can deliver manure with an
economy and a certainty which pleases his customer and repays him.
Besides, the horse contributes in other ways.

One day very soon Mr. Jenks will buy himself a little truck and thereby
he too will break through the 'oats' barrier, something that was first
accomplished about 1830 when the horse yielded place to the locomotive,
sail to steam, and the present rushing avalanche of technology began to
stir.

Manure for the fields of England; food and goods for the underfed and
rapidly increasing millions of the world. Neither need space ships, or
missiles, or jets, but just safe and certain means of carriage so that losses
and the cost to the consumer may be as small as possible.

If Mr. Jenks's horse became Pegasus and took wings, then he could perhaps lift those books on the table of the House to the tune of 15 lb. or so and carry them through the air. But if we taught his horse to swim, then he could tow 50 or 60 Members through the water; 15 lb. through the air; 9,000 lb. by sea at 1/50th of the cost, albeit far more slowly. That is what the power of one horse can do. Is it therefore any surprise, Sir, that 99.9 per cent of the world's freight still goes by sea?

Sea power, maritime supremacy, admiralty, call it what you will, does not mean aircraft carriers or frigates or nuclear submarines. Sea power depends on traffic and it includes the ability to traffic. The world being what it is and given to war and piracy and privateering (which is only nationally approved piracy), a Navy is an essential element of sea power. But the need for a Navy stems principally from the possession of a merchant fleet and the need to ensure the merchant ship's unhampered passage over the sea routes of the world.

I said sea power or admiralty. What do we understand by admiralty? Nine out of ten would say, 'It's that old building on the north side of the Horse Guards against whose denizens the House so often delights to rail.' I prefer this definition:

> 'Admiralty', writes Paul McGuire,[2] 'is the understanding of sea power. It must be fed from the blood and marrow of a people accustomed to the sea; but as an instrument it is shaped by skill and wisdom enduring from generation to generation of seamen and statesmen who understand the sea. So wisdom and understanding are kept alive only in the constant exercise of power at sea.'

Do we believe this today or are we in danger, in the words of the old proverb, 'of walking into a well from looking at the stars'?

We are the wanderers, Sir, the traders and the brokers of the world; the carriers over that four-fifths of the surface of the globe covered by water. We came to greatness on this and stayed great on our coal, our railways, and our ships – always our ships.

Satisfactory as it may be, I wonder if it subtracts one point from the cost of living if a million people fly BEA or hustle over the Atlantic by BOAC. Do the many hidden and many more obvious subsidies to our aircraft industry (£300m. a year has been quoted recently) add in any way to our

---

[2] *The Price of Admiralty*, Paul McGuire.

strength in waging the cold war? Does aviation even warrant a separate Ministry? Surely, it's our big steamers or our diesellers, our cargo ships and our tankers, and our 'dirty British coasters with salt-caked smokestacks' on which, as a nation, in the last resort we depend. Why is this not universally comprehended? What a strange doctrine it is for this island – and make no mistake about it, commercially we are still and we shall always remain an island – what a strange doctrine it is that takes careful and calculated steps deliberately to neglect, to stultify, and stifle the one great world industry in which we excel and by which we have always lived. Strange doctrine indeed that also deliberately encourages this mass aerial hypnosis.

Have I made my point? Do I make clear, what all must believe who study objectively the condition of the shipping industry today, that indeed 'we have walked into a well from looking at the stars?' Now we have to climb the sides once more and they are steep and slippery.

Richmond has told us what to do:[3]

> 'Ships', he said, 'cannot be built unless a shipbuilding industry exists with its yards and its slips and machinery and a skilled body of workers in that industry, so the fostering of that industry is an essential duty of the statesmen in regard to sea power.

Do our statesmen today measure up to this? Does the Government regard it as its duty to foster this shipbuilding industry of ours? Few who have listened to this debate would believe they do – yet the whole of our island history, and history is only experience, stands witness to the truth of Richmond's words.

Amongst the many tendentious things that have been said there has been the implication that our shipbuilders neglected their duty in not fully modernising their yards. What would have been said of our great ship-yards, I wonder, if they had laid off their workers for two or three years immediately after the war to start modernising? Where would the world have been with the German, the Dutch, the French, and other continental yards obliterated, with Japan on her knees, if Britain had not built and built and built at a time when even our warships were loaded with fruit and milk and eggs to feed our children? Surely it is safe to say that food and oil would have been even more scarce, rationing even more strict, and those grey, grim, post-war years even more prolonged. No Sir, we owe a debt to the shipbuilding industry not only for what they did in the war but

---

[3] *Statesmen and Sea Power*, Introduction, p.x.

for what they did for us afterwards as well. And have we in the span of only 30 years altogether forgotten the agony of Jarrow and Wallsend and Clydeside? Of course there have been faults. Of course, with hindsight, matters might have been arranged better. But, Sir, that agony meant a lost generation in the shipbuilding industry and even the accumulated wisdom of the House is not always right on every issue.

A few years ago there was a revue at His Majesty's Theatre called *Paint your Wagon*, and there was a lyric in it which went like this:

'Where are you going? We don't know.
What are you doing? We can't say.'

That seems to sum up the situation today and surely we can do better. First, however, we must try to guess at the world conditions in which British sea power will necessarily operate in the next 40 years.

Doubtless we shall still live under the threat of annihilation; but safe and certain means of carriage over the oceans at the cheapest possible rates will always be an essential even when people go backwards and forwards to the moon. And how much more even than today will this safe and certain carriage, sea power, be needed. More people in the world, more food needed, more industry, more trade, more ships, more nationalism, more restrictions on free passage on the high seas. The three mile limit yesterday; the twelve mile limit today. Extensive farming of the sea to get more food, and the fifty mile limit tomorrow.

The purpose of our long series of Navigation Acts was to secure for ourselves the largest share of the world's trade. Where we showed the way, is it surprising that others have followed with Cargo Preference Acts and Flags of Convenience? Human nature changes very slowly.

In the days of wooden walls and sail our strategy centred round the Baltic timber trade. Today it centres round the supply of sterling oil from the Middle East. But there are other and even more significant factors. Indonesia is athwart the great focal point of the Far East trade route. Population explosions are occurring, or about to occur, in that country, in Africa, in China, and in South America. Australia, possessing the greatest untapped resources in the free world, is as yet undeveloped and under-populated.

What does all this spell out? Surely, Sir, just the old, old story. Ships to carry goods hither and thither and the other instruments of sea power, a shipbuilding industry, and a Navy. For, as Roskill writes:[4]

---

[4] *Strategy of Sea Power*, p.16.

'But devotion to trade being an acquisitive practice and the accumulation and enjoyment of wealth by man having always aroused the envy of his neighbours, it has invariably been necessary for a trading community to defend the ships and craft which carry its goods to and fro across the sea; for if the sea is not ruled as well as used, losses are bound to be suffered, and may reach such dimensions as will imperil the community's existence'

Piracy did not go out with Henry Morgan.

And so, Sir, I conclude once more that nothing fundamental will change in the next half century. The only question is, 'Are we to live?' If we are to live we must trade. If we are to trade we must have highly competitive cargo ships and tankers and a Navy to ensure their free passage. And before either, a thriving and forward-looking shipbuilding industry to give us the ships.

How do we achieve this? Sir, few would dare to stand up and give any certain answer, but there are obvious points of attack at which, given goodwill, a clear purpose, and a little (by aviation standards only a very little) money, something can be done. There are other points which need close study before an attack can be launched.

It is a fact that world shipbuilding capacity exceeds that necessary for replacements and for the growth of tonnage and service which depends on world trade. Various conclusions can be drawn from this vis-à-vis the British shipbuilding industry:

(a)   we could close down the British shipbuilding industry altogether;

(b)   we could reduce it in proportion to the world excess in the usual British way of fair shares for all or low enough to build only for us;

(c)   the British industry could become so tremendously competitive in the world market that it could remain at about its present size and the world would look to it as they now look to Mitsubishi or Verolme.

To me (a) and (b) seem equally illogical. At any given moment there are probably more cars being produced world-wide than are strictly needed. Does the British car industry decide to close down and cut back? Certainly not. It looks for new markets. The whole basis of the economy of the free world, and in particular of the UK, depends on our ability to create jobs that men can work at, and be proud of, and make money by their work. Industrialization in the emerging countries is inevitable; it carries with it, as inevitably, the need for sea transport. That sea transport Britain must provide. Our shipping salesmen must get out and ensure that we do so, and we, on our part, must ensure that our facilities for executing orders are realistic, simple, and quick to react to new markets. I continue therefore on the basis that there must be no chicken-hearted talk (rightly or wrongly attributed to the Ministry) of cutting back the industry by one-third. Instead it must all be brought to a high state of competitive efficiency so that world markets can be conquered.

This, of course, is so easy to say; and I must concede that Government assistance in the short term needs to be vigorously applied. A 'scrap and build' policy has much to commend it, and at least it can be proclaimed and made economical for British shipowners to buy British. In the Royal Navy, with the helter-skelter advances in weapon technology, there are strong arguments for building new hulls and propulsion machinery round each new generation of weapons rather than wasting time and effort and a great deal of money adapting new weapon systems to hulls a quarter of a century old and to propulsion systems with hundreds of thousands of rough sea miles behind them.

Hull form, means of propulsion, cargo handling, interior layout, corrosion resistance, economy of operation, reliability of material, economy in operating and maintenance personnel; this is the sort of stuff of which a thriving shipping industry is made.

Computers and a rising degree of automation are being introduced by some of the more far-sighted shipbuilders. But the best hull form for particular classes of vessel, the best angle of entrance and angle of run, the best prismatic coefficient, are all still largely a matter of habit, or predilection of the owner, or sheer hunch. One day soon, perhaps well within five years, a break-through will occur and an equation for hull form for whatever particular qualities are needed will be discovered. Then models and automated plate cutting and welding machines, already introduced in many yards, will finally revolutionize the long drawn out process from the drawing board, through the mould loft, to the launching slip.

Fibre glass and plastics are in common use. Steam, diesels, gas turbines, and (why not) well proved long life aircraft engines like the Avon, nuclear propulsion, all these systems provide a fascinating choice of power plant. Hydrofoils, hydrokeels, submersibles, hovercraft, new hull forms such as that for the proposed Cunarder, have their merits and give wide opportunities for imaginative study and development.

The British diesel industry, as D.S.I.R. reports have shown, must concentrate on recapturing the shipping market. 'Packaged' forms of power plant with absolutely standardized layouts and a world-wide spares service must be provided almost 'with the propellers turning over' for the shipbuilders to mount before launching.

As I said earlier, there is a lost generation in the shipbuilding industry, and somehow a greater number of brilliant men than seem attracted to it at the moment must be brought back into the fold. The shipbuilding and the shipping industry should combine, perhaps with the help of the Chancellor through the University Grants Committee, to endow more Chairs of Naval Architecture; with lectures in dock layouts (perhaps the Rochdale Committee could help), in cargo handling, in marine engineering; whilst a well defined programme of research must be instituted under a liberally minded and preferably fairly young directing council into the whole problem of sea transport. Sweden can show us the way.

The scheme agreed years ago by the Admiralty and industry (but shelved for want of a few thousand pounds) to allow the training of civilian marine engineers at the great new Royal Naval Engineering College must be revived and instituted.

The French were the originators of modern naval architecture. Their broad training at the *Polytechnique* (Napoleon's great foundation), and the ubiquity of the brilliant men of the *Génie Maritime*, both in the Navy and in the French shipping and shipbuilding industry, sets a pattern which in some respects we might follow. These are only some of the ways in which we can lay the proper academic foundations of sea power which, today, are so sadly lacking.

This business of restrictive practices, Sir. Do you know the different trades involved in shipbuilding? There are shipwrights, loftsmen, platers, welders, blacksmiths, fitters, electricians, plumbers, coppersmiths, painters, woodmakers, riggers, sailmakers, and a hundred others.

Again and again in this debate it has been suggested that if the employers were to give security of employment, then a start could be made at once on the abolishing of restrictive practices. But, Sir, the Admiralty, the biggest shipyard employer in the country, already gives established security and pension rights. It has done so for years. Let the unions be invited to abolish restrictive practices in the Royal Dockyards and, when the difficulties (which I do not underrate) are ironed out and settled, the other two-thirds of the country's shipbuilding and repairing industry can follow. Even, Sir, if for some reason this argument is irrelevant, surely where Esso have shown the way at Fawley, others can follow.

The Royal Navy possesses the most highly sophisticated surface ships in the world. It gets by with three uniformed groups of craftsmen, each of whom have their well defined roles; whilst within each group are appropriate specialists. The Navy can do this because of the quality of its apprenticeship training which, as the House has acknowledged before, is the finest in the country. The way is therefore signposted for industry if only we can bring ourselves to follow the road.

And now for nuclear propulsion. No single action, or rather lack of action, has done more to depress the shipbuilding industry than the Government's decision to do nothing practical about getting a nuclear ship to sea. Four interests are involved in addition to national interest and national prestige: the Admiralty, the shipowners, the shipbuilders, and the nuclear industry. The Admiralty, rightly, must spend the country's money in the best way that will further whatever strategic directive is given by the Cabinet. If that directive can be met without resort to nuclear power, or if resort to nuclear power on the surface implies that there will not be enough money to meet that directive, then the Admiralty may not, of its own, adopt nuclear propulsion. In these day the shipowners cannot support, alone, a venture which, almost certainly to begin with, would produce a substantial loss. Neither the shipbuilder nor the nuclear industry can produce power plants if there is no demand. Unless, therefore, the Government pulls the trigger, all four are absolutely hamstrung. Yet all four have much to gain and need only the faintest of shoves to get into the business and each contribute quite a substantial proportion of the cost.

Sir, our ability to analyse technical situations has markedly increased since the early days of steam, and with this has arisen a terrible tendency to scare ourselves and confuse ourselves with a morass of technical complexity. Always it seems so much easier to make one more technical study; so much safer to await one more vital development; so much wiser to listen to one more Faint Heart. We pretend that today things are so much more difficult than yesterday. Yet are they, Sir? Are our difficulties any more baffling than those, for instance, which faced the man who turned the Navy over to oil. This is what he had to say:[5]

'Owing to the systems of finance by which we had bound ourselves, we were not allowed to borrow even for capital or 'once

---

[5] The World Crisis, W.S. Churchill. Vol. I, Chapter VI, *'The Romance of Design.'*

for all' expenditure. Every penny must be won from Parliament year by year, and constituted a definite addition to the inevitably rising and already fiercely challenged Naval Estimates. And beyond these difficulties loomed up the more intangible problems of markets and monopolies. The oil supplies of the world were in the hands of vast oil trusts under foreign control. To commit the Navy irrevocably to oil was indeed 'to take arms against a sea of troubles.' Wave after wave, dark with storm, crested with foam, surged towards the harbour in which we still sheltered. Should we drive out into the teeth of the gale, or should we bide contented where we were? Yet beyond the breakers was a great hope. If we overcame the difficulties and surmounted the risks we should be able to raise the whole power of the Navy to a definitely higher level; better ships, better crews, higher economies, more intense forms of war power – in a word, mastery itself was the prize of the venture. Forward then!'

I spoke of Faint Heart, Sir. Perhaps we should not forget that his fellow rogues were Mistrust and Guilt; that they lived in Deadman's Lane; and that it was Little-Faith who slept and was set upon.

How do we dare to doze and dream up our funny little paper dreams? Most of those who know about the application of nuclear power to ships assert that this source of power will replace oil for all but the smallest units. Advances in shipbuilding and marine engineering have always possessed an inherent element of danger. What advances, anywhere, have not been dangerous? But, surely, Sir, the greatest danger, is not to advance at all.

It isn't the lack of paper studies, there are masses of them. It isn't the lack of scientific development, there is plenty. It isn't even the lack of money (for the sum by aviation standards is infinitesimal) which is holding up further advance. It is quite simply the lack of operational data, the lack of practical experience in the design, building, and operation of a surface ship with a well proved reactor system. Sir, statistics and the polished briefs of permanent officials cannot possibly interpret the rewards we should harvest from an immediate and sustained assault on the engineering frontiers associated with getting a nuclear merchant ship to sea.

Already five projects are in hand in Germany, and the first nuclear ship will be afloat in 1965. There is a French idea for an oceanographic research ship. Norway, in conjunction with Sweden, has plans for a

20,000-ton ore carrier; a 65,000-ton tanker suggested originally by Britain has now been taken over by a team working in Holland. Russia and the United States are well ahead. Only Britain lags and awaits with tranquillity the moment when her merchant fleet and her Royal Navy will sail only by permission of one of the oil-rich States of the Caribbean or the Middle East, disappearing as they seem to be, one by one, behind the Iron Curtain.

I have not touched on our fishing industry, which is another element of sea power of increasing significance in the years to come; nor on the problem of manning the ships we must build and operate. It was in this House, just under 200 years ago, that a Member said:

> 'Give up the fishery, you will lose your breed of seamen, and I know no way that the country has of breeding seamen but this one the fishery, and the other the coasting trade.'[6]

It was the 'Teddy Boys' of their generation who found Australia with Captain Cook; who sailed with Gilbert and Drake and Hawkins and Anson; who raced their clippers round the Horn. Our Borstals are full of the same fine young men who have sought the same excitement and adventure in ways less suited to our modern society. There is a lesson here somewhere if we could only learn it. In the *Otaio*, a trading cargo ship built for the simultaneous training of their very highly selected deck and engineer apprentices, the New Zealand Shipping Company have a most splendid concept. I wonder if this idea could not be extended to the training of deck and engineering hands drawn from Borstals and approved schools. A background of the rough sea provides a natural education which stone walls and warders, however devoted and dedicated the latter may be, can never give. Instead of doing anything like this we have turned our eyes to the air and we have allowed Russian sputniks and American spacemen to lead us from our destiny. I repeat 'We have walked into a well from looking at the stars.'

All I have said, Sir, could be done tomorrow given the willpower, the drive, and a little money. Just a modicum of understanding of the problem of sea power; just a mite of goodwill, leadership, and enthusiasm; just a little appreciation of what the shipping and shipbuilding industries have endured in the last half century; and a great step forward could be taken.

The southern shipyards pose a special problem of their own in the solution of which Admiralty help might be necessary. For instance, if the

---

[6] Admiral Saunders, quoted by Archbishop David Mathew in *Naval Heritage*

Government were to buy their shares and allot to them the Dockyard quota of the shipbuilding programme, then there would be an easement of the heavily loaded Royal Yards. The building experience which is so essential to the Dockyard professional grades could still be catered for by exchange service; but the sudden impact created by unforeseen, but inevitable, operational changes in the repair and refit programme would be restricted to the Royal Dockyards themselves and insulated from the new construction programme.

But there still remains the nub of the matter, the rationalisation of the vast shipbuilding complexes of the Tyne and Clydeside; for on these two great rivers, and on the shipyards of Liverpool, Belfast, Barrow, and the Tees, and the other smaller shipyards on the east and west coasts, the life of this country depends. Depth of water, size of yard, type of order book, affiliated companies, geography of the yard, and a hundred other factors all come into it. The problem of the cost of gas and coal and steel must be looked at, for this assembly industry of shipbuilding can control, at the most, only a third of its own costs. Only a Royal Commission, I believe, could plumb the peculiarly difficult topographical, technical, and human problems involved.

Last of all, Sir, sea power is indivisible. The Navy, though an essential instrument which ensures free passage to our merchant fleet, is only the secondary instrument of sea power. Our merchant fleet and the industry which builds the ships are now sponsored by the Ministry of Transport; logically the Admiralty should also be transferred to this Ministry. However willing and able the officials in the Ministry of Transport may be, there are conclusive arguments for putting them once more under the Admiralty and allowing it the same increased numbers which the Ministry of Transport is now (so very rightly) employing on the shipping and shipbuilding task. As I've said, sea power is indivisible, Sir. The Admiralty is the largest employer of shipyard labour, the largest single customer for the shipbuilding industry, the largest shipowner, the Government instrument for the direction of the Royal Navy. It is staffed by devoted officials who, in their work, are necessarily in daily contact with the shipbuilding, the shipping, and the ship repairing industry, and who, through long association, understand the problems of sea power in their widest context.

Whatever artificial arrangements may be made, the Admiralty in fact will always remain the Ministry of Sea Power. It is to the Admiralty that the whole industry turns for and will always turn for advice.

Lord Hailsham said recently:[7]

> 'We live in a land hungry for leadership and idealism, for deftness of touch and imagination, for dash and resolution, for technical skill coupled with the flash and glitter of genius. We live in an age surfeited with the cliché and the platitude, weary of mere words and yet longing for inspiration, tired of activity but in burning need of action. In such an age it is well to look back to the past not so much in admiration as in hope, that in the desperate shifts of the present something may yet be granted to us of the qualities which made our people great.'

Surely, Sir, it was our ability in the past to use the oceans on which this country rose to prosperity and, as we neglect sea power, so our greatness and prosperity diminish. It is the bounden duty of our statesmen to look to those industries which can give us that sea power by which we have always lived. If they neglect this duty and fall prey to the temptation to procrastinate, or if they look instead to the skies, they betray their trust; and soon we shall have no ships to move on the one open highway of the world, and my children and your children will starve.

---

[7] Speech at a Trafalgar night dinner at the R.N. Barracks, Chatham, October 1957.

PEACE IS OUR PROFESSION
JOURNAL OF THE RUSI MAY 1964

This title was cribbed from the large sign over a US nuclear Air Base in Oxfordshire which I visited with the Imperial Defence College in 1963. The article gives my views on the trend that British strategy should have been adopting at that particular moment and I think this was the first time that I launched the 'Constabulary Concept' as the basis of the UK military effort rather than the vast outpouring of money on a Continental Strategy against a Soviet foe who would invade Western Europe (which the Kremlin coveted as an industrial power house) only as a last resort.

The Concept was aimed at providing a 'maritime holding force' which could hang on in any area where British interests were involved until a full Brigade Group could be flown to the scene. It was in fact a modern version of Gunboat Diplomacy and Sir Barnes Wallis' ideas of integrated transport (in this case integrated military transport) were uppermost in my thinking.

Of course the Constabulary Concept was never adopted to the extent that I postulated but senior figures in NATO were interested. It was brought up at meetings I later attended when Admiral Moorer and Admiral Holmes (successive SACLANTS) were bringing the Standing Naval Force Atlantic into being in the late 60s; and that was as far as it got. The terror invoked by the acts perpetrated during the Soviet invasion of the Eastern areas of Western Europe in 1945, together with the French aptitude for playing their own game regardless of the national interests of others succeeded in stifling what I still regard as a potentially viable strategy. Like most of my other ideas at the time, the viability of the Constabulary Force rested on surface nuclear propulsion for major warships and major tankers and other elements of the Fleet Train. The successive Boards of Admiralty, starved of resources by our adherence to

50

large continental Army and Air Forces, could never see their way even to try for the extra monies involved.

Once more the fault was a lack of imagination in successive governments brought about by the large numbers of retired soldiers and airmen in Parliament and of politicians who understood little of maritime problems. Instead they visualised an eruption across the German Plain (for which of course contingency plans are now known to have existed), as the main threat and were totally uncomprehending of the maritime noose around the Western world which so nearly succeeded. With one or two honourable exceptions most academics studying strategy fell into the same pit.

The title of this article is borrowed, with respect, from the Strategic Air Command, whose motto of course it is, and to whose courage and professional skill, with that of their comrades in the V-Bomber Force, we owe our continuing existence. Indeed, to those who have had the privilege of visiting the aircrews in Bomber Command and their friends in S.A.C., there remains an imprint of intense professional skill and complete dedication, not easily forgotten. Daily, as they fly, or wait at a few minutes notice, they carry with them the death of the world as we know it, and if they are ordered to use their weapons then the rest of us have failed. For it is true to say that all of us, civilian or military, in different ways and degrees, manipulate the wide variety of graduated deterrents, whether moral, economic, political, or military. In whichever field we are engaged, our success or failure can help to spell the difference between peace or escalation into a flaming holocaust.

Peace, then, is our profession too. For those of us in the armed forces, whose profession also is war, the active pursuit of peace is no longer a paradox.

The Threat in the Seventies

War, the Prime Minister has said on several occasions, is no longer a valid act of deliberate national policy. And perhaps we may hope that within the next decade even China will come to accept such a doctrine. But even then little will have happened to lessen tension between men, or the causes of conflict between the multiplying sovereign states.

A wholly communist world will remain the aim of Russia and China, and communist 'blackmail', in a wide variety of guises, will constantly increase. Thus the West will continue to need a really credible deterrent to ensure that any attempt to start a world war remains an irrational act, and also to make it plain to any irrational 'bonehead' who might succeed the existing sophisticated leadership in Russia that any attempt to revert to the old Stalinist dogma of the inevitability of war carries with it the certain risk of world extinction.

Thus the West needs a first strike and, more important, a second strike capability which is palpably real. In Europe, too, where more than any-where the situation will remain tender, there is need for sufficient land and air forces to ensure its territorial integrity without the necessity for an immediate nuclear exchange, whether tactical or strategic.

But it is in the countries outside Europe that the greatest danger threat-ens. If the free world is to escape gradual erosion, it must be able to avoid the *fait accompli* of communist occupation. It will always be impossible to protect every area locally; but the very minimum aim, by political means and by aid, must be so to nourish and sustain the local defences that the possibility of a cheap communist victory is excluded.

In the Middle East and in South-East Asia in particular, the communist bloc, with its inner lines of communication, is always able to concentrate its manpower and material against countries which are militarily weak. It is true that the political penalties, either for a 'peaceful takeover' or for stark aggression, might be great and the vast uncommitted world thereby rallied to the West; but the risk remains and the temptation towards aggression with the prospect of dramatic initial victories is always present.

As well as the deterrent, therefore, the West needs forces 'in being', poised and readily launched, as an essential element in the defence of the free world outside Europe.

The Keepers of the Peace

The United States, as the most powerful nation in the free world; the United Kingdom for her Commonwealth links and her unique place in the world as a trading nation; and France for her close connections with North and West Africa, all have a special responsibility, on the world stage, for preventing the spread of communism.

In the Indian sub continent and in Asia the answer to communism will be determined not by any abundance of Western military forces but by the success or failure of the governments of the Indian subcontinent to dem-onstrate that freedom works. The economic, social, and cultural develop-ment of this part of the world is thus the greatest bastion that can be raised against communism; and so must such a development be regarded by free Europe and by America.

Perhaps, indeed, in the years to come, it will be the Commonwealth which will play the major part in the prevention of world communism. For the Commonwealth, as Mr. Baldwin once said, 'stands in the sweep of every wind, by the wash of every sea, a witness to that which the spirit of confidence and brotherhood can accomplish in the world'.

There are many of little faith who today delight in proclaiming that the Commonwealth is breaking up. Certainly it is changing; and the wealth and majesty of the British Empire have given way to something far less tangible. But as the years go by and the Colonial Empire disappears and the free association remains, there will emerge something far more lasting and deeply inimical to the arid philosophy of communism. For the Commonwealth is not a political, or economic, or military alliance, it is a free association of a complete cross-section of the world's population who, on the whole, acknowledge that more of their interests are in common than in conflict. Those which are in common must be strengthened and those which are in conflict must be discussed, and perhaps resolved, without hate and without animosity.

A Commonwealth secretariat, a clearing house for ideas, would be one further step along the road to really constructive discussion, and a Commonwealth agreement on overflying rights another prodigious step in uniting for peace. Though either or both of these would be welcome to many, the time to launch them is not perhaps ripe at the moment.

The Role of the United Kingdom
The Enemy

In establishing the role of the United Kingdom in the prevention of communism, the importance to any plans of the former's economic health is plainly fundamental. The repercussions throughout the sterling area and the world of an economic disaster in London would vastly benefit the communist cause. This has been said before; but there has been no sign yet that the public realises how the threat of world communism is made more real and more urgent by the bursting population of the developing countries and their increasing poverty. But unless the ordinary man and woman is made aware of the widening gap between the 'haves' and the 'have nots', and how effectively we can diminish it, then there is probably nothing that can save the world from disaster in the reasonably near future.

The BBC and the Press

In all this the BBC and the British Press could play a noble and effective part, but the former desperately lacks money and still more overseas relay stations and the latter is the despair of those who travel abroad and have to listen to comments on it. In the fight for freedom in which we are all engaged the British Press could be such a staunch ally but at present is a poor one. If it could only be brought to divert just a small stream of its daily torrent of criticism to putting its own house in order, the cause of freedom would be advanced.

The UK, then, through its economic integrity, through the integrity of some of its newspapers and its broadcasting, through its Commonwealth links, through its 'image' of political stability and dynamic industrial advance, through its forces well armed but never aggressive, could be the greatest of all world influences for the success of freedom and democracy.

The Role of the Military Forces of the U.K.

Deployment

There seems to be several well defined and alternative, though mutually exclusive, patterns of deployment for the forces Great Britain can afford.
We could:

(a) make a massive contribution to the nuclear deterrent;

(b) withdraw all our forces East of Suez and fortify the Atlantic Alliance;

(c) turn our backs on the deterrent and on the defence of the U.K. and Europe, and concentrate on dominating, mostly by sea and air, the high seas (especially around Africa and between Aden and Singapore) over which the ideas and goods of the free world must flow to the developing countries.

Alternatively we could afford a mixture and a little bit of each.

The quality of judgment needed to weigh the needs of foreign policy; to stretch the tenuous resources of the Exchequer; to spot the real danger points in the Communists' erosive drive; to evolve the quality and quantity and best type of answer to that drive, demands in the first place a comprehensive and far-reaching intellectual analysis by a wide variety of disciplines.

Defence Analysis

Writing in the RUSI Journal,[1] three officers said: 'There is no doubt that a large part of the original strategic thinking comes from America and France. Many strategic thinkers active in American university seminars

---

[1] *R.U.S.I. Journal*, August, 1963.

are among the President's closest advisers and the Service attitude to these resources of thought is perhaps more sympathetic in America than in the U.K. At the same time it is difficult for defence planners in White-hall to give strategic problems the intellectual analysis they deserve: the pressure of day to day work and the sudden peaks and dips of the political and international barometer limit the opportunities for measured thought . . . This seems an opportune moment for the establishment of a 'British Institute of Strategic Affairs' where civil and military defence planners could join in debate . . . with the best brains from the universities . . . and the many disciplines essential to any realistic analysis of policy. The scientist, the engineer, the economist, the industrialist all have their part to play and it is essential that they should come together when strategic concepts are being discussed.'

Dr. Kissinger, in the last paragraph of the last chapter of *The Necessity for Choice*, defines the universal 'Commissar' of our time and refers to the 'pedantic' application of administrative norms by the adminis-trator 'whose world is defined by regulations in whose making he has no part.'

'Our challenge,' concludes Dr. Kissinger, 'is to overcome an atmos-phere in which all sense of reverence for the unique and therefore the capacity for real innovation stands in danger of being lost. The obsession with safety and predictability must produce an attitude fearful of risk and striving to reduce everything, including man himself, to manipulable qualities.'

'What we need,' he writes in another chapter, 'is men at the apex of our organisations who somehow can create a framework of purpose for those who work at the base of the pyramid.'

In the age in which we live, where the speed of communication and advance of technology have in so many ways outstripped the limited ability of the human brain to peer through the maze and realistically to define policy, every effort must be made to assist those who hold positions of great responsibility to retain their creativity and to prevent routine from becoming an end in itself. Such arrangements are not yet common enough in the U.K.

The Application of Science and Technology

In all this it is a variety of disciplines, and not any single discipline, which is needed. Especially we must be on our guard that in our national life and sometimes in the arming and deployment of our forces, the scientist, in some curious form of exclusive wedlock with those whose education has had a classical background, does not come to occupy too dominant a position. Both fundamental scientists and classical scholars are apt to consider that the man who does something useful is an inferior being. As Professor Garner once said,[2] 'It is apparently considered to be of higher service to mankind to study classics or literature or to carry out so called fundamental research than, in the words of the Charter of the Institution of Civil Engineers, 'to direct the great services of power in nature for the use and convenience of man.' Indeed more recently Dr. Ogorkiewicz[3] has charged that some of our failures in the weapon field are due to the lack in the Government service of what he calls 'the inbuilt defence mechanism against an imbalance between research and down to earth engineering in its ultimate need (in private industry) to produce marketable products.' He concludes, 'the scientific Civil Service, by tradition and recruitment policy, favours the research scientist and the analytical research attitude to problems. As a result there is a tendency to pay more attention to analysing problems than to synthesising knowledge into useful equipment, and more concern with perfection and experimentation than with getting out workable equipment, which would be the case if product-conscious engineers figured more prominently.' And on 21st November, 1963, Professor Sir Willis Jackson, F.R.S., said,[4] 'Finally the Civil Service is also not free from responsibilities in so far as the majority of the professional engineers whom it employs forms part of the so-called 'Works Group of Professional Classes,' a term which suggests that their status is lower – as their career prospects undoubtedly are – relative to members of the Scientific Civil Service.'[5] Whatever the truth may be, much is heard in Parliament and elsewhere about the shortage of scientists and the drain to America; far less, if anything, is ever recounted about the disastrous drop in the last decade in numbers of mechanical engineers on whose skill in the main the great prosperity of the country once was built and on whose efforts, and those of electrical engineers, the effective arming of the Services, as well as the economic well-being of all in the country, including the scientists, really depends.

---

[2] Professor F.H. Garner, Redwood Lecture 1951.
[3] *Brasseys Annual*, 1963. Chapter XI. 'Failings of the Weapon Development System.' R.M. Ogorkiewicz.
[4] *Scientific, Technological & Technical Manpower*. Sir Willis Jackson F.R.S. The Tenth Fawley Lecture of the University of Southampton.
[5] The recent inauguration of the Admiralty Engineering Services is a notable advance.

British Strategy

Many, perhaps the majority, would assert that Britain's world role is far from over and her influence for peace is still profound, ubiquitous and often decisive. Once she loses the urge to have a finger in every pie her future as a world power is finished, and the world would be the first to notice, and feel, the loss.

The Deterrent

There are many arguments for retaining a nuclear deterrent capability, and almost as many against doing so. Three facts stand out stark and absolutely incontrovertible:

(1) Britain and Britain's scientists were founder members in the nuclear deterrent business.

(2) Once out of the business there is for all practical purposes no readmittance.

(3) So long as we retain even a small but credible nuclear second strike capability, this country can never be susceptible to blackmail and the threat of individual nuclear extinction, unless the aggressor is prepared to pay at least an equal price.

So Britain must keep the deterrent and, to identify her interests with those of Europe, sufficient British troops must always be stationed there to show her allies that she is committed, irrevocably, to its defence.

Limited War

General Hackett has said,[6] 'Total war we have to avoid. But acts of organised violence between groups of men which we are unlikely to be able, entirely, to prevent, we must do something about.' And again, '. . . situations are easily conceivable in which the only hope of avoiding something worse may lie in taking a hand in it. We may well be working towards a position in which the main purpose of the profession of arms is not to win wars but to avoid them; that is to say, by timely warfare to lessen the risks of general war. The chief function of the armed forces becomes the containment of violence. The function and duty of the military professional is the orderly application of armed force . . . his duty is to develop his skill in the management of violence. We are moving,' suggests General Hackett, 'towards what Janowitz calls a constabulary concept.'[7]

---

[6] *The Profession of Arms*, Lees Knowles lectures of 1963. Lt-Gen. Sir John Winthrop Hackett.
[7] *The Professional Soldier*. Janowitz (Free Press of Glencoe 1960).

The detailed implications of such a concept will be examined further. Meanwhile in a world which contains the UN; in a world where a few men armed with spears crossing a frontier cause headlines in the Press everywhere; in a world which knows that there are two great systems of destruction poised and ready to destroy it; the thought that three of the great Powers who have most to lose if control is lost are still prepared, until some better system evolves, to keep their forces poised and ready instantly to contain violence and to create a pause until the slower moving forces of sanity and conciliation can be marshalled and brought to bear, is a comforting one.

The Constabulary Concept

Geographical Considerations

While France has an interest in North and West Africa and the U.S. in China, the main area of possible U.K. involvement lies in the Singapore, Darwin, Cape Town, Aden quadrilateral. In particular this includes:

(a) *Malaysia*, with whom it seems likely we shall have a continuing Defence Agreement for many years and for whose peaceful self-development the U.K. carries a very considerable responsibility.

(b) *S.E.A.T.O.*, in which the U.K. is a partner and which, as the years go by, is likely to play an increasingly significant part in the maintenance of peace.

(c) *Hong Kong*, in which, for internal security and for general stability, the U.K. must continue to maintain a presence.

(d) *The Arabian Peninsular*, to parts of which the U.K. is bound by treaty obligations and whose oil supply, both as to cost and availability, could drastically affect the price, at home and abroad, of British manufactured products and thus the whole economy.

(e) *The Developing States of Africa*, where the turbulent history of the Congo may well be repeated in other States. This could require unilateral short term intervention for the protection of the white population.

(f) *The High Commission Territories*, where until South Africa abandons apartheid, the U.K. will carry a continuing responsibility for their integrity and the maintenance of law and order.

(g) *The Indian Subcontinent*, where the dominant strategic factors of the Indian Ocean area are the Indian Ocean itself and the land mass. Neither India nor Pakistan can afford to build up the naval strength necessary to dominate the entire area. If the Indian Ocean and the Bay of Bengal were to be sterilised by hostile naval forces operating from Rangoon, Indonesia, or Mogadishu, then the indigenous defence industries could not for long support the armies and air forces in operation in the north.

(h) *Gan*, which is a good fleet anchorage and an extremely valuable air staging post.

Military Implications

If, then, General Hackett's proposition is applied and the U.K. sets about providing an effective Constabulary Force in an area, mostly sea, covering nearly a quarter of the globe, some more precise idea of what can and cannot be accomplished needs to be spelled out. The Constabulary Force is by definition a highly mobile and relatively lightly armed force which can provide an armed garrison in some troubled area almost at the drop of a hat. Behind it lies a sufficiently massive and quick follow-up able to stabilise the situation for as many hours or days as possible while diplomacy tries to settle the issue. The greatest weapons of the Constabulary Force, in fact, are speed and resolution.

Limitations of the Constabulary Force

In particular the Constabulary Force:

(a) could not resist effectively any all-out sea, land, or air offensive by a sophisticated and fully industrialised country possessing its own arms industry;

(b) could resist aggression by a second class Power plentifully supplied by Russia or China with non-nuclear sea, land, or air forces for a short period only, which might well prove costly in life and treasure. In spite of this the pause would allow diplomatic activity to be maximised and powerful (non-nuclear) air power deployed from the U.K. and made ready to strike at the aggressor if all else failed;

(c) could contain local rebellion and unrest, whether fostered initially by Soviet communism or not, until the arrival of reinforcements;

(d) could thwart the forces of disruption, and by its obvious ability to react instantly and effectively, induce a feeling of security, and thus a great support for those men of goodwill in the area who seek, by peaceful and constitutional means, to lift their countries from poverty and squalor into nationhood.

The ability in each one of these cases effectively to operate the Constabulary Force would depend in the end on the possession by the United

Kingdom of a nuclear weapon capability whereby the ultimate military force of Soviet communism, the nuclear missile threat, could be kept at arm's length whilst attempts were made to restore peace and stability and allow diplomacy to work.

It is clear from the above that a judgement needs to be made which will fundamentally affect the level of success in the four situations postulated, and that in particular the Western Indian Ocean (in the absence of Aden as a base) presents a difficult choice. A force the size of the U.S. Seventh Fleet, in conjunction with the navies of India and Pakistan, could certainly dominate the whole Indian Ocean and the Bay of Bengal while at the same time fulfilling the Constabulary Concept to an extent which could raise the expected level of complete success from (c) to (b) above. But such a force is beyond the financial resources available to the United Kingdom today. This leads to a discussion of our strategy in general in this area, and naval strategy in particular.

Area Strategy

So long as our defence agreement with Malaysia continues and so long as her Government deems it necessary for British forces to help defend her country, then we possess a base in the South-East Asian area from which any action to contain violence and to maintain peace would almost certainly be permitted. If, in the future, Malaysia should feel herself sufficiently secure against the dangers of communist subversion and erosion and invites us to withdraw, then the Australian mainland is not far away. And there is small doubt that in such an event a powerful U.K. presence in northern Australia would not be unwelcome to the Australian Government as part of the defences against possible Chinese or Indonesian aggression, particularly in a period in Australia's history when so many of her resources are necessarily and rightly occupied in building up her population and economy.

Two problems then remain to be solved: (a) the maintenance of a Constabulary Force in the Western Indian Ocean; (b) the protection of the trade routes to India and Pakistan.

The Sea-Air Threat

From west to east in this area the sea-air threat consists of:
  (a) Egyptian or Communist (Russian or Chinese) forces operating from Hodeida, Berbera, or Mogadishu;
  (b) Chinese forces operating from Rangoon;
  (c) Indonesian forces operating from Sumatra or Java;

(d) Communist submarine forces operating from any of the above or from supply and depot ships.

Superficially this Soviet threat appears substantial and likely not only to place any Constabulary Force in a perilous position but also to have the ability effectively to blockade the Indian subcontinent. On the other hand, though the weapons are sophisticated, the backing, at the moment at least, is minimal and, in the event of a shooting war in which the Indian subcontinent was involved, drastic air action could be taken from India against Soviet naval bases and, with effective maritime air reconnaissance, against Soviet depot ships and submarines also. This should reduce the threat to reasonable proportions until stronger free world resources could be brought to bear.

It does not, however, solve the problem of the sea-air threat against the Constabulary Force operating off the coast of Africa or Arabia. This threat could come from Egyptian forces or Soviet submarines.

Strategy and Ship Design

Lord Fisher once wrote:[8] 'Strategy should govern the types of ships to be designed. Ship designs as dictated by strategy should govern tactics. Tactics should govern details of armaments.'

Over the last decade and a half the extraordinary technological advances in every field and the unpredictable political events on the world scene, coupled with the normal historic cycle of post-war neglect of naval affairs by statesmen, have left us with an all too small navy. Throughout this period, however, the Board of Admiralty have somehow still managed to maintain the highest quality of ships and weapons, and equally, if not more important, have managed to train ships' companies to use them in a manner which is unsurpassed anywhere. This is not to say that there are not still many things wrong, but in conceiving a strategy and matching ship design to it, well-informed judgement and experience of every aspect of naval warfare is readily available. The only parameters are financial.

In propounding the concept of a Constabulary Force based on nuclear power, this article suggests that on balance a more effective force can be achieved within the same financial parameters, albeit a less well armed one.

The Constabulary Force

In broad terms, the requirement for a Constabulary Force is to be able to place a battalion of soldiers or a Royal Marine Commando ashore, with

---

[8] *Naval Necessities*. 1904 (Published privately)

armour, artillery, and air support, and to maintain it, possibly in contact with an enemy, for as long as it takes to bring it up to Brigade Group strength. Thereafter the Brigade Group will have to be sustained.

In terms of lift, the forward wave will consist of a Commando ship and an assault ship with a carrier. These in turn will need tankers and store ships, all with an adequate escort which will itself need refuelling. If suitable airfields were available, the subsequent follow-up troops and immediate supplies could come by air; but in any case a further considerable sea follow-up would be needed with suitably designed ships preloaded and situated well forward.

The theatre of operations has already been defined in broad terms: namely the littoral countries of the Western Indian Ocean, other than India and Pakistan.

Some facts relevant to the mounting of a maritime Constabulary Force

At this point certain relevant facts, mostly of a technical nature, need to be stated, together with one or two more or less obvious implications.

1. Oil-fired ships use about twice as much oil at 30 knots (720 miles per day) as they do at 25 knots (600 miles per day).

2. Ships have to refuel every three to four days. In a task force, this refuelling process is nearly continuous, as ships need to keep 'topped up.' All this severely reduces the actual speed of advance. Ships when refuelling are good submarine targets.

3. Prolonged high speed steaming causes considerable wear and tear on boiler room equipment. The electrical load from modern weapons and equipment is so great than the amount of oil available for steaming is diminished. To offset this there has been a drive for higher thermal efficiency; but in some cases this has affected reliability.

4. The fuel consumption of a large task force continually at sea and steaming at high speed calls for a large number of 'replenishment at sea' and freighting tankers, all requiring escort.

5. The need continually to conserve fuel severely restricts the speed and tactical handling of individual ships and task forces.

6. Air down-takes and funnels create difficult ship construction problems. They also make it impossible to exclude radiation and blast damage.

7. A Bill is now before the U.S. Congress[9] which if passed makes it certain that by the mid-seventies most of the U.S. merchant marine will be

---

[9] 88th Congress 1st Session H.R. 1071. Jan. 9th. 1963.

nuclear-powered. Nuclear propulsion for surface ships and for warships over 3,000 tons will be the rule rather than the exception.

8. A warship's hull and machinery is built to last the life of the ship (the armament can be changed). Machinery installed now will still be in use in 1980.

9. Due to the slowing down of the power station programme there is surplus reactor manufacturing capacity in the U.K. The U.K. is the last of all the great powers to get into the nuclear ship business. Indeed she has hardly started.

10. To guard against radiation dangers the capital cost of reactors and reactor machinery is higher than for oil-fired boilers. But this cost includes the price of an enormous built-in 'reliability factor' which gives a valuable dividend in the shape of prolonged high speed, trouble-free operation.

11. An oil-fired task force creates a demand for a large fleet carrier able to dominate the area for 300–400 miles around. A task force with continuous high speed available and no refuelling problem is in an immeasurably stronger position to avoid trouble. It is possible that the carrier size could be reduced whilst retaining an offensive and defensive capability with V.T.O.L. aircraft.

12. The concept of a nuclear tanker/accommodation ship could mean a new class of small single-purpose A/S frigates, conventionally powered but refuelled by and the crews relieved from the parent ship. This could reduce the cost and increase the number of frigates. The savings might also result in money being available for a nuclear-powered escort cruiser armed with powerful anti-submarine and anti-aircraft missiles.

13. With oil-fired ships the need for material refit is more frequent than the need for relaxation and recreation of personnel. With nuclear ships the reverse is the case and some form of wholesale crew relief would be essential. This would immensely simplify the naval welfare and training problem.

14. High speed is still the best form of defence against submarine attack. Only a nuclear ship can maintain high speed more or less for ever.

Oil versus Nuclear Fuel

The arguments for and against nuclear propulsion can be summed up as follows – an oil-fired task force would:

(a) cover less mileage in any given time due to its slower average speed and its need to refuel;

(b) need more duplication to keep one credible task force on station;

(c) need a heavy fleet carrier escort;

(d) be more susceptible to submarine attack than a nuclear-powered task force;

(e) be cheaper on a ship-for-ship basis;

(f) be more expensive as a task force because:

> (i)   more ships would be needed to maintain any given front line density;
>
> (ii) more supporting tankers would be needed;
>
> (iii) more aircraft and escorts would be needed.

From the above it seems that the idea of a nuclear-propelled force merits examination.

The Order of Battle of a Constabulary Force

Task Force 1 at sea

(a) Commando ship (one Royal Marine Commando and its helicopters)

(b) Assault ship (tanks, lorries, artillery, broadcasting station).

(c) Small carrier (25,000 tons) with V.T.O.L. and AEW aircraft and helicopters.

(d) Escort cruiser with A/S helicopters and A/S and A/A missiles.

(e) Hunter-killer submarine.

(f) Tanker/accommodation ship.

(g) Eight small A/S frigates.

All these ships would be capable of 30 knots sustained speed, and (a) to (f) would be nuclear-propelled.

Task Force II

As in (a) to (g) above but stationed at Gan at 24 hours notice. In addition at Gan (or forward with Task Force I) there would be one nuclear-powered 'warehouse ship' preloaded with landing craft, ammunition, petrol, and stores to support a Brigade Group, and one aircraft support ship to assist with servicing facilities.

Task Forces I and II would rotate in the seagoing role, being relieved periodically by Task Force III.

Task Force III

As in (a) to (g) (Task Force I) but refitting at Singapore or Darwin at 72 hours notice. Able to reach Gan in 10 days.

Task Force IV

Refitting in, or *en route* to or from, U.K.

In addition there would be a need for accommodation in Australia/ Malaysia for the Middle East Strategic Reserve (one Brigade Group) and a considerable echelon of Transport Command sufficient to lift them to Gan in a specified time.

As postulated earlier, the Constabulary Force should provide a highly mobile, relatively lightly armed, quick reaction presence, and such a concept, if acceptable, must be applied not only to the scale of weapons but also to the building and arming of the naval ships employed on this duty.

Conclusions

General

There is no indication that, even in the distant future, the battle for the hearts and minds of men will have diminished. As always, the U.K. will have to be in the forefront of this battle. To remain effective her economy must flourish, and investment, both from the government and from the private sector of industry, must flow overseas into the developing countries. This will not occur unless there is a reasonable degree of stability in these countries. Powerful international organisations like U.N, or the give-and-take of inter-Commonwealth discussion, can all help to create stability, as also can the greatly respected U.K. means of publicity through the BBC World Service. If the British Press could adopt a more responsible outlook, it too would have a part to play. British and Commonwealth statesmen and the instruments of their policy, the armed forces, have a vital role in this battle.

The Role of the British Armed Forces

British armed forces have two missions to which they are already committed, the provisions of a deterrent and the commitment to Europe. Both of these are inescapable if British influence is to operate on the world stage. They also have a third mission, which is more difficult to identify with a precision as it is ubiquitous and world wide. Broadly, it is to assist British influence (by which is meant the whole great tradition of British democracy) to induce that stability which will let the developing countries go forward in peace.

The need for a Comprehensive Analysis of British Strategy

In the mixed up world of today, this is an incomparably more difficult task than the armed forces have ever faced before. British strategy urgently needs the impacts of minds skilled in many disciplines, not only to assist in its evolution but also that men of influence in the country, and hence eventually the country generally, may feel committed to it and back it to the hilt.

Financial Considerations

If the need for Britain to maintain a presence is conceded, then in the absence of foreign bases there seems to be no alternative but to deploy our armed forces in some effective maritime fashion. In terms of today's weapons, such a role would probably not be more expensive than a series of bases (and in terms of overseas payments it might be cheaper); though the getting to it involves a double stance, and this is costly. But our era is one of steadily mounting weapon costs and this, together with the provision of a nuclear capability, makes the financial equation progressively more impossible of solution.

Political Considerations

On the political side the adoption of a double stance has, at once, a generally upsetting effect; whilst any apparent intention to abandon bases is likely to engender immense pressure on the U.K. to abandon her interest east of Suez altogether. Before embarking on the surrender of any bases, therefore, it is essential to possess a politico-military alternative which is well known and, if possible, widely acclaimed.

To the more or less informed public at home and abroad, an effective maritime presence suggests a U.S. 7th Fleet type organisation which possesses a 'sledge hammer' capability highly appropriate to its present task. But, and especially in the eyes of Afro-Asians, there is political dynamite in such a solution for a stabilising influence on the littoral countries of the Western Indian Ocean.

It would also be manifestly beyond our financial means to support.

Three Alternatives and an Answer

All this adds up to the need to equate the adjective 'effective,' when applied to a military/maritime presence in the Western Indian Ocean, with the financial and political realities of the situation. The three possible solutions might all need, in one way or another, the backing of a Brigade Group and a correspondingly large echelon of Transport Command; and certainly in the background, the possession of a strategic nuclear deterrent.

The three solutions are:

1. A 'sledgehammer force' of the 7th Fleet type; immensely powerful and therefore politically unacceptable; immensely expensive and therefore financially impossible.
2. A similar 'sledgehammer force' done 'on the cheap.' Immensely powerful (and also politically unacceptable) when available; but lacking sufficient backing and resources to render it continuously militarily credible.
3. A 'Constabulary Force'; nuclear-powered, fast-moving, always available, independent of any substantial supply chain, armed only with long service sailors, soldiers, and airmen, very conventional weapons, and a powerful broadcasting station.

It is the submission of this article that if 'Peace is our Profession,' then the maintenance of peace and stability in the area here discussed and the essential economic viability of the U.K. would be best served by the Constabulary Force type of maritime presence.

ALL OCEANS LEAD TO ENGLAND[1]
JOURNAL OF THE RUSI 1966

I only met Sir Barnes Wallis once and that not long before he died. But in his Presidential Address to the Engineering Section of the British Association entitled 'The Strength of England' he used the phrase I have taken for a title and with his permission I borrowed it.

Barnes Wallis was a marine engineer by training although better known for his 'bouncing bomb' with which the Mohne Dam was destroyed, as well as being the inventor of the geodetic aircraft design derived from the studies he had made in the design of the R 100 Airship. His ideas for an integrated world transport system on land, sea, under the sea and in the air, which he put forward in his Presidential Address seemed to me then, and still do, to make good sense. But my main preoccupation at the time this article was written was with sea transport and the obvious fact Wallis so vehemently proclaimed that 'All Oceans Lead to England'.

Had we had an iota of imagination or sense of our maritime history Britain could have been the entrepôt of the Western world as Hong Kong and Singapore are of the East. But Rotterdam overtook London and the fact that the Channel and the Straits of Dover are becoming now so dangerously crowded that the great Port of Falmouth and Carrick Roads and Plymouth, together with the Channel Tunnel, should have been developed instead, never occurred to anyone.

'It is extremely important', writes Mao Tse-tung,[2] 'to keep the enemy in the dark about where and when our forces will attack.

---

[1] From 'The Strength of England'. Presidential address to the Engineering Section of the British Association, by Dr. Barnes Wallis.
[2] Mao Tse-tung, '*On Protracted War*'.

This creates a basis for misconceptions and unpreparedness on his part . . . In order to achieve victory we must as far as possible make the enemy blind and deaf by sealing his eyes and ears, and drive his commanders to distraction by creating confusion in their minds.'

General Beaufre[3] has written, '. . . In spite of Raymond Aron in France and Liddell Hart in England, questions of strategy make no impact on the general public or indeed on the military, who continue to think merely in terms of technical progress and tactics.'

A suggestion[4] by three officers, one from each Service, at the Imperial Defence College, that a British Institute of Strategic Affairs should be created where the broader and less secret aspects of national strategy could be studied, analysed, publicly discussed, and debated, so that a corpus of informed opinion could be generated, seems now, in spite of much initial high level support, to have been effectively killed.

Various articles in this Journal[5] and in Brassey's Annual[6] over the last three years arguing that British sea power and 'maritime strategy' are not solely the business of the Royal Navy but comprehend everything from the farming of the sea (the only hope of feeding an increasingly protein-hungry world population) to the fostering of technology which will ensure the safe, cheap, and rapid passage of goods over 'the one open highway free of international political hindrance', have evoked more interest in United States' universities and the U.S.N. than in the U.K.

It seems highly probable that the Presidential address to the Engineering Section of the British Association by Dr. Barnes Wallis, a marine engineer by upbringing and by any standard a not unsuccessful aircraft designer by profession, will suffer the same fate. His confident and much more authoritative assertion that the future greatness and strength of England depends on the proper use of sea power and the use of a different sort of air power seems also to have fallen on stony ground. 'All oceans lead to England', writes Dr. Barnes Wallis, and 'England is the Clapham Junction of the air routes of the world.'

---

[3] *Introduction to Strategy*, p.21. André Beaufre.
[4] *JOURNAL* of the R.U.S.I., August 1963.
[5] 'The One Open Highway', August 1962; 'World Population and British Strategy', August 1963; 'Peace is our Profession', May 1965.
[6] Brassey's 1963, Chapter VII, 'Sea Power'.

Communism today, whether in Vietnam or as manifested in British industry (by the revealing weekly bulletins of the Economic League which exists to counter subversion by exposing it) continues, as Mao holds it must, 'to blind and deafen us' and 'creates confusion in our minds'.

Clearly, if we are to surmount Communism's erosive strategy, a great public education has to take place and an imaginative and practical policy has to be evolved. Vague exhortations by politicians are no longer sufficient in a democracy daily becoming more literate and educated. Sir Leon Bagrit in the concluding paragraphs of his great series of Reith Lectures said:

> '. . . one of the purposes of good government is to help each member of our society to make his optimum contribution to our national life . . .', and later, 'In spite of the smallness of our country and our lack of raw materials there ought to be no wavering in our determination to remain an important force for good, not only to help ourselves but to be active in helping mankind in general'.

Increasingly the press, the public, and even Parliament are beginning to recognize and respect fact; and the facts of the communist assault must be clearly and publicly identified and equally clearly divorced from near fiction and emotion, which in an educated people can only breed cynicism and disbelief.

Unfortunately Britain still lacks an informed national forum where the great issue of Communism which faces this country and the free world can be confronted, debated, and a strategy to counter it evolved, or at least a degree of public education of what is at stake, achieved.

The suggestion referred to above, put forward three years ago, not only in this journal but by the press, the Institute for Strategic Studies, and often in the universities, and echoed again only recently, for a properly constituted British Institute for Strategic Affairs or a National Institute for Defence Studies (as some would call it – though the name matters not at this stage) simply must be pursued.

Rumour has it that the suggestion has been condemned on a variety of grounds:

(a) that a pragmatic approach is the best way to construct a defence policy;

(b) that national security would be endangered by such an Institute;

(c) that 'advice to Ministers' cannot properly be given, or received, outside official channels; and that advice from such an Institute would be unconstitutional.

All these, the writer of this article would hold, may be superficially true but in importance are not to be compared to the national benefits which would accrue.

The Soviet Threat to British and Western Sea Power – Some Facts

A. Soviet ice-breaker class diesel-electric motor vessels began this season's winter sailings from Europe to Canada on 2nd December 1965; they will make twice as many trips this winter as last. Last winter, for the first time ever, three Soviet vessels, the *Indigirka*, *Volkhovges*, and *Lena*, made six trips to Canadian ports, and on two occasions they delivered cargoes to Quebec and Montreal at a time when the St. Lawrence was closed to conventional shipping. The Canadians have already chartered six Soviet ships to make twelve trips on the Europe-to-Canada route this winter.

B. On 20th October 1965, Kachanov, Secretary of the Krasnodar Kray C.P.S.U. Committee and a Deputy of the RSFSR, gave a talk on the Black Sea tanker fleet. He said it would not be very long before tankers of 100,000 tons and even 200,000 tons cargo capacity would be built. In the seven year period the Black Sea shipping line had doubled its tonnage and a further 12 tankers would be delivered before the end of 1965.

C. According to a Soviet radio broadcast on 15th November 1965, Mikhail Yegorov, U.S.S.R. Deputy Minister of Shipbuilding, told a press conference to mark the 150th anniversary of the launching of the first Russian steamship that in five years' time the Soviet merchant marine would be the fifth biggest in the world, with an aggregate tonnage of 13,600,000. Between 1960 and 1965 it had moved up from eleventh to sixth place. Soviet ships now sailed to 92 countries and the U.S.S.R. had 'become an equal partner even with such a maritime power as Britain'.

D. A Moscow radio broadcast for seamen on 10th November 1965 said: 'The cargo capacity of the Black Sea Shipping Line has increased by almost 300 per cent during the last seven years and now the line carries annually as much cargo as was carried by the whole Soviet merchant fleet 10 years ago.'

E. (From a lecture to British Army officers!)

'While we are on this question of trade I must call attention to the rising strength of the merchant fleets of the Soviet bloc, made up mainly of fast modern ships. They, and the shipbuilding capacity of the bloc countries, constitute a serious and growing challenge to the merchant fleets of the West. The same applies to their trawler fleets. Soviet trawlers are now fishing off Northern Australia, right down both coasts of Africa, and in the south-west Atlantic.

'This expansion forms part of the pattern of Soviet naval strength, for in no country are the naval, merchant, and fishing fleets more closely integrated. Some people are just waking up to the fact that the Soviet merchant fleet is the sixth largest in the world, and that her submarine fleet of 465 or more is the largest. She has at least 32 nuclear-powered submarines and about 45 equipped with Polaris-type missiles.'

The quotations above are only a few snippets culled in the last few weeks from non-confidential sources available to the writer. The real story is even more grim.

Yet British sea power, the means whereby this country clawed its way to greatness, is still looked at by the majority as a function of the sailors within the Ministry of Defence rather than as a national policy on which much of the strength of England, and indeed the future of the world, if the population is not to starve, depends.

Sea power in its classic sense means the ability to transport goods across the oceans and, if called on, to deny this ability to the enemy. Today it comprehends trans-oceanic transport below, on, just above, and far above the oceans. Aircraft, hoverships, ships, and submarines are all involved and no longer are sailors, and certainly not Royal Navy sailors, the only ones concerned.

The Constituents of British Sea Power in the old meaning of the term

Nevertheless, perhaps it would be convenient here to list the various agencies of one sort or another which today have fairly major interests in British sea power, though only in the old, historic sense. Amongst them would be:

Chamber of Shipping and the Shipowners
Shipbuilding Conference
Ministry of Defence
Board of Trade

Ministry of Transport
Ministry of Technology
Ministry of Agriculture and Fisheries
TUC and many individual unions
Great parts of British industry
Docks and Harbour Boards and Port Authorities throughout the
country
Trawler owners and fishermen
White Fish Authority
Institute of Oceanography
Lloyds Register of Shipping
The Atomic Energy Authority

It would take several volumes of the journal to discuss individually the dimensions of these various interests; but in an increasingly competitive world, where our resources are so strictly limited and where the right aim is so essential, it would seem logical to examine and analyse this whole system so that the problem, as it affects the strength of England, can be comprehended and then confronted.

This article is being written before the Geddes Report is issued; but even Geddes, Devlin, Rochdale – however brilliant each individual report may be – will never bring together all the vast complexity into which some agency should delve if our 'misconceptions and unpreparedness' are not to continue.

Productivity and Distribution

The Trade Unions and many others in this country are still living with that 'olde worlde' thought that over-production is a danger leading to unemployment; that if we keep the same working hours and increase productivity we shall need fewer workers. Of course this can never be true whilst ⅘ths of the world is crying out for goods and services, and it can only arise when the system of distribution has failed to produce the raw materials which are the basis of increased productivity and to distribute the manufactured goods, the results of increased productivity.

Dr. Barnes Wallis's Concepts

Dr. Barnes Wallis raises the twin concepts of nuclear submarine merchantmen using the polar route to the Pacific and STOL aircraft capable both of supersonic speeds for stage lengths of 10,000 miles and efficient subsonic performance for much shorter distances. With Sir Leon Bagrit he brings into juxtaposition two related problems:

(1) the possibility of almost unlimited productivity that automation brings to this country, to be profitably and beneficially exploited;

(2) the possibility that we can devise the necessary means of distribution throughout the world; and by inference the collection, by the same means, of the raw material that we cannot provide ourselves.

Here, then, we begin to approach a new and up to date concept of sea power. Though not everyone would concede that Dr. Barnes Wallis's sub-polar nuclear merchantmen are the immediate answer to our problems, his thesis that, as a nation, we are lost if we lack rapid and economical means of world-wide, trans-oceanic distribution is impossible to deny.

Furthermore, it is difficult not to agree with him that we possess all the engineering and other skills, both on the sea and in the air, necessary to provide these essential means of transportation, whether below, on, just over, or above the oceans, and that only a proper comprehension of the need is lacking, and a means of transposing these (often) military-held skills into the world carrying trade.

So to the vast list of agencies interested in sea power must be added an equally lengthy list of those who in one way or another contribute to air power.

The Study of Trans-oceanic Transport

In its splendid series of Adelphi Papers the Institute for Strategic Studies produces detailed analyses of world problems which are of the greatest possible help to people who seek an inkling of what faces those who come after us. Yet nowhere are our national problems subjected to this same comprehensive analysis; certainly not when, as many of them do, they sprawl across the interests and responsibilities of different ministries in Whitehall.

The ceiling on defence costs calls into question the very existence of a navy and an air force if costs cannot be controlled or reduced. At the same time cheaper (commercial) means of transportation to and from this country are essential if we are to live.

The bringing together of military, air, and sea power in the Ministry of Defence has already set a pattern which could be followed (or imposed) nationally on all the civilian agencies involved in sea and air transport.

The population of the globe will double within our children's lifetime; and if Europe and the West, and in particular England, to which all oceans lead and where all the air routes meet, are to maintain their standards of living and help the underdeveloped countries to survive, they must import, manufacture, export, and distribute.

The communist world, split perhaps a little at the moment, nevertheless continues purposefully to blind us and to muddle us while quietly taking over the carrying trade of the world.

The Role of the Ministry of Defence

The Minister of Defence is reported as saying that defence expenditure is the costing of foreign policy. Surely there are immense dividends which could also accrue if the allied problems of military, sea and air power and the need for cheap transport were looked at together. So far, this article has played down the role of the Ministry of Defence in the future development of British sea power; but in fact it has a vital 'triggering' role to play.

The Navy possesses the most elegantly designed marine propulsion machinery in the world, whether steam, diesel, gas turbine, or nuclear. Because of the limitations of warship design and past systems of costing and controlling expenditure, some of the earlier versions of each design do not possess the reliability that the second and third generation possess; but even Mr. Aubrey Jones has paid tribute to the increased warship utilization which is now becoming the rule. The Services between them constitute the single biggest customer the British shipbuilding industry possesses. Increasingly the British Chamber of Shipping and Lloyds Register are working with the Services by precept, example, and financial inducement to lead the shipbuilding industry out of the doldrums into which it was allowed to sink. It is to be hoped that Geddes will clearly chart the way.

It is the cost of small warships which is the really big problem today, and the high cost of warship building may be attributed in part to a vicious circle, difficult to break.

There is a ceiling to defence expenditure, and as the cost of small warships is so high, fewer are built. Yet the cost remains high because the design of warships is still, by tradition and to some small extent by need, a 'custom' design, and contracts to build are parcelled out to the Warship Group in dribs and drabs on a sort of 'lucky dip' principle, the winner often being the firm prepared financially to risk the most. So short production runs preclude the shipbuilder from redesigning and re-equipping his shipyard to make series production possible and thus really facing up to the job of reducing construction costs.

The answer is that single non-competitive designs, which often mean 'over design' and designs which tend to eliminate initiative by the shipbuilder leading to 'overbuilding', need to be eliminated if costs are to come down.

All this may seem a long way from broad national strategy. The point is this: the Ministry of Defence for some years has been in a very powerful position to 'jack up' the shipbuilding industry – or a portion of it – and full use has not been made of the opportunity.

But now, by combining the shipbuilding needs of all the Services, an opportunity presents itself to introduce new concepts and up to date methods not only within Ministry of Defence procedures but also into the industry, and to lower the cost of warships and associated auxiliary vessels. The dividends to the Services could be immense and together with reducing costs could lead to more ships, to shorter life ships, and therefore to less subsequent expensive conversions in the Royal Dockyards (which take ships out of service and overload the dockyards) and thus to greater overall operational availability in the fleet.

Benefits to Industry

The Ministry of Defence possesses the single most powerful and skilled cell of ship designers and engineers in the country. The 'trade-offs' to industry of their search for economic high speed trans-oceanic movement could be widespread, healthy and invigorating.

The need for Study and Analysis of Trans-oceanic Transportation

But somewhere all this has to be studied. Research associates have to be employed. Blind alleys have to be explored and discarded. The right road has to be found and charted.

A British Institute of Strategic Affairs, suitably staffed and situated near the Ministry of Defence, could make use of much of the immense technical (but often quite unclassified) 'know-how' which exists in that emporium and could work with men of vision, such as Dr. Barnes Wallis and Sir Leon Bagrit, to evolve a national strategy for overseas transport and distribution, compounding all that is best in air and sea power in the very broadest sense of these terms.

To achieve just this one study would be to achieve something that Whitehall is simply not attuned to do. It would show that as a nation we are at last waking up to the threat of a Soviet takeover of the carrying trade of the world; but much more it would demonstrate the usefulness of the sort of agency which has been suggested.

The Royal United Services Institute

'Remember then that your vocation, deliberately chosen, is war. War as a means of peace, but still war'. (*Alston's Seamanship Manual* as used in the old *Britannia*).

Between them the three Services comprise probably the greatest concentration of engineering, leadership, and modern management talent in the country. Generally speaking, their entry and selection procedures are in advance of any other profession and their officer and technician training, by general consent, is superlative.

The majority of those serving today fully understand the totality of the war which we are now fighting and they comprehend better than most that the shadows of this war stretch far beyond the responsibilities of the Ministry of Defence. Very responsible opinions founded on knowledge, experience, and deep study are often expressed at the Imperial Defence College, in the corridors of the R.U.S.I., and in other places where officers of the three Services meet. A great many people outside the Services also have views on defence policy (sometimes jejune and frequently naïve) and these views are widely proclaimed to the great bewilderment of the general public.

The basis of the letter written to the *Journal of the R.U.S.I.* three years ago was that the best way to build up an informed public opinion which might give rise to some enlightened strategic thought would be to create a dialogue or debate between the Services on the one hand and some of the people mentioned above; and that the R.U.S.I. provided an almost ideal venue for this purpose.

Since the original letter was written, 'military studies' have become an accepted feature of several forward-looking universities and at Cranwell, and this is a great step forward. There still remains, however, a need for some 'centre' where officers from the Services, students of military studies, defence correspondents, and others interested in future strategic thought can come together and debate the various issues, to the general education of public opinion.

THE FORGOTTEN THREAT

Leeds Castle, August 1982

I was asked at fairly short notice by Mr Geoffrey Stewart-Smith on behalf I think of the Institute for Foreign Policy Analysis to present and read a paper on the Soviet threat with particular reference to the submarine threat, at a conference to be held at Leeds Castle. For various reasons I could not be there for the first day which sadly prevented me from hearing the Rt. Hon. Sir Alec Douglas-Home expound. However he had to leave early and so I was allocated the most luxurious bedroom in which I have ever slept. The following is what I said.

The number of permutations of the total Soviet threat to the Western way of life is almost limitless. However, even to an audience as sophisticated as this one, especially when the proceedings are being recorded prior to publication for those who do not possess your deep insight, there is one intransigent problem that cannot be too often emphasised. I refer to the almost total inability of most politicians, and many Service people, a great many academics, a large number of churchmen, most of the media and the vast majority of ordinary folk in the West, to comprehend that the moral imperatives governing society in the Soviet Union bear no relation at all to those in which most of us have been steeped, in our Judaeo-Christian civilisation.

In Soviet society to murder, cheat, steal or lie, especially to lie, is no better and no worse than to be kind, to be honest, to be truthful. The only yardstick to be applied to moral behaviour is how best should Soviet Imperialism be advanced. Thus the information and propaganda constantly spewed out is nearly always judged in the West against a wrong premise and, worse still, is iterated and reiterated by well meaning Western folk whose main and perhaps only faults are often a too transparent honesty or an adolescent naivety.

The Two Main Threats

That having been said I shall try to group these permutations under only two very simplistic headings. Indeed in a short presentation such as this dealing with a subject of the utmost philosophical, geo-political and technical complexity almost everything has to be expressed in generalities of a very simplistic nature.

The first group of threats then is the continuous and unwearying attempt by the Soviet Union to suborn the political and societal institutions of any country not already, more or less, within the Soviet orbit of influence. The aim is to push for the installation of governments which will be at least inclined to accept the legitimacy of any policy directives from Moscow, whether promulgated openly or in a covert and surreptitious manner.

The second group of threats is to breed fear (and this is rather different from frightening) in the governments and peoples of the countries beginning to appear susceptible to subversion, or to the activities of those sympathetic to the doctrines of Moscow. Apart from the ever present and intensely terrifying possibility of a nuclear exchange (which I shall hardly discuss as I consider it unlikely) this second group of threats breaks down into three main elements.

(i) The overwhelming nuclear, chemical, and conventionally armed military build up in Central Europe and on the Northern and Southern flanks.

(ii) The establishment of large, well equipped, airborne élite 'shock troops', the Spetznaz Brigades, as advance guards for the eight highly trained, more heavily equipped airborne divisions – one obvious target being the British and Allied airfields which bisect the middle of Britain. The neutralisation of the UK by a mass airborne invasion on to these airfields would pull the rug out from under the feet of NATO.

(iii) The massive and still rapidly growing maritime capability. This can be divided into a number of sub elements:

  (a) An almost worldwide maritime aircraft ocean reconnaissance capability. This is reinforced by photographic and other passive satellite detection capabilities and by active, nuclear powered radar satellites oblivious to cloud cover.

  (b) A surface 'narrow seas' and 'ocean going' warship capability with its own organic airpower and with a land based naval air component.

  (c) A growing ballistic missile submarine force.

  (d) A large and growing diesel-electric and nuclear powered submarine capability armed with a wide range of anti-ship and anti-submarine weapons.

(e) A large intelligence gathering fleet.
(f) A large and growing and well subsidised merchant fleet under central naval control. This fleet has three roles: economic warfare, intelligence gathering and (in the cruise ships), subsidised subversion of Western European tourists.
(g) A fishing fleet engaged in stripping many of the world's fishing grounds for conversion into Fish Protein Concentrate (FPC) and in intelligence gathering. This fishing fleet is also centrally naval controlled.

Contrasting Views on Elements of the Second Threat

The term 'The Forgotten Threat' could well be applied in the UK to every aspect of Soviet maritime capability. I first bloodied my own nose drawing attention to it in the late 1950s and early 1960s but my perhaps rather hysterical pleadings fell always on stony ground. Even today when the more stentorian voices of the pilgrim band led by Admiral of the Fleet Lord Hill-Norton and Dr Luns are heard across NATO, the governments of the Western Alliance and Japan (with the notable exception now of the United States) are still suffering from the 'Ostrich Syndrome', their heads are buried well in the sand.

This, in all conscience would be bad enough were it not that all of them are suffering also from what I christened twenty years ago* 'The Chicken's Beak Syndrome'.

Those who were at Leeds Castle two years ago may recall I said that if you place a chicken with its beak on the paving and draw a chalk line from it, there it will stay with its backside in the air convinced in its tiny little mind that it is firmly tethered. That is precisely the attitude of most governmental leaders and their permanent officials as well as, very sadly I believe, most Army and Air Force leaders in the Alliance. Indeed my own country is suffering from a particularly virulent strain of 'Chicken's Beak Syndrome' at the moment. I hardly think I need explain to this audience how that chalk line stretches out across the German Plain.

The defence of Western Europe has come to depend, in practice, on the early release of tactical nuclear weapons. And, although it is arguable, I believe, and I think most people believe the Mountbatten/Zuckerman view, that the use of tactical nuclear weapons will quite quickly be followed by a total strategic nuclear exchange. For such a terrible event the

---

* Brassey's Annual, 1963. Page 52.

Soviets are probably better prepared than the West but the Kremlin knows that such a holocaust would not be of any benefit to their Marxist-Leninist dreams. Marxism/Leninism has not worked the economic miracle that was hoped and the Kremlin's aims are somehow to divert to Soviet control the flourishing industrialised Western Europe. A nuclear desert is the last thing they look for.

Similarly an airborne invasion of the mid-UK airfields carries with it, certainly with the present (1982) British government, if not the absolute certainty, then at least the very strong risk of a major nuclear strike obliterating Moscow. And the Kremlin would be faced with the fact that the cream of their Army had been dropped into the UK and that their Soviet nuclear missile counter-blow, if launched against the UK, would wipe out their own forces and, the prevailing wind being from the South-West, the heartland of the industrialised Europe as well.

So there is a paradox here. The least desirable options to take over Western Europe from the Soviet point of view carry with them the certainty of the destruction of the industries of the Ruhr, France and the UK, the very prizes that the Soviets seek. But these options, particularly an eruption across the German Plain by the Shock Armies in East Germany are regarded by the Western Leaders as the most likely options for the Soviets to follow!

So here, once more, we come back to what I have termed the 'Chicken's Beak Syndrome' from which Western Leaders continue to suffer. They still are unable to comprehend what in Brassey's Annual in 1963 I described as the 'Noose At Sea'. In the last twenty years the Soviets have slowly begun to draw the noose tight so that one good pull could strangle the West or more likely could bring the West so near to strangulation that the only alternative would be to trim to Moscow's diktats.

Soviet Policy. Cautious Opportunism Inclining To Adventurism

The Soviet Policy which they believe will carry them towards world hegemony, as I perceive it, is one of cautious and occasionally not so cautious, opportunism. Today we all live in a world of mounting tension; in a world where Western Europe exists in a climate of difference, division and dither; in a world where in the United States, to quote Dr Chester Cooper, 'policy makers have still to learn how to cope with threats that are less urgent and cataclysmic than the menace of strategic nuclear war.' In parentheses I would now guess that Dr Cooper might except from that comment the most remarkable speech by Secretary Lehmann reviewing the US Navy posture to the House Armed Services Committee last February. But overall I still believe that in looking towards the West the Soviets must perceive a climate of dissension tending to incline their own (Soviet) policies towards adventurism rather than the very cautious opportunism which has generally been the Soviet hallmark in the last few years.

Pressures on the Kremlin

However, before I examine the particular path down which such opportunism or cautious adventurism may lead the Kremlin, we should consider what other pressures are on the Soviet leadership. Three years ago at a conference on Strategic Direction in Chicago I spoke of my optimistic hope and expectation that The Law of Colonial Ingratitude, something about which my own country knows a lot, would spread to the Socialist Republics within the Union: and the Union would break apart. But now after a letter from Professor Hugh Seton-Watson (and who should know better than he) I am far less optimistic. He wrote:

> The Russian people seem to have a tremendous capacity for civilisation. They have produced writers and musicians and great scientists and thinkers whose ability to probe and stimulate and explain the mysterious depths of the human mind put them in the top league. But this tremendous capacity has been and still is inhibited from its full flowering by the persistent armour plated barbarism of their ruling autocrats and bureaucrats which has been demonstrated over a period which stretches back for five hundred years or more.
>
> It has perhaps been made easier too by a specific national defect which seems to recur century after century, namely an inability to stand up to tyranny from their rulers or (on the few occasions when a new élite has shaken off the old by force) the ability only to rule anew in a tyrannical way. It is as if one vertebra is missing from the spinal column of the whole nation.

A couple of months ago I asked Professor Dahrendorf (who was dispatched to a concentration camp in Germany at the age of 16 for establishing an anti-Hitler society at school) whether there were many 'little Dahrendorfs' in the Soviet Union willing to risk their lives for a similar end. His answer was a categorical 'No'. He felt, I think, that the human instinct towards freedom had either been virtually bred out or knocked out of the Soviet young, or it remained quiescent, for they could see no light at the end of the tunnel as he and his young friends believed they saw in Germany in 1944.

From all this I conclude that opportunism or cautious adventurism will continue to be the policy of the Soviet Union unless the spread of dissidence in Eastern Europe, such as we are aware of today and such as we see in Poland and Czechoslovakia and perhaps Hungary, reaches a level (which will not be very high) that the Kremlin begins to see as unacceptable; or the Soviet subversive and politico-military threats against the Western Alliance start to give a diminishing return and the Alliance shows signs of recovering from its present acute ague. In such circumstances I foresee that the Soviet search for non-nuclear opportunities for pressures on the West will mount and then the maritime options will appear even more favourable to those men in the Kremlin.

The Geo-Political Scene as Viewed from the Kremlin

If I was presiding in the Kremlin then, at this point, I would survey the geo-political scene.

I would note that there are in the world a number of what I would call 'slow matches'. Some are burning brightly and some are just smouldering. But near each match there is a powder keg which could explode and trigger world conflict and a nuclear holocaust; and this, as a Soviet statesman, I most earnestly wish to avoid.

One of these 'slow matches' burning rather brightly at the moment and therefore to be handled very delicately is in the Middle East, Israel, the Lebanon, Iraq/Iran, Afghanistan and the turmoil not far below the surface in the Gulf States generally. Iran particularly is showing that its military power is still considerable. My Soviet policy of subverting the Baluchis on both sides of the Iran/Pakistan Border is beginning to pay off. There may well be an opportunity here to drive down from Afghanistan through Iran to Char Bihar or possibly down the Khyber and so to quite nearby Karachi. In either case the long looked for Soviet warm water port outside the Straits of Hormuz would be achieved.

Then there is South-East Asia. The awkward, tough, belligerent Vietnamese have already allowed the Soviet navy to use Camranh Bay, so obligingly equipped by the Americans. From here I can put the Kremlin's hands on the tap controlling the flow of oil to Japan and, when the South China Sea oil reserves are developed, on the oil supplies to China too. I think I can afford to be a bit more adventurous here than in the Middle East.

Next I turn my eyes to the South Atlantic. I once had my hands on Chile, but the CIA defeated me. But I still believe Chile is a long term aim and Argentina now seems to be a fertile ground for the Soviet Union to cultivate. I must encourage Argentina's claim to the splendid harbours in the Falklands and South Georgia. They are the key to the extraction of minerals from Antarctica. When Panama comes under Kremlin influence, something we in the Kremlin are working on, we shall have our hands on both routes from East to West of America, Cape Horn and the Canal.

On the other side of the Atlantic there are opportunities galore. The West has excommunicated South Africa and so denies itself the use of those splendid harbours like Durban, East London, Cape Town and Simonstown. This 'excommunication' must certainly be sustained and though meanwhile I can base what SACLANT calls my 'Fifth Fleet' in Luanda, I must move it further down towards Walvis bay in Namibia and thus reach even nearer to 'The Roaring Forties', through which passes a large percentage of Western Europe's energy and many of the materials needed by the industry of the whole Western Alliance.

Now Ladies and Gentlemen, I desert my office in the Kremlin and resume my talk to you in Leeds Castle.

All these 'slow matches' are burning near the global ocean choke points through which passes and must continue to pass the energy and materials on which the industries of Western Europe and Japan depend. So all of them, without exception, present the Kremlin with opportunities for the exercise of maritime power. There are other 'slow matches' of course, but I believe the three I have mentioned to be the most critical.

The Forgotten Threat

In the early part of this paper I defined for you the different sub-elements of the Maritime Threat. But within this (by the West) only vaguely discerned and wholly neglected Soviet threat, this acquisition of aircraft operating facilities in surrogate territories, this expensive development of reconnaissance satellites, this ocean surface naval capability with its own organic and shore based air power, these centrally controlled and subsidised merchant and fishing fleets breeding deep sea sailors and a vast intelligence gathering fleet of specialised ships, there also exists what I call 'The Forgotten Threat', the submarines on the ocean trade routes, our lifelines. Many people, and in particular those of our rulers suffering from the Ostrich and Chicken's Beak syndrome, find such a threat incredible and indeed even welcome the Soviet Union's vast expenditure on all matters maritime because (they so naively believe) otherwise that money might go into greater land and air forces for an advance across Germany which the Soviets regard as a last and wholly unsatisfactory resort.

Broad Characteristics of Soviet Submarines

Without boring you with precise figures let us briefly analyse the weapons of this 'Forgotten Threat'. There are three families of Soviet submarines. There are the launch pads for the strategic nuclear weapons and these submarines are also nuclear propelled. These I shall only mention in passing. The other two families divide into nuclear propelled and diesel-electric propelled and are armed variously with anti-ship and anti-submarine weapons and sensors and they have various roles. They are known as Hunter-Killers.

The various hunter-killer roles are as follows:

(1) The shorter range nuclear ballistic missile submarines normally stationed off the Eastern and Western American seaboards have hunter-killer escorts.

(2) The new great Typhoon strategic nuclear ballistic missile nuclear propelled submarines, though stationed in the under ice, reasonably safe haven of the Arctic Ocean, take up so much sea room that more of the smaller ballistic missile submarines with hunter-killer escorts will seek the open oceans.

(3) There are constant nuclear hunter-killer patrols off UK bases and I suppose off US bases also.

(4) The Soviets see a need to 'mark' with nuclear hunter-killers, the increasing number of US carrier battle Groups whenever these are deployed in significant strategic areas such as the Straits of Hormuz or towards the North Cape. Such a requirement will increase when the measures set out by Secretary Lehmann begin to evolve.

You will appreciate that though nuclear submarines have virtually unlimited fuel endurance they have to return to a base or some sort of facility to reprovision with food and to rest or change the crew and, in time of conflict, to re-ammunition. Whilst this 'servicing' can be done from land bases or depot ships (and of course the Soviet Union has managed to find suitable positions for both around the world) there still comes a time when every submarine has to return to its home port. All in all therefore it is my tentative conclusion that a large proportion of the nuclear hunter-killer submarines will be engaged in escort duties but that is no great cause for optimism. Nuclear submarines and especially Soviet nuclear submarines are noisy and easy to pinpoint but they are steadily improving though I doubt whether they will ever be as silent underwater as the diesel-electric submarine propelled by electric motors driven by batteries. These are the most silent of all. The Soviets have very sophisticated batteries, thus the opportunities for detecting such submarines charging on the surface or using their 'Snort Mast' to run their diesels and charge when submerged, are few and far between.

To sum up – whilst nuclear propelled submarines can stay dived they tend to be noisier and therefore more easily detectable by acoustic means; the diesel-electric submarine whilst far quieter has to risk coming to the surface to charge batteries or to snort, when it may be detected; further, its fuel has to be replenished probably from a nuclear propelled submarine milch cow or tanker or by returning to one of the many Soviet depot ships or bases around the world.

So, though a few nuclear-hunter killer submarines may be available for attacking Western energy or trade, my belief is that the main threat to Western Europe's lifeline comes from the growing Soviet fleet of very silent diesel-electric submarines.

Let me again stress that I discount, except by mistake or misunderstanding, (and who would have believed it possible for a barefooted man to penetrate the security of Buckingham Palace and finish up unchallenged, in Her Majesty's bedroom) that the Soviets will initiate nuclear war which would entirely erase their whole drive to bring a thriving Western Europe into the Soviet orbit. I also believe that whilst continuing to appear menacing to keep the Chicken's Beaks firmly fixed they will never assault the Central Front and trigger first a battlefield and then a total nuclear exchange. Should the unthinkable happen however, and should the nuclear exchange up the escalation ladder be slow, measured and discreet, which I most profoundly doubt, then the main maritime battle will be over, on and under the North Atlantic.

Lessons from History

Even if we put aside Qaddhafi's quite recent attempt to sink the *Queen Elizabeth 2* by torpedo from a submarine as she proceeded with a full passenger load of Jews to Haifa, history can demonstrate two scenarios very relevant to the rising tension in the world today.

The first of these is the Spanish Civil War and the indiscriminate sinking of merchant ships ostensibly by Spanish submarines but, as was soon revealed, by Italian submarines on the direct orders of Mussolini. Let me quote you a letter from Winston Churchill, then out of office, to Anthony Eden the British Foreign Secretary:

> Submarine piracy in the Mediterranean and the sinking of ships of many countries without any care for the lives of their crews must be suppressed. For this purpose all Mediterranean powers should

agree to keep their own submarines away from certain defined
routes for commerce. In these routes the French and British
Navies should search for all submarines and any found should be
pursued and sunk as a pirate. Italy should be asked in the most
courteous manner to participate in this. If however she will not do
so, she should be told that this is what we are going to do.

So what today would be termed a Submarine Exclusion Zone was effectively initiated and in due course Eden replied to Churchill as follows:

The really important point is that we have emphasised that co-
operation between France and Britain can be effective and that
the two Western democracies can still play a decisive part in
European affairs . . . if we include French help in the air we shall
be working on a 50/50 basis.

This was called the Nyon Patrol and there were no more sinkings but
lessons were derived.
(1) It is now not novel when one country is wracked by an internal
struggle for another country, backing one of the sides, to do so by covert
submarine attacks against international trade.
(2) The repercussions of such action stretch far beyond the actual area of
operations. Merchant crews will not be inclined to sail without danger
money. War risks insurance suddenly escalates. Depending on the area of
attack the movement of world trade can be seriously impaired or dislo-
cated.
(3) Even if political agreement can rapidly be achieved as it was at the
time of Nyon, in these days of sophisticated submarines it would take time
to muster and deploy the instruments of anti-submarine warfare.
  As the Nyon Patrol taught us in 1937 so the recent Falklands battle has
re-emphasised, namely that the destruction of submarines calls for a vast
expenditure of acoustic devices and many different sorts of munitions.
But the main point which must be hammered home again and again is that
submarine attacks on trade are covert and therefore deniable; and in the
wholly amoral struggle we face it is irrelevant who is actually manning
the submarines.
  My second scenario relates to that period of tension when there is no
way, short of precipitating hostilities, of stopping Soviet submarines leaving their bases. They could be counted and tracked probably to their
destinations but there is no way that they could be prevented from taking

up their stations in Soviet or surrogate ports or at sea in the global choke points through which Western trade must pass.

Should tension continue to rise but the Soviet Forces in Europe remain behind their frontiers a similar situation begins to emerge to that when the German and Allied land and most Air Forces glared at each other for the first eight months of World War II. But just as the sea war started on September 3rd 1939 so, in this case, there would be a knife across the West's jugular ready to be inserted at the first sign of any Western hostile act.

Possible Future Western Policy

What then should be the prescriptions which the West should look for to deter or counter the Soviet Union from either of the two, from the Soviet point of view, eminently desirable options whereby the Kremlin may push the West hard without actually triggering nuclear war?

First, of course, is the need to cure the governments of the Western Alliance of their Ostrich and Chicken's Beak syndromes. This will not be easy because, apart from Dr Luns, there is no statesman in the European end of the Western Alliance who understands maritime power. I think President Reagan does and a lunch *à trois* with Al Haig makes me believe he does too. I hope that Vice-President Bush's influence, as he certainly does, will soon be felt.

But curing the syndromes does not mean abandoning the land and air defence of the West. It would not do to show the Soviets they could have such a quick walkover that nuclear release permission for tactical weapons would not be produced by SHAPE in time. But it does mean discarding outdated shibboleths by which Allied Commanders now abide. I find much to commend in that recent book *The Uncertain Ally* by Mr John Wilkinson MP and Commander Michael Chichester. Let me quote its last paragraph:

> NATO has come to display all the characteristics of ossification that affect any official organisation, national or international, which is not regularly overhauled by strong leadership. In concert with President Reagan's new Administration Mrs Thatcher's government could help to provide that leadership by stimulating both official realism about the threat which the Alliance faces and the determination to put into effect new and imaginative policies to release British strategy from the rigidly set immobility in which the UK's defence policy has been set for far too long.

The Moorer Concept. Regional Maritime Pacts

To get some movement in the UK in the direction at least of acknowledging in Ministerial circles the need for change would be a most significant advance. But beyond that I have always wondered where Admiral Tom Moorer's initiative in 1969/70 came to grief though I know the First Sea Lord of the time was sympathetic for I sat in on the discussions, somehow, though, the UK official line later became far less forthcoming.

The Moorer concept proposed that naval representatives of those countries adjacent to the great global choke points should, as a start, gather together at the US Naval War College at Rhode Island to thrash out a series of possible joint naval exercises directly related to the threat of intimidation in those areas. I think he hoped that if he could obtain some general consensus that these choke points were the most important strategic spots in the Western Alliance then the US and UK jointly, in those areas where each had some influence, might approach the governments concerned in the hopes of obtaining political approval for some contingency planning, maritime exercising and command and control arrangements.

The US, UK, France, Spain, Portugal, Japan, Brazil, Argentina, Chile, South Africa, Pakistan, India, the Oman, (but not at that time Iran), Singapore, Indonesia, Thailand, Malaysia, Australia, New Zealand, would all have been included either because of national self-interest or because the availability of convenient bases made them obvious participants.

Perhaps Admiral Moorer tried to work too fast. Perhaps at that rather difficult moment in US political history the time was not ripe. But it seemed to me then, as it does now, a historic idea and I strongly believe on a regional basis it should be revived if the 'freeish' world is to achieve concerted action against the steadily mounting ability of the Soviet regime to bring politico-military pressure to bear in those vital points. There must be regional strategies which would go some way to raise the stakes and provide a deterrent if any such hostile Soviet action was contemplated.

South East Asia. A Maritime Flash Point

You will note that having mentioned South East Asia I have hardly referred to it again. Time prevents a closer analysis. Nevertheless I believe the rising tide of piracy in that area will soon call for international action to control it. Here too may be a tempting area for the Soviets to practise the tactics and problems of covert submarine attack. Piracy and submarines go well together and it is no secret that Soviet submarines have already practised attacks on merchant ships off the Cape of Good Hope.

Conclusions

I do not for one moment minimise the horrendous political difficulties of establishing the sort of regional naval pacts which Admiral T. H. Moorer envisaged. Even to mention in my country the participation of South Africa in such a pact (and without South Africa there can be no regional arrangement adjacent to the greatest choke point of all) would send what we used to call 'the media' but have come to call since the Falklands either the 'talking or chattering classes', into further quite unprecedented heights of emotional hysteria. At the same time on the other side of the coin the Soviet nuclear powered hunter-killers have their escorting duties away from the Trade Routes. Western surveillance of diesel-electric submarines, rendered more difficult by their silence, presents opportunities when they are 'snorting' or refuelling. The Soviets too face many difficulties.

If there is any real intention by the West to confront the maritime threat to its main trade routes it has first to establish the credibility of such a threat – and therein is the rub. My own country, which used to have leaders who understood 'seapower' or, as it is now called to include the essential air component, 'maritime power', no longer seems to have such people. The reasons would take another long talk to explain.

You who have so patiently listened to my overlong diatribe may still not share with me my profound belief, expressed in service journals and newspapers over twenty years, that the Soviet maritime option and the 'Forgotten Threat' either in the Nyon or Phoney war mode as I have tried to explain, are what, in reality, we in the West most have to fear. Such threats I submit are the most acceptable to the Soviets as being the least likely to consume Western Europe and the Soviet Union in a nuclear holocaust.

But perhaps at least you may feel, like Abraham Lincoln as he remarked when he first saw the model of that early Ironclad warship *The Monitor*, 'All I have to say is what the girl said when she stuck her foot in the stocking, "it strikes me there's something in it".'

SPEECHES AND LECTURES IN U.S.A. AND U.K.

COMMISSIONING ADDRESS TO CLASS ZERO SEVEN AT THE NAVAL AIR STATION, PENSACOLA, FLORIDA

Admiral Hayward USN invited me to conduct this ceremony and sent his private aircraft to Washington DC to fetch me. Due to a misunderstanding in my office I was told I should not have to make a speech but in fact that escape referred to the ceremonial dinner the night before. At the ceremony itself a suitable speech was definitely required as, soon after they had qualified as aviators, all these young men would be going off to that bloody war in Vietnam. Reinforced by a fair measure of Jack Daniels I therefore laboured through a hot Florida night composing and learning by heart something suitable to say to the young men concerned, in the presence of senior officers of the USN and a whole bevy of parents and beautiful girl friends.

There was a small crisis when I returned to Washington as it was suggested that no one could be commissioned (or ever had been commissioned) into the USN or USNR by a foreign officer. However after Counsel to the Pentagon had been consulted it was agreed that as the Oath of Fealty to the United States had been administered by a US Naval Officer all was well. What I had to say apparently found some favour with the parents as, at their request, the recording was subsequently printed and sent to each of them.

I found it of interest that the father of Mr Fucci, the elected Class Leader, was an ice cream vendor in Connecticut, while his deputy was the son of a millionaire from California.

The Class kindly sent me a group photograph later and some of them stayed with us in Washington when on leave. Then they qualified and went to Vietnam; and we heard no more.

Ladies and Gentlemen,
With all the quite distracting beauty on one side of me I find it difficult to concentrate on this very serious ceremony but concentrate I must because these are serious, indeed very serious times.

Class Zero Seven has just sworn a solemn Oath of Fealty to uphold the Constitution of the United States and now, as a British Admiral, I am very privileged to be asked to hand to Mr Fucci and his companions their commissions in the United States Naval Reserve.

Superficially, because they have not been long in the Service, perhaps it could be said that this ceremony only recognises that the US Navy, after testing them for eleven gruelling weeks, still thinks that these young men remain good bets who can be turned into naval aviators; but I think in reality it means much more than that. It means that Captain Haynie, Captain Hoesch, Sergeant Greelish and the many other first class leaders and veterans who are on the Staff here have recognised, in these cheerful and physically tough men those elements of ability, character and will-power without which no one can hope to become an officer in the United States Navy; without which no one can hope to lead.

Ability, professional ability, as I understand it, is a quality of the hand and mind after which we all have to strive and which, by hard work and enthusiasm we ourselves, by our own efforts, can always improve and constantly seek to improve.

Character, on the other hand, is a quality of the spirit. It often stems from deep religious conviction and I think that Major Pless* and others will agree with me that the man of character in peace is more often the man of courage in war.

Courage is of two sorts, physical and moral, both of these I believe, we can improve if we work away at it constantly.

Then there is will power. That too can be developed. The strength of purpose to lead, to care for and to transmit to those perhaps less gifted and less fortunate than Class Zero seven who, in years to come, will be committed to their care and look to them for leadership.

There is personality, of course. The ability to put yourself in the other man's shoes, to develop the human touch, the ability to laugh at yourself and life in general and never, never, to become pompous.

---

*The Chief Instructor at Pensacola who had recently been awarded the Congressional Medal of Honour (the equivalent of our VC) for bravery in Vietnam.

Lastly discipline. Discipline runs through all our lives like an undertone. A great friend of your Admiral Sims, the British Admiral Jellicoe, put it like this:

> In a consideration of the question of discipline one is, in these days, at once brought face to face with the prevailing spirit of the times. This spirit is roughly described as 'democracy', but to a large extent it means a disinclination to accept any form of restraint and a desire for unrestricted freedom of life and action. From the point of view of the Nation, any nation, this attitude of mind is regrettable and may be dangerous. In the Naval Service, any naval service, such an attitude to discipline is quite incompatible either with efficiency in general or the well being of any unit be it submarine, surface ship or aircraft squadron.

Therefore I suggest to you gentlemen that if by discipline we mean 'self-control' we need more, not less discipline in democracy today.

What, you may well ask, do we gain by discipline? How does it help to establish the high morale after which we seek? I suggest to you that discipline engenders a spirit of calmness in emergency – the same spirit that keeps a disciplined man at his post when all his comrades have fallen, will keep a man more cool in the midst of emergency, panic and disaster. In other words discipline renders a man more capable of facing the changes and chances of human existence.

Secondly I suggest that discipline produces a certain determination and firmness of character. A disciplined man who has been given a difficult task to accomplish is more likely to carry it through to a successful conclusion than the undisciplined man who may be turned aside at the first obstacle. The man of discipline has learnt to resist, to bear up, to hold on in spite of all difficulties.

Lastly discipline teaches sentiments of confidence and self respect, for having learnt to obey, a man has gone a long way to learning to command. In a word, the object and result of true discipline is to inspire men with bravery, firmness, patience, self respect and a sentiment of honour.

Your Navy, in recognisable form, has served your nation for nearly two hundred years. And during that time a great many men – some famous but the great majority unheard of – have created in the sum of their lives, your imperishable naval tradition.

Tradition, if you understand it in these days of explosive technological progress, can be a weight pulling you back. But tradition, if you regard it as something of the spirit, is a force which strengthens the community in which you serve because it inspires men, when working and fighting their ships and aircraft, to emulate the standards of those who have gone before them. Study tradition therefore and contribute even more to the great US Naval tradition to which aviators in particular have added such lustre, by interpreting the best of the past into the difficult and perplexing present.

Ladies and gentlemen, as I travel around America I see the glitter and the froth, but I see more and more what someone described as the great solid sea of the American Nation, as simple in its aspirations and as traditional in its virtues and with a consciousness of its high destiny at least as great as I believe exists beneath the equally tawdry glitter in my own country.

These sons and brothers and husbands and fiancés of yours have chosen a hard and dangerous life. Help them all you can because often there will be a clash of loyalties between their love for you and their love of their Country which has brought them to this proud moment when they will receive their commissions.

And so, at last, in wishing Class Zero Seven the greatest good fortune and success in their careers may I read you something by one of Scotland's greatest authors about one of Scotland's greatest sons, the Duke of Montrose, who ended his days on the scaffold while all around him the common people, who loved him, wept.

> First there must be fortitude, the power of enduring when hope is gone, the power of taking upon oneself a desperate responsibility and daring all.
>
> There must be self-forgetfulness. A willingness to let worldly interests and even reputation and honour perish if only the task be accomplished. The man who is concerned with his own repute will never move mountains.
>
> There must be patience, supreme patience under misunderstanding and setbacks and muddles and interferences of others.
>
> There must be resilience in defeat, a manly optimism which looks at all the facts in all their bleakness, yet dares to hope.
>
> There must be a sense of the eternal continuity of a great cause, so that failure will not seem the end; and a man sees himself as only a part in a predestined purpose.
>
> Leadership depends, then, primarily upon moral endowments.

May I commend those words to you as you strive to become qualified pilots in the United States Navy and later as you become operational. They have hung by my desk or in my cabin for many years now. After my all too frequent failures I read them and take comfort and try again, as we all have to do in these often frightening but also often inspiring times.

SPEECH IN HONOUR OF ADMIRAL THOMAS H. MOORER

Chief of Naval Operations US Navy
October 21st 1968

His Excellency the British Ambassador, Sir Patrick Dean, G.C.M.G., having proposed the toast to 'The Immortal Memory' it fell to the British Naval Attaché to propose the toast to Admiral Moorer who a few months later assumed the even greater responsibilities of Chairman of the US Joint Chiefs of Staff. As before the speeches were relayed to our home where my wife was entertaining the wives of the US officer guests.

Your Excellency, Admiral Moorer, General Chapman, Gentlemen.

It is my great privilege tonight to speak of our principal guest, Admiral Thomas H. Moorer, Chief of Naval Operations of the greatest Navy the world has seen.

In many ways it would have been more fitting if what I said on this occasion last year had been said tonight in Admiral Moorer's presence. Last year I read a short passage from Sir Winston Churchill's book *The Second World War* in which he paid tribute to the gallantry of the US naval aviators in the Battles of Midway and the Coral Sea. The moment, as I surmised last year, that the US Navy effectively took over from the Royal Navy as the principal instrument of seapower and peace on the oceans of the world.

In that context I could have paid tribute, as I do now, to Admiral Moorer's extraordinary personal heroism at and after Pearl Harbour, to the wounds he suffered in action and to the many medals for gallantry he now wears. Those were historic days as the United States, with its Navy and Marine Corps in the van, fought its way back across the Pacific, in that long series of desperate and bloody amphibious campaigns.

Tonight is Nelson's night, and so we on the British Navy Staff, in our small way, felt we could do no greater honour to Admiral Moorer and through him the great Navy over which he presides, than to ask him to join us here in the presence of Her Majesty's Ambassador, on the one evening when we celebrate the life of our greatest sailor whose Immortal Memory His Excellency has so eloquently recalled. At the same time we are very conscious – indeed deeply conscious, of the privilege Admiral Moorer does us, in sparing the time to be our guest tonight, in the middle of that great crusade the US is fighting in Vietnam.

Admiral Moorer has many problems which Nelson had to face: but he also has much that Nelson lacked. Greatest amongst these assets Admiral Moorer would rate, I am sure, his lovely wife, whose gracious kindness makes any chance of meeting her a pleasure to be looked forward to and, once met, a recollection to be cherished. It is from her and his happy home and his children, if I am a judge, that he must find a great deal of the strength which today enables him to carry his incredible burden apparently so effortlessly and so easily.

But there are two further resemblances between Nelson and Admiral Moorer. One of Nelson's great friends was Admiral Lord St. Vincent, closely associated with our Royal Marines. And so I am sure Admiral Moorer would wish that I should mention General Chapman, I dare to say a friend always standing beside him, as the US Marine Corps and the US Navy have always stood together in peace and war.

When the Army and the Navy come to gaze on Heaven's scenes,
They will find the streets are guarded by United States Marines.

Was there ever a truer couplet?

The second similarity is love of people, a quality that Nelson like Admiral Moorer so well understood.

It was Shakespeare who put into the mouth of Henry V the phrase, 'A Band of Brothers.' But it was Nelson after the Battle of the Nile who wrote to Admiral Lord Howe, 'I had the happiness to command a band of brothers.' Nelson was known throughout the Fleet, in an age of appalling cruelty, for his humanity and his common touch. He loved his fellow creatures and he strove always for the betterment of those he led. In the end it was the spirit of the officers and men of the British Fleet which proved them so unbeatable.

Next year, when the unhappy time comes for me to leave the United States, it will be the courtesy and kindness, the sense of discipline, the cheerful dedication and the ability to work for and, if need be to die for, a Cause which, all of we Britons here this evening, have so often observed amongst the officers and enlisted men of the US Navy and US Marine Corps, which I shall carry away with me.

When such a spirit exists, as I know Your Excellency has seen and as we on the British Navy Staff constantly witness, it is a spirit which has spread downwards. It is a spirit which can only exist when there is someone at the top who understands people, as Nelson did, and who has around him a 'Band of Brothers', united in their sense of purpose and giving a personal leadership for which technical virtuosity is a help but never a substitute.

I like to think that in that Annapolis Class of 1933, which has given such an unprecedented galaxy of distinguished officers to the United States Navy, and of which, with Admiral Moorer there are nearly sixty still serving, and so many of whom we are so privileged to have here tonight, there is the nucleus of that modern 'Band of Brothers,' the Admiral's List of the United States Navy. We are glad too that Admiral Draper Kauffman has permitted two midshipmen from that great Navy Academy to be our guests tonight. Who knows the destiny of the Class of '68?

Your Excellency and Gentlemen, before I ask you to rise, may I invite you to remember for a moment all those devoted men and women serving and retired from the United States Navy, and of General Chapman and those who serve with him and with General Walt who we are so proud to have here tonight in the United States Marine Corps, and also of Admiral Smith, a most welcome guest, and the men and women of the United States Coastguard, the third largest Navy in the world.

Now may I ask you to stand up and drink a toast to our principal guest and, if I may be allowed, to his gracious wife also.

Your Excellency and Gentlemen – Tom and Carrie Moorer.

DINNER IN HONOUR OF MR FRANK BARNETT, 1982

President, National Strategy Information Centre

Speech on behalf of the British guests in the presence of the Honorable Jack Marsh, Secretary of the US Army.

This was a very memorable occasion. Frank Barnett had been a corporal in the US Army and had distinguished himself greatly in the fighting around Bastogne in the winter of 1944/45. In some way his decoration had been awarded but never presented and this had been brought to the attention of Jack Marsh, Secretary of the US Army and a friend of mine from other days.

One morning, in the Pentagon, although it was seven years since I had been Naval Attaché and having been flown over by courtesy of the US Army, I was amongst those invited to witness the presentation in the company of an otherwise very distinguished gathering and a small Guard of Honour dressed in War of Independence Uniforms.

In the evening there was a big dinner attended by many old Washington friends and I found myself seated next to Mrs Casey and one removed from her husband, the Director of Central Intelligence and Head of the CIA. Like many dinners in the United States this was a very grand affair and the speeches, of which, surprisingly, mine was the shortest, took over an hour.

Mr Secretary, when we last met at a Conference in Brighton four and a half years ago you might just remember that I started my keynote speech with this quotation: 'Judging happiness to be the fruit of freedom and freedom of valour, never decline the danger of war.'

Surely, Sir, we are fortunate that at this critical moment in history our two countries are led by a man and a woman who both, so resolutely, uphold that sentiment. But democracies today are less easy to lead than those small city states from which democracy was born.

People have to be informed and educated objectively or the never ending din of political conflict will deafen and bemuse them – and as in a maze they will lose their way. It is by disseminating such information and by patient education that Frank and his colleagues fight so hard to keep the West on course.

Some fifty years ago Demetri Manuelski said in Moscow at the Lenin School of Political Warfare:

> 'War to the hilt between communism and capitalism is inevitable. Today we are not strong enough to attack. Our time will come in twenty or thirty years. To win we shall need the element of surprise. The bourgeoisie will have to be put to sleep, so we shall begin by launching the most spectacular peace movement on record. There will be electrifying overtures and offers of concessions. The capitalist countries, stupid and decadent, will rejoice in the opportunity to co-operate in their own destruction. They will leap at another chance to be friends, and as soon as their guard is down we shall smash them.'

The last war has delayed Manuelski's programme but recent world events suggest it is now being closely adhered to.

Mr Secretary, the winds of change have surely lifted the roof off the world as most of us here tonight once knew it. Never have the powers of destruction been so limitless. We face daunting dilemmas. We are dogged by uncertainty. Though we live in space and travel the abyssal depths we are rapidly losing that Faith which has carried the world forward over the last several millennia. We in the West face a rabid imperialism backed by the belief that Man is just a tool making animal. We are too often beguiled into sacrificing the hopes of the future to the clamorous demands of the present – and when we do we are surely betraying the traditions of our Judaeo-Christian society founded on the belief that while hope is a virtue, despair is a sin.

The radicals, the sceptics, the iconoclasts seek to destroy that relationship which exists between our two countries and of which your President and Secretary Weinberger gave us such proof in the Falklands War. But it is that background which enables us to open our hearts to Frank Barnett and, I think too for him to speak his mind without reservation to us.

What it seems to me we lack in the West is that quality of patience which Frank so manifestly possesses. Do you remember the old saying?

> Faced with the Gordian knot,
> Cut it, if you dare,
> Undo it if you can,
> If you can do neither, don't despair,
> The rope will rot.

For two thousand years Western culture has established order where chaos has been endemic – and we should be proud of that. We must cease to beat our breasts because of thoughtless and deliberate subversive criticism.

This morning, Mr Secretary, at that wonderful ceremony in the Pentagon, you decorated Frank for his valour in those dreadful bitter months of 1944–45, when the courage and fortitude of American soldiers at Bastogne pulled final victory, if not from actual defeat, at least from a reverse that would have allowed Soviet troops to hold the Rhine today. Tonight we surely once more applaud Frank's valour and leadership in the even more critical battle for the very survival of civilisation, in which all of us are engaged.

Mr Secretary, I know Annapolis well and my cousin General Ben Le Bailly ensured that I should visit your great US Air Force Academy. But tonight I remember my visit to The Citadel at Charleston, South Carolina and to the Virginia Military Institute, and particularly the forty-eight hours I once spent at West Point. At all five I saw much of the best of America's youth but I recall particularly the young officer who looked after me at West Point. Like Frank Barnett he had won a Rhodes Scholarship to Oxford but he had put that aside because he believed his duty lay in Vietnam. I so well remember him pointing out to me those words with which General McArthur, who I had once watched accepting the surrender of Japan, gave as a charge of duty to the West Pointers. If I recall it correctly it went like this:

> 'To BUILD courage, where courage seems to fail. To REGAIN faith, when there seems to be little cause for faith. To CREATE hope, where hope becomes forlorn.'

Those of us who had the privilege of serving in your great country in the late Sixties are only too well aware how many of those very young men from West Point and your other great military academies answered that charge and now lie buried in Arlington National Cemetery or enrich the earth of a foreign field. Surely McArthur's words, as those of Pericles I quoted earlier, will echo down the centuries. But, as of now, they seem to epitomise what, to me, Frank (and his bride who somehow keeps him going at full speed) are seeking to achieve in these perilous days.

I know I speak for the British here tonight and for the many in Britain who know Frank and who are not here, when I say we salute them both and together with Frank and his wife, his faithful colleagues who keep the National Strategy Information Centre the dynamic instrument for freedom which it so surely is.

DINNER GIVEN BY THE ROYAL NAVAL ENGINEERING COLLEGE, KEYHAM, FOR THE LORD MAYOR, ALDERMEN AND COUNCILLORS OF PLYMOUTH.
March 20th, 1957

The old RNEC at Keyham (originally Kaime), the home of naval officer engineering training since 1879, with which the city of Plymouth had so many connections (Councillor Hunt for instance was also a Hall Porter at the time of this dinner at which he was an honoured guest), was soon to be abandoned as the College moved out to Manadon where the Foundation Stone of the new College had been laid the year before.

It could be said that in some ways this long relationship between 'Town' and 'Gown' had been an adversarial one. The 'Kaime students' as they were always called by the local Press had been known to put butter on the tram lines which ran past the College so that the trams developed wheel spin and failed to reach the top of the slope; at one dreadful variety show at The Palace Music Hall in Union Street the students' booing was so loud that the 'bouncers' were sent in only to find the culprits all padlocked with handcuffs to their seats, while the holder of the key, later the first Rear-Admiral (E) actually to fly his flag, sat quietly well away from the fracas. A well known and very portly officer found his way on to the balcony of her political HQ when Lady Astor was re-elected MP, and to the cheers of his messmates down below made an inspiring speech in her honour.

But it was in the Blitz that the College and the Town came together. Students, with their own motor cycles provided an invaluable messenger service; others manned auxiliary fire appliances and fought fires with hand pumps, while one small posse raised steam and drove an ammunition train out of Millbay docks towards the safety of Tavistock. Students were killed and there were several wounded.

My Lord Mayor, Mr Town Clerk, Captain Sir John Walsham, Gentlemen,

The fact that you, my Lord Mayor, (it doesn't sound quite right and a bit patronising to call you *my* Lord Mayor but your eminent Town Clerk tells me it is and he should know) together with many distinguished Aldermen and Councillors and senior officers of the City have joined us at dinner tonight gives us all a great sense of privilege.

Though this small hall where you are seated is the oldest Officer's Mess in continuous use in the Royal Navy, we have been here less than 100 years. You celebrated your fifth centenary 18 years ago.

Nevertheless, Sir, we feel that even in our comparatively short span we have become a little bit of Plymouth. I know that I speak for the officers of the ten nations under training in the College when I say we are proud to make that claim. Even amongst them there are personal links. We have an officer of the South African Navy whose ancestors lived here and bore the same name as the Lord of the Manor of Kaime, the older and more correct pronunciation. We have a Bunbury, a relation of that Bunbury who was charged with telling Napoleon on board the British ship in Plymouth Sound, of his banishment to St. Helena. One of your most famous sons, the first President of the Royal Academy, Sir Joshua Reynolds, was the son of a Master at Plympton Grammar School. We too have an officer, the son of a Master at Plympton Grammar School who, if he has not yet won fame as an artist has represented his country in the Olympic Games. Your old Beadle, Sir, Ballemay, may well be an ancestor of our Instructor Captain Bellamy, the Dean of the College. I suppose if he had followed in his predecessor's footsteps we would see him whipping our College rogues and vagabonds and dispatching them to Compton whilst, though perish the thought that there should ever be undesirable females in the College, he would be sending those to Stonehouse or Stoke. Your famous Chief Constable, Mr Skittery, honours us also with his presence here tonight. I think I first heard his name while I was a cadet at Dartmouth when he led 50 enormous Devon constables with truncheons drawn through the main gates of Dartmoor prison and quickly stopped a mutiny of the inmates. Should he wish to take some leave I'm sure the Instructor Captain as Beadle, would be willing to take over. Captain Bellamy's ancestor was paid 3d for each whipping and the inhabitants of the Three

Towns all had to be indoors by 8 p.m., certainly an aid to the academic achievement the Dean tries to impart and a relief for the constabulary in their occasional nocturnal dealings with the young officers. For what it is worth too, my Lord Mayor, we have a John Shepley, surely a descendant (though I have yet to notice the resemblance) of your exceptionally pious predecessor of 500 years ago.

But to be serious, this long and sometimes not untroubled relationship with the City, this 'Town and Gown' relationship was tempered and made strong in the fires that swept your great City just sixteen years ago tonight. Indeed it was at about this time on the evening of 20 March 1941, just after the King and Queen had left North Road Station, in the 279th air raid since the first fire bomb attack in the previous November, but after a month's respite, that the bombers struck at the beginning of your six weeks of devastating agony and death when, in the words of Winston Churchill, 'the city's heart was cauterised and its streets were ragged ribbons'.

Under the inspiring leadership of Lieutenant-Commander Walsham, now our Captain, Sir John Walsham, Baronet, the Kaime students went out to fight the fires, to carry the messages through the burning and half blocked streets on their own motor bikes, to help the homeless and the stricken and in some cases to die alongside the citizens of Plymouth. It was in those days and nights, amongst the rubble and the bodies and the smouldering streets that the real link was forged between Kaime and the City, a link which we all hope will grow stronger as the years go by.

As you know so well Sir, because you graced with your presence the ceremony last year when Admiral of the Fleet the Earl Mountbatten of Burma laid the Foundation Stone of the new College, we are soon to leave this old Mess. In exchange for all this too small but beloved building which has given so much to the Royal Navy we shall find ourselves the trustees of a great estate which has existed at Manadon over at least 1000 years of recorded history. A period, Sir, which has seen Plymouth rise to its present greatness through the activities of our two indivisible Fleets, the Royal and Merchant Navies.

It was the men of Devon and of Plymouth (and my wife came from Buckland Monachorum, the home of Sir Francis Drake), who by their daring, courage and willpower founded the world trade by which this country had grown great. Today things are more difficult and our greatness depends on that mundane and, to me, rather inexplicable science called economics. Last year, Sir, you heard the First Sea Lord say that this College gave the finest engineering training in the world today. In saying that he was also echoing the remarks made by such hard headed industrialists as Lord Hives of Rolls-Royce. Some, I fear, believe that all this wonderful training for which the public pays is being devoted solely to the wretchedness and wasteful misery of violence and war.

That is not so. The Royal Navy, as always was the case in those days with any new idea, reluctantly borrowed the idea of steam propulsion from the Merchant Navy and, for many years, neither advanced their techniques very far. But since the war, thanks to the vision at the Admiralty of officers such as Captain Walsham and others, a quite new concept of our naval engineering responsibilities has arisen. It is in the Royal Navy's interests to harness all relevant design and development and adapt it to the improving of our propulsion machinery. It is in the country's interests that the lessons we learn should be fed back into the improvement of our merchant fleet so that it can always operate with maximum economy and compete successfully in the markets of the world. For as you well know, it is only by our seaborne trade that our country can remain great. Ten years ago that feedback was a trickle – today it is becoming a flood. There is a paper from our Captain wending its way round the bureaucracies of Whitehall suggesting that without any increases in our College overheads a number of Merchant Navy Engineer Officers should be trained here alongside their Naval brothers.

Many would agree with Rupert Brooke when he wrote of 'English western Plymouth where men tread softly and there is love and beauty and old houses and the brown black splintered haunted moor. . .' But I would rather quote you from a letter from a young officer who, perhaps with a touch of the Elizabethans caught during his training here, sailed alone from Cremyll to Auckland, New Zealand last year in a 25 foot, 2¼ ton folkboat, the smallest craft ever to cross the Pacific. Just a year ago last Sunday he completed the last 42 days of his trip across that ocean without sighting a single other ship. He wrote to me: 'I have seen the wonders of which I have always dreamed and places so beautiful beyond my wildest imagination. I think every time that each of them must be the most lovely in the world. Then I remember that last supper with you at the College on that summer's evening; and the lawns at Manadon and the big cedar and the great chestnut and the roses and the tulips and, last of all, the sight of the Mewstone and the Sound while twilight turned to darkness as I sailed into the setting sun.'

There are trees at Manadon, the old cedars, the oaks, the sequoias which were planted before the first stage coach reached Plymouth. Now in the last six weeks we have been planting the same sort of trees and many others given us by all the nations who have officers training here. I wonder what the world will be like when those trees have reached the heights of those we now so enjoy.

My Lord Mayor, as a small token of our affection for the city in which all of us have trained and of the ordeal we faced together in those dreadful years of war, may I ask you to accept as a gift to which all the officers have subscribed, this print of Old Plymouth. It may serve as a reminder of the great city Plymouth was before it was destroyed and of our certainty of the even greater city it will be when it is once more, fully restored.

TRAFALGAR NIGHT 1975

Much of this speech was originally due to be delivered on Trafalgar Night 1973 at the Royal Naval Engineering College. In the early hours of that morning the United States put its forces on a high state of alert due to intelligence reports that the Soviets were embarking parachute divisions with the intention of intervening in the Yom Kippur war. So, to my acute embarrassment, I had to cancel at the last moment but thanks to the kindness of the Captain, later Admiral Sir William Pillar, I was again invited two years later. Those were difficult days. I was still Director-General of Intelligence at the Ministry of Defence, so it seemed to me right on this occasion to strike what I believed was a true note, however sombre and perhaps out of place such a speech might seem in a training establishment full of effervescent young naval officers, as Manadon always is.

Mr President, I am sure there are many here tonight who question, as I have often questioned, why it is that on one of the nights near to the Anniversary of the Battle of Trafalgar, in the Queen's ships at sea and ashore we, in the Royal Navy, recall in particular that Admiral who died on board HMS *Victory*, in the moment of victory.

In an often too conservative Service is not this 'wake', if I may call it that, just one more manifestation of a tendency to look backwards that has too often bedevilled the Royal Navy?

I certainly used to think so. But as one reaches an age which Sir Walter Scott so aptly described as 'over the hill' things look different. When you are young and climbing upward you see before you only the next peak to be scaled – or, occasionally looking over your shoulder, what has gone before. But once over the top one can look to the far horizon, clouded it's

110

true, in mist and ultimate darkness, but the perspective somehow appears different.

Tradition, it seems to me, especially in this materialistic age, is something very valuable if only we understand clearly that it is something to be lived up to. I would agree with anyone amongst you that tradition is a very poor diet on which just to exist.

Before I speak for a few moments of the relevance today of Nelson's qualities, let me apologise for the fact that two years ago, when you last asked me down, I had to cancel literally a few hours before the dinner.

You may recall that the Yom Kippur war was reaching a climax. The Israelis were just holding the Syrians on the Golan: the bloody battle of Mt. Hermon was being fought and Arik Sharon had swept across the Canal and was carving out a piece of Egypt behind the Egyptian Third Army.

Two streams of great transport aircraft, one from the USA to Israel and the other from Russia, over Hungary and Yugoslavia, down the Adriatic, and around Greece had during the preceding week been approaching Cyprus, where they were effectively converted by our British flight controllers into three streams – or six if one thinks of the return flights – the Russians to and from Syria and to and from Egypt, and the Americans to and from Israel.

Quite suddenly the stream from Russia stopped; intelligence from central Europe assessed that men rather than material would soon be the freight and that the prime Soviet intervention capability, their (then) seven, (now) eight, powerful airborne divisions were being readied. At the same time something not far short of an ultimatum was delivered in Washington DC.

And so, about 0200 Eastern Standard time (0700 our time on the very day of your dinner) the United States raised the alert status of all her forces. Airborne Command Posts were sent aloft; B52s from overseas returned to their bases to be armed; missile crews started their checks preparatory to a countdown. The world was inching towards a holocaust; and there was much criticism of American action, some of it by people and politicians who should have known better.

However, as you will readily understand, by that very act those great men in Washington DC showed the Soviet Union the risk she was running and so, by ordering that alert, war at once became less likely. Nevertheless, for a few hours those of us in the intelligence community dare not leave our posts however tempting an evening at Manadon.

Yet the Yom Kippur war has brought the West in general and this country in particular, to the brink of disaster – and tonight we are still poised on that brink. The whole fabric of our economy is at risk and if it tears I see no floor in the abyss into which we shall fall.

In Nelson's day virtually the whole of Europe was arrayed against us and the odds against the survival of our country and our way of life must have seemed terrifying. In this time of economic crisis the odds today seem just as high and to try and reduce them we must relearn some of those lessons Nelson taught us.

It's true, as Solzenitzyn said in a speech not long ago, that 'the third world war has already been fought'. In the non-Soviet elements of the Warsaw Pact powers more people have been ceded to an alien tyranny than ever before in the dark lamentable history of Mankind. So now it seems we are engaged in a fourth struggle and we have to understand certain facts as Nelson, with his great political flair, would have comprehended them.

Firstly, the Soviet government and the Communist Party of the Soviet Union operate on two utterly separate but closely linked planes. The opportunist but genuine policy of the Soviet government today is *détente* which means a relaxation of tension, and such an aspiration is surely the heartfelt prayer of all ordinary folk, West or East of the Iron Curtain. Unhappily there are differences between the ability of ordinary folk to express such views depending on which side of the curtain they live. Although it is slowly being eroded those of us in the West still have a fair measure of freedom.

East of the Iron Curtain there is none. I often recall to myself Winston Churchill's words written 60 years ago: 'Russia, self outcast, sharpens her bayonets in her Arctic night and mechanically proclaims through self starved lips her philosophy of hatred and death.'

The Lubyanka Prison, the preserve of the KGB has, so they say, the best view in Russia from its cellars. You can see as far as Siberia. And if by good luck you miss the Lubyanka there are plenty of pseudo-psychiatric clinics.

The Soviet government hope for two things from *détente*:

(a) The import of management and production techniques from the West so that the productive capacity of the military complex and particularly the so far starved civilian sector of their economy may be improved.

(b) The encouragement of a sense of greater safety in the West and therefore a relaxation and a lowering of its guard.

As you well know *détente* depends on some form of political and military balance and if either of these is eroded then the general equilibrium is upset. Here is a paradox: the existence of a military balance certainly provides the material for armed conflict; but a common perception of that balance makes the outbreak of active conflict unlikely, with the corollary that the political equilibrium is preserved. That is why genuine mutual and balanced force reductions are so terribly important.

As I see it the situation today is similar to that which would prevail if two strong men were facing each other, each holding one end of a very stretched piece of elastic. The best way to ease the tension would surely be for each man, one step at a time, to walk towards each other. But that is not happening. Over the last 3 – 5 years the Eastern Man has made a great effort to improve both the quantity and quality of the equipment available to his Army, Navy, Air and Rocket Forces, and he is continuing to increase the tension in the elastic by raising his military budget at the expense of the civilian budget by at least 3½% per year in real terms. That is the threat from without.

But the Eastern Man is also embarrassing the Western Man, and this is where the Communist Party enters the fray. Through the well oiled Party machinery Eastern Man is casting down gallons of subversive muck which turns to mud and so makes it difficult for Western Man to keep his feet in this tug of war, thus constantly Western Man finds himself being drawn towards Eastern Man as the tension on the elastic increases and Western foothold becomes more slippery.

Western man does not help himself much. Whereas Eastern Man has standardised boots which help him to hold his ground, Western man has old slippers and anyway talks so much that he is always out of breath. Western man also is shedding his equipment as being too expensive. Indeed if we in the United Kingdom continue with our 'Recessional' very soon all that will be left to defend those freedoms we cherish will be the Americans (if Congress permits) and the Germans, I repeat, the Germans, the one now more or less constant or improving military force in Western Europe.

I think there is a tendency to feel that these great international matters are largely beyond our ability to influence. That is a defeatist attitude and one that Nelson would certainly have deplored. After all he was spurned at Court; left ashore on half pay for years by a totally corrupt Admiralty, and he was someone with no personal influence. We may feel lonely today. How did he feel when he set no foot ashore for nearly two years?

So we have to consider what we can do personally, and nationally, as we go about our training and in our service in the Royal Navy, to confront and overcome the threat from without, and as we bring up our families and as we try to do our job and earn our daily bread, to confront and overcome also the threat from within. We have actively to confront these separate but closely related and well orchestrated external and internal conspiracies which seek to undermine and finally destroy the fruits of 2,000 years of Western progress, halting and uncertain progress it is true, but progress nevertheless.

It seems to me we have to be rebels. Nelson was a natural rebel. The natural rebel is not an iconoclast, a man who pulls down and sneers and denounces giving nothing in return. Nelson rebelled against what he hated because he knew what he loved. He was stimulated by a divine discontent with matters naval, as he saw them.

Nelson believed in his country and surely we must too. There is certainly much still wrong, but I have seen a lot of the world and I believe we have achieved over the centuries, through a well ordered properly operated democratic process, quite possibly the fairest society anywhere today. That fact is often obscured these days by the politics of envy. 'My Country, right or wrong' Nelson would have said. 'My Party, right or wrong' I'm afraid far too many would say today. Therefore I suggest to you that a belief in and love of Country is something that you must teach yourselves. Not just the fields and hedgerows but the sort of society we might enjoy if only all would recognise it.

Next Nelson (with ship's companies more often than not pressed and unwilling men drawn from the dregs of a dozen countries) altered for all time to its true meaning, the word discipline. In a service where the cat of nine tails was in daily use it is said that Nelson never ordered a man to be flogged. He recognised, as communism has failed to recognise, that man has a spirit – and to that spirit he appealed and won. The communist thinks that man can be changed like the edition of an evening paper. Men, men and women, the hearts and minds of men and women, that is what we have to hold today, as Nelson held them.

Then I suppose Nelson taught us love of service. One of the most heart-warming things I have seen as I have 'gone over the hill' in these last years, is the way our three Services have come to grips with the prevailing spirit of the times. This spirit is roughly described as democracy, but to a large extent it means a disinclination to accept any form of restraint and a desire for unrestricted freedom of life and action. That is what so many of those little pygmy men and women who dance and prance and mouth Moscow's platitudes across the pages of our newspapers and TV screens, mean by democracy.

In the Services today there is I think, uniquely, a large measure of that true democracy which is the mark of true discipline. It is something to do with a man's spirit, as Nelson would have recognised; it is something to do with self control; it is something to do with patience; and above all it depends on moral and physical courage. All qualities Nelson possessed in such measure.

Discipline is the root of the matter. Discipline keeps a man calm in an emergency. It keeps him cool in the midst of panic and disaster. It gives him the determination to resist and hold on and face up to the changes and chances of human existence.

I have been so privileged to see that sort of discipline amongst those very young soldiers of all ranks in our incomparable Army as they go about a distasteful and dangerous job in Ireland and do it far better than anyone believed it could be done. I have seen it in lonely little RAF stations collecting intelligence so vital to the threat from without and so secret that they may not even know the importance of what they collect. I have seen it in my own beloved Service where the changes from coal to oil and then to gas turbines, from guns to missiles, has meant an increase in sophistication so that every man now has skills I could barely start to learn, but where too each man seems to have retained the same firmness, patience, self respect and that sentiment of honour which, together, were Nelson's particular legacy to the Royal Navy. It is a privilege to meet such men and those in our Police Force, men like my faithful bodyguard who I see you are so well entertaining tonight and to whom my family and I owe such a debt in these last troublesome years. These four Services together are our Nation's front line of defence against the threats from without and within.

Gentlemen, not long ago in a talk to the Staff College in Australia I quoted G K Chesterton:

> *I tell you naught for your comfort,*
> *Naught for your desire,*
> *Save that the skies grow darker yet,*
> *And the sea rises higher.*

I would say the same today. We are still beating into the storm. But let us, in the Services, count our blessings, as Nelson so often had to do. In Roy Mason we have a Secretary of State, as I have good cause to know, who by any yardstick that I recognise, is a great patriot. We have a Chiefs of Staff Committee united as never before and each, like Nelson, a renowned master of his own profession and each like Nelson a great innovator, unafraid of new ideas; all working in concert with each other and with an experienced Permanent Secretary, Sir Michael Cary, uniquely for the

Civil Service, an electronic engineer, and lately the last of a long line of Secretaries of the Admiralty stretching back to Pepys.

As I have travelled the last five hectic years, seeing war, terrorism, revolution and a rising tempest of violence, I have come to discriminate more and more in our Country between the tawdry glitter and the froth and the demagoguery and brutish intimidation so often, too often, reported on the one hand and on the other the great solid sea of our nation, as simple in its aspirations, as traditional in its virtues as it was in Nelson's day.

Remember then how Nelson faced up to the dangers at the beginning of this cataclysmic era through which it is our fate to travel today, dangers which must have seemed as terrible to him as those at this very moment do to us. We, the British, with our NATO allies face a highly trained, highly mobile, heavily armed Army and Air Force backed by huge reserves, all battle-ready and trained to surge forward regardless of casualties. General Sir Harry Tuzo and our superb British army of the Rhine face the huge Soviet 3rd Shock army, ready, able and willing if need be to give it a bloody nose. At sea we face a threat from over, on and under the ocean which, in sheer numbers, though surely never in skill, outmatches the whole of the NATO fleet. But do not fear that because their ships look heavily armed they are omnipotent. It would not be proper for me to tell you what we know of their deficiencies. Ask Admiral Sir Terence Lewin, the Guardian of the Eastern Atlantic – all is not gold that glitters.

At one end of the scale we face war from satellites and space vehicles and missiles; and in all these threats from without it is the Soviets who constantly increase the spending. It is NATO which as constantly reduces. At the other end there is the threat, new to us in its intensity, ancient in its origin – war by guerillas, insurgents, assassins and more and more by subversion. War by ambush and infiltration, war by hostage taking and unimaginable torture, seeking victory by exhaustion. War by the active erosion of the pillars on which our society rests.

Nelson, Pitt, Wellington, these men moved the world and helped to give 100 years of near peace. Down through the ages there have always been men and women who have shown us the way and I shall always recall once hearing Bobby Kennedy's harsh anxious voice, 'Some people,' he said, 'see things as they are and ask why. I dream of things that never were and ask why not.' Nelson put it another way in the language of his times. He always said that he saw before him his 'Golden Orb', something that went ahead and lit his path. Both meant that hope and faith were the answer, and that, above all, is Nelson's message to us today.

Mr President, Gentlemen, in this College from where so much new thought has come and where I know there still exists that divine discontent with things as they are which Nelson in such measure possessed; in this Port of Plymouth, hallowed by Drake and Hawkins and Raleigh and Grenville and the last piece of his Nation's shores which Nelson saw before bearing off towards Trafalgar; in this Britain today so beset by her enemies from without and particularly from within, I shall ask you in a moment to rise. And in the sure and certain knowledge that tradition, if we understand it, can help us to bear up and hold on in the face of all odds, to drink to the Immortal Memory of Horatio, Viscount Nelson, Earl of Bronté, Admiral of England who, in the moment of victory fell covered with undying glory, leaving to us a legacy of self discipline, endurance and courage which we neglect at our peril.

Mr President, Ladies and Gentlemen – THE IMMORTAL MEMORY.

THE HEART OF THE WEST'S MARITIME CAPABILITY

LECTURE TO THE ROYAL NAVAL STAFF COURSE
1970

Before I left Washington DC (where for nearly three years I had been Naval Attaché) the First Sea Lord, Admiral Sir Michael Le Fanu, asked me to prepare a lecture for delivery to the Naval Staff Course and possibly the then Joint Services Staff College, giving my views of the US Navy and Admiral Moorer's theory (the CNO) as to how a naval regional organisation, if practical, might evolve to counter the Soviet's increasingly worldwide naval presence which was having such a considerable measure of political influence. Because of the international audience I should have to address and because the First Sea Lord wished Moorer's views to be known widely, the lecture was to be completely unclassified and I was directed to make Moorer's views known as widely as I was able. It was Tom Moorer's view that because navies always got on well together his scheme would help greatly to bind the West and other non-communist countries together not only navally but perhaps, eventually, politically as well. Although the then Board under Admiral Le Fanu agreed with Moorer the scheme foundered in the Chancelleries of various countries including, I suspect, the UK. While Admiral Moorer, the mainspring behind the idea, went on to become Chairman of the (US) Chiefs of Staff preoccupied with the winding up of the Vietnam war . . .

Because of my admiration for the US Navy I called this talk 'The Heart of the West's Maritime Capability'.

I have chosen this title for my talk for three reasons. First it is the phrase used by the First Sea Lord in his message to the Royal Navy when *inter alia*, he explicitly referred to the US Navy.

The phrase acknowledges that pre-eminence at sea to which the US Navy acceded after the Battles of Midway and the Coral Sea, a pre-eminence that the Royal Navy had held since Trafalgar.

Secondly, this title enables me to speak of the West's maritime capability and to speculate how best it can be mobilised to confront and deter the Soviet worldwide threat at sea.

Lastly it permits me to discuss the subject of maritime capability itself.

I debated for some time the order in which I should place these three items, but I concluded finally that these subjects are so closely interwoven that I must jump from one to another, trusting to the intelligence of my audience to follow my rather grasshopper thought processes.

As regards the US Navy I'm afraid I make no claims to be objective. I remember Admiral Sir John Frewen saying to me before I sailed for the USA that when he first met them he fell for Americans in the first 24 hours. I am made of lesser clay and I lasted only about 10 minutes.

The United States Navy certainly does not need me to defend it. In company with its sister services, however, it has been going through one of those periods, which we in Britain know so well, when the whole military establishment becomes the object of scorn and derision directed at it almost wholly by people whose knowledge (in this case of naval affairs) is jejune in the extreme and whose shrill virulence is a constant encouragement to the enemies of the West. I always remind my American friends of a passage from those great Lees-Knowles Lectures which General Sir John Hackett gave seven years ago. 'Man,' he said, 'obstinately remains what he is and not what the radical reformer thinks he ought to be. The very existence of the profession of arms is a constant reminder that this is so and the rancour it sometimes arouses in the radical breast is easily understood.'

However it would not be considered a disservice to the US Navy if I made some observations in the light of the two and a half happy years my wife and I have spent amongst them.

I should say here that it has been an additional privilege to be accredited also to the US Marine Corps. If I mention them only occasionally in my talk it is surely because General Chapman's tough body of veterans, whose numbers and tactical air power exceed the whole of the British Services put together deserve a lecture to themselves.

When the Army and the Navy come to gaze on Heaven's scenes,
They will find the streets are guarded by United States Marines.

I fear the words of that old Marine song have become too terribly true in the Tet offensive, in Hue and in Vietnam, in the last two or three years.

When I first met one of the great Americans to whom our country and the West owe so much, Admiral Rickover said to me, 'Never forget in everything you do or say in the United States you are the Trustee for the Royal Navy.' Although I never take anything Admiral Rickover says lightly it took me several months to convince myself that the US Navy, this greatest ever manifestation of seapower, really does value its association with the Royal Navy, however small we may be, however misguided our political direction may sometimes seem and however much we may appear to be relinquishing our worldwide role. I honestly believe a 'Special Relationship' does exist between the two Navies which, if we understand it and use it properly, can be of immense benefit to the West in meeting the Soviet threat at sea. As I listened to Ambassador David Bruce when, uniquely, he was dined by the Pilgrims in New York on return from his great eight year embassy to the Court of St. James, I heard him use the phrase 'Special Relationship' and then go on to say that was too weak a description for what he proclaimed was in fact an 'Anglo-American Alliance'. I thought to myself that our two navies could perhaps claim that first but much maligned phrase as their own and that the extraordinary close affinity between us was basic to the Anglo-American Alliance and therefore well worth working for; and so I began to understand the real meaning behind Admiral Rickover's words.

Inevitably there are divisive forces between the two navies. There is growing up in both a generation who were too young to have fought together in World War II or Korea; and only the RNZN and the RAN have sided the ships on Yankee Station and in the Riverine war as they fight the communists in Vietnam; while increasingly ships flying the Red Ensign enter the Vietnamese port of Haiphong. That was why I always insisted that when, on Trafalgar Night we, the British, dined the senior officers of the US Navy and US Marine Corps, there should also always be present as guests a number of Midshipmen from the Naval Academy at Annapolis. Nevertheless, in facing the main threat the warship navies of the West in contradistinction to the merchant and fishing fleets are well united and in this potentially great naval alliance the increasingly close partnership of the US and Royal Navies is a fundamental fact – indeed I would hold it to be the linchpin. I shall return to the more concrete possibilities later.

If the US Navy is the heart of the West's maritime capability then I suppose its people are its lifeblood. With a budget over five times that of the whole UK Defence Budget, the US Navy has some 900 ships, 9000 aircraft besides another 5000 aircraft in the US Marine Corps. There are ¾ million naval officers and enlisted sailors, over 90% of whom are on a 4 or 5 year engagement. With some 15,000 officers entering every year (only 900 or so from Annapolis) and about 200,000 recruits annually, the turnover in manpower and the training task is mind boggling, certainly to a mind brought up in a small 'long service' navy like ours.

Inevitably in such a gigantic organisation with its four great Fleets, its vast air component, its huge submarine service and its tremendous surface power, all backed by a mammoth R. & D. and Shipyard, Supply and Aircraft Maintenance Organisation there are wide differences in outlook, morale and technical excellence. Inevitably too there is ample opportunity for mistakes and I understand that many of these have quite naturally been highlighted in our press and media as they have been in the United States.

Indeed if one was to sit in Washington DC and read the press and listen to the TV and to Congress one could easily assume that the whole affair was one big mistake. Gentlemen, I wish I had the time or wit to convince you of the opposite. I wish the press could tell you of Admiral Moorer, the CNO, and his Band of Brothers, the Annapolis Class of 1933, so many of whom, with 36 years of close friendship since they joined the Naval Academy together, now side him in his great responsibilities. I wish the press could tell you or TV could show you their subordinates right down to the ardent young Air Officer candidates that I was (uniquely for a foreign officer) allowed to Commission into the US Navy. I wish the Press or TV could show you the sometimes scruffy and long haired recruits from the Chicago slums streaming into the Boot Camp and the smart and well disciplined young men leaving after only 11 weeks, or of those nice (usually) country bred boys, brought in under Project 100,000 for the underprivileged and being kept back for a few more weeks to teach them to read and write a little better. I wish I could tell you of the sixteen hour day which the young and sometimes not so young ex-university graduates put in for three months on end at the Officer Candidate School; or per-haps, as the BBC did two or three years ago, of the eager and articulate and polite young men at Annapolis; or of that outstanding officer who is the present Superintendent who fought the Germans with the French Army, then with the Royal Navy and finally the Japanese with his own Navy. I wish I could show you some of the people like the hard bitten old Chief Petty Officer who shook my hand and recalled a day in 1944 when his Captain broadcast, 'The British who have now nearly finished off Germany are sending their ships out here and the British Carrier Squadron is coming into sight over the horizon.' 'We knew then we could not lose,' he said to me. I wish I had more time to tell you of life at sea in a ship of the US Navy, of the letters I received from ordinary sailors to whom I had spoken when on board, or of a picnic I attended with several hundred enlisted men and pilot pupils at a Naval Air Station. The USN has had its Pueblo and Guittari and other problems too. But after all some of you here who have read Naval history will know of the Invergordon and Lucia mutinies, of the collision between *Hood* and *Repulse*, the affair of Bandmaster Barnacle and even PQ 17. Such blotches in either service, some inexcusable and some, with hindsight quite understandable, must be set against the wonder of the whole canvas.

I always take every opportunity of recalling to young US navy officers, as I do our own officers, Admiral of the Fleet Lord Jellicoe's treatise on discipline written 50 years ago:

> 'In a consideration of discipline, one is in these days at once brought face to face with the prevailing spirit of the times. This spirit is usually roughly described as 'democracy', but to a large extent it means a disinclination to accept any form of restraint and a desire for unrestricted freedom of life and action.'
>
> And after giving his views on the need for discipline and the ways it can be infused he wrote, 'A Service so disciplined is less expensive to the State and at the same time provides the State with citizens who, on their return to civil life, will be a real strength to the community.'

I suppose that perhaps the critics of the US Navy think they could do better themselves but personally I believe if Lord Jellicoe could see what I have seen I am sure he would recognise that the problems of discipline in the US Navy, as in our own Navy, have not really changed from those he set down. I think he would commend the end product who is now leaving the US Navy for civil life as being a disciplined man who could meet most, perhaps all, the criteria which he so succinctly established. In a service so vast and with personnel changing so quickly I have constantly been amazed and uplifted at the spirit and the efficiency and the enthusiasm which is so patently apparent.

Now if the men are good – and as I say I believe they are usually superlative – the same cannot be said about the ships. Their average age is seventeen and a half years.

Nearly half the officers and enlisted men have been in their ships for less than a year – and even enthusiasm which works an 80 hour week at sea and in harbour is no substitute for experience. So there is finger trouble and old machinery does not like that much.

Ships are averaging 70% of their time on station actually underway or at immediate notice. That is more than we have been achieving and our ships in the last few years have generally been running at more than World War II tempo. Breakdowns are frequent and sometimes catastrophic. Corrosion is taking its toll and so on.

I do not think that Congress has given the US Navy the tools its officers and enlisted men deserve, if they are going to play their part in any Western Naval Alliance of the future.

With their current operational tempo there is also very little time or opportunity to evolve and practise the ideas and the tactics which the West must use, should the mounting Soviet pressure on the oceans rise towards the danger point.

All this places a big responsibility on the other Western Navies especially on the Royal Navy, the only other deep water Navy which, albeit in a tenuous way, still practises all forms of maritime war. We have a role and a vital one. We are not preoccupied with a war at the other end of the world. We must continue as we do to strive for professional naval excellence. We must constantly consider contingent means to maintain and strengthen what is now an historic relationship between our two Services despite the vast disparity in size and resources between us.

Now I will try to examine the world problems which involve the sea and how they affect the Western Maritime capability.

Even if Mr Robert McNamara had not defined the problem statistically there is little doubt in anyone's mind that starvation breeds chaos and violence. But Mr McNamara puts the seal on this assumption when he points out that major outbreaks of violence have increased from 34 in 1958 to 58 in 1965 and prolonged insurgencies from 23–40 in the same period. Further in this time scale 89% of the very poor nations, 60% of the poor nations and 48% of the middle income nations have suffered serious violence. And the economic gap between the 'haves' and the 'have nots' is constantly increasing.

My own view is that Europe apart, Britain certainly and the USA probably, will never intervene militarily by a conventional invasion of another nation. It is national wars of liberation through political effervescence which are likely to set back progress, arrest development and create anarchy that are the danger, rather than wars of conquest by one nation over another; and this fact seems to me to require an altogether more subtle strategy.

The 20 year programme of 'Anti Imperialist Liberation Revolutions' was first enunciated by Kruschev in his speech to the Communist Congress in 1961. It was Lord Attlee who spoke of 'the vast outpouring of political energy in any new nation' and certainly this is true of the hundred or so countries now caught up in the transition from traditional to modern societies. Generally they are anti-landowner, anti-rich, anti-middle class and nearly always anti-white. Their birthrate is skyrocketing and there is emerging a whole hemisphere of youth, whose frustration and starvation has already erupted into intense political activity and often violence.

Lin Piao, now the heir apparent in China, wrote just four years ago, 'The countryside and the countryside alone, can provide the revolutionary bases from which the revolutionaries can go forward to final victory . . .' Looking at the entire globe, if North America and Western Europe plus Japan can be called 'the cities of the world' then Asia, Africa, and South America constitute the rural areas of the world.

Sir Robert Thompson returns to this theme in his book *No Exit from Vietnam*:

> With the failure of Western methods of defence in Vietnam all Western methods will be downgraded even in the political, economic and technical fields. The development of freedom and democracy, through plural economic and political societies and the concept of free enterprise will cease to be attractive because they will appear to render States vulnerable to subversive attack. The great majority of the countries concerned are basically agricultural (the 'countryside of the world') where millions are acutely anxious, less about their form of government than about where the next bowl of rice or maize is coming from.
>
> If the industrial countries of the West led by the United States (the 'cities of the world') fail, or because of Vietnam default on their obligation to remedy this situation and to close the widening gap between the rich and poor nations of the world, then these so called 'newly emerging forces' will be in great danger of becoming the future starving masses. It is hard to think of a more explosive situation looming ahead than that a large part of the world, with its backward agriculture and expanding population, may become both communist controlled and starving.

It is at this point that the application of seapower in this vast problem has to be studied. What we are all seeking on both sides of the Iron Curtain is time. Time somehow to organise the emerging world so that hunger is reduced; so that violence is diminished; so that freedom may become a way of life, say the West. Time so that hunger is reduced, so that violence is controlled; so that Marxism may become a way of life, say the Soviets and China too.

The primary struggle will be political and economic; a struggle for men's minds through their hearts and through their children's minds and stomachs.

Clearly the West, not only because of the risk to its own security if it does nothing, but because so many of its countries fall within the rich bracket and have a moral duty to do so, has to assist in the development of the under developed world. Development means economic, social and political progress and a reasonable standard of living – and please note the latter is a comparative term, constantly changing.

It is not the purpose of this talk to try and define the role of the military in helping to induce and maintain the minimum degree of security and order without which development cannot proceed. But there are whole areas of the problem of development which concern the sea and which the Soviets have grasped, which the West still seems incapable of comprehending other than in purely military terms.

Protein deficiency is the biggest single child killer. The oceans could provide all that is needed in the way of Fish Protein Concentrate (FPC). Only the Soviets, in any meaningful way, are starting to meet this world deficiency.

High freight rates inhibit the easy passage of goods and raw materials. Only the Soviets, by devoting part of their GNP to reducing freight rates (and incidentally thereby undercutting the West) are contributing with their brand new merchant fleet to this reduction in world transport costs and thus to the development of the less developed countries.

Apart from the periods of the First and Second World Wars the Royal Navy virtually guaranteed that the oceans were a highway free of political hindrance. Since World War II (unhappily to a decreasing extent) the US Navy and the Royal Navy together, have usually been able to deploy sufficient power at sea to continue such a guarantee, but there have been failures and there will be more.

Today there are many areas in which the Western naval writ no longer runs and it might no longer be possible to make it do so. The Soviet fleet is moving in with the power to deny access to raw materials and the free passage of goods on the high seas. Whether or not such power is exercised either in quasi-military ways (proclamation of exercise areas at focal points as has happened, for instance) or in actual military ways, it would take place in a neutral environment; it could be sporadic and protracted; whilst any actual 'Western' decision to confront such activity would be extremely difficult to achieve. Even if no actual quasi-military or actual military activity is indulged in, the presence of Soviet warships is a powerful political pawn. Furthermore, because Soviet Russia owns the heartland, countermoves against her merchant fleet or the merchant fleet of the Warsaw Pact powers could damage developing countries much more than the West.

Then there is the sea bed itself, already man can live and work down to 600' or so, that is to the defined limits of the Continental Shelf. Nuclear power, new steels, titanium, fuel cells, underwater TV, all these and remote control techniques are permitting vehicles of extraordinary capability to explore and harvest the sea bed in the deepest oceans and soon perhaps in the abyssal depths. The USSR with her expanding submarine fleet, deep diving, very fast and increasingly quiet, is making the ocean bed her stamping ground. Already the sea bed has become a source of potential conflict and, perhaps all too soon, of actual conflict.

In a recent paper entitled 'Maritime Strategy in the 70s' General Moulton, if I read him correctly, holds to what I call the Enoch Powell theory that 'defence of the Homeland is the only true justification for military vocation.' Personally I believe this is taking too parochial and nationalistic a view and certainly out of touch with what I believe the young are thinking. General Moulton also seems to go on to suggest that it is not a far step from this to what he calls a European Maritime Strategy. Further he appears to postulate that such (European) maritime forces earmarked to undertake the reinforcement of the flanks of Europe might also form part of some international Constabulary Force, available to give limited backing to indigenous forces facing an internal opponent in a 'War of National Liberation' (as such conflicts are often called). This seems to me to be an idea worth pursuing.

I have been for nearly three years a member and in my time Chairman of the Military Staff Committee of the United Nations Security Council. The other members were from the USA, Nationalist China, France and the Soviet Union.

Although the committee has met every two weeks for twenty-five years it has never done any business. Yet if the Security Council were ever unanimously to agree to the establishment of a Constabulary Force this committee would be the designated instrument for the organisation and operation of such a Force. The Soviets and the French committee members have often told me that one day they believe this will occur. I would like to think that was the way the remainder of Western thinking and modern Chinese thinking is going too.

Such, however, is the mess that the politicians of the world have got us into that this will be a long time ahead. (In parentheses was it not Admiral Lord Fisher who used to say what really gave him a profound Belief in the beneficence of the Almighty was the state of the Empire despite the politicians?) Although it may now seem that the Almighty has deserted us what I am concerned with is how the Western world (we used to call it the 'Free World' but that is clearly a misnomer) can capitalise on the vast fund of naval understanding and mutual goodwill, largely created here and at the US Naval War College at Rhode Island, so that a contingency naval presence, such as Admiral Moorer USN has suggested, can be made available to confront the Soviets on each regional basis.

I agree very much with Hanson Baldwin when he says that by clever propaganda and by extensive (and sometimes excessive) Western Press coverage the Soviet Fleet has acquired a political and psychological influence quite disproportionate to its combat effectiveness; and also with Professor Laurence Martin when he asserts that 'the significance of maritime capability varies greatly according to the political context; and that the Soviet quest for 'dominance' has different implications according to whether we have in mind a state of peace or war. Thus Soviet seapower in the Mediterranean and the Persian Gulf is an effective instrument for forward diplomatic policy although it would often be very much on the defensive in open hostilities with the West.' And Professor Martin adds a pregnant sentence which, in my view, is the key to our future Western Naval course of action. He says, 'It is consequently a vital Western interest to see that the overall naval balance never shifts in the Soviet favour to an extent that would encourage Soviet leaders to reassess and minimise the dangers of military action.' Personally I would add to that sentence what I have called quasi-military action also, but in Martin's sentence it is the overall naval balance which is really important.

Let me now try to summarise the present situation:
1. The US Navy is the heart of the West's maritime capability.
2. The US Navy has been run off its feet and, although well manned, its tools are getting blunt and old and are not being replaced sufficiently fast.
3. New and perhaps revolutionary tactical doctrine more appropriate to a war at sea has not been given the chance to develop, because future

strategy and weapon systems have not fully been examined, largely of course because of pre-occupation with the Vietnam war.

4. The Royal Navy, although tiny by comparison with the US Navy, has been through a series of traumatic experiences, mostly due to lack of national resources, but has emerged still just able to field a small fleet with good weapons appropriate to modern maritime war and the ability to deploy worldwide.

5. Some of the RN skills such as the operation of Polaris have been borrowed from the US Navy; others, such as the operation of SSNs, have been borrowed and perhaps subsequently improved.

The earlier than expected phasing out of the large carriers has left a gap which has not yet been filled. But this has stimulated new thought and new ways of deploying organic airpower economically. In this field the RN may once more be able to help the USN.

6. Although I have not specifically referred to it, this audience will be aware of the Standing Naval Force, Atlantic and the Maritime Contingency Force Concept. With these and the pooling of national surveillance (however nationally secure the actual means of surveillance may remain) NATO has gone some way to showing how multi-national maritime power can be co-ordinated and exercised effectively in the interests of the West.

7. The oceans of the world fall into several reasonably defined regions in which the littoral countries, as well as others, have a common interest in preserving the rights of free passage on and under the sea.

8. This common interest can be defined broadly as the need to preserve stability particularly where stability is already only marginal due to political effervescence or poverty or hunger or all three.

9. Security and stability, and order and development, go hand in hand. As Mr McNamara has said: 'Development means economic, social and political progress. It means a reasonable standard of living and 'reasonable' in this context requires continual re-definition. As development progresses and when the people of a nation have organised their own human and natural resources to provide themselves with what they need and expect from life, and have learned to compromise peacefully in the larger national interest among competing demands, then their resistance to disorder and violence will enormously increase. Conversely, the tragic need of desperate men to resort to force to achieve the imperatives of human decency will diminish that resistance to vanishing point.'

10. The common interest among the Western Nations in general and the wealthy nations in particular is to encourage the building of security and

stability by every form of aid and assistance, whilst, if possible, excluding communism from those areas where starvation is already rife and where there is a ready made breeding ground for anarchy and chaos.

In all this endeavour and in a world whose population will have doubled by the time our children are our age, I hold that the sea has a great part to play.

The sea as a vast and largely untapped reservoir full of food and protein.

The sea bed as a vast and as yet largely untapped source of power, minerals and fresh water.

The sea as the one open highway free of international political hindrance, over which all the goods and services to ensure development of the undeveloped world must flow.

The sea as a source of political issue and even conflict.

I think all of us would agree that the thrilling and fascinating techniques of air and aerospace engineering developed in the West over the last 20–25 years have effectively focused people's eyes on the stars. Perhaps in the words of the old proverb, 'We have walked into a well from gazing at the stars.'

I so well remember, when I was Naval Assistant to the Controller of the Navy (who was desperately worried about the malaise affecting all parts of the British shipbuilding industry), talking to an MP for a shipbuilding constituency and trying to enlist his help. In effect he said to me, 'Give up. Shipbuilding is a primitive industry not suitable for anything but an undeveloped country and certainly not something on which our country should waste its resources.'

I wish you could see as I have seen what is going on in the USA. The tremendous new shipyard at Pascagoula in which Littons, the great aerospace firm, and the State of Mississippi have invested so much treasure; the Advanced Marine Technology Group at M.I.T. under Dr Frankel (who fought so gallantly in our Navy at Crete and elsewhere); the plans that Boeings and Lockheeds and Grumman and Litton and Electric Boat have for the future of surface and sub-surface ocean transport.

These great firms certainly do not regard shipbuilding as a primitive industry, but as one where there is almost infinite scope for innovation, improvement, revolutionary ideas and development.

I wish I could spend time telling you too of the Federal Maritime Academy under an American admiral of Scots extraction, himself an ex-Chief Engineer, his father a British merchant service captain and his grandfather a Scottish shipbuilder, or of the fine young deck officers he turns out uniquely holding also qualifications in nuclear and marine engineering. I wish our Board of Admiralty could meet him.

Then let us turn to the sea bed for a moment. It is true that in the last few months Britain has shown some small signs of waking from its lethargy. But listen to this small quotation from a recent US report:

> The driving force and urgency of our new concern for the sea stem from the changing character of the world itself – from mounting economic needs, from congested populations, from our own deteriorating shores. The need to develop an adequate national ocean programme arises from a combination of rapid and interacting forces.
>
> The potential for expanded economic activities is evident in today's marine industrial operations. Offshore petroleum, gas, and sulphur recovery attests that the wealth in the land under the sea is available to Man; the mining of tin, diamonds, sand, gravel and shell from the sea bed shows the possibility of recovering other important minerals. Deep submersibles and undersea habitats demonstrate the ability of Man to live and work under the sea. Yet technological development for economically important work in the sea remains largely in the future.

And then let us mention briefly, for it makes one ill to dwell on it, the utter chaos in the Western 'ocean carrying trade' and Western fishing fleets. What can be done short of nationalising them and then internationalising them all just as we have nationalised navies and are working towards (as Admiral Moorer would have it) an international or at least co-operative western navy it is difficult yet to see. Because first of course we have to convince the western governments of the importance of the whole 'Sea Affair'. Very few people in government on either side of the Atlantic or indeed anywhere in the Western camp itself would admit that a problem exists at all.

Finally then let us turn to the Western naval problem in the light of:
(a) The problems facing the European Community.
(b) The vast areas of the world from which any British presence is being withdrawn.
(c) The limitations of the US Navy, the Royal Navy, the NATO Navies and the other navies which feature vaguely in the Western camp.
(d) The continued retention by the Soviets of the naval initiative.

(e) The Soviet possession of the 'Heartland'.

(f) China.

It seems to me that there are two main actions which can be taken to improve matters on the naval front.

First with the Standing Naval Force, Atlantic, and the Maritime Contingency Force of NATO (both the products of Admiral Moorer's foresight) as examples, we should, with the USN, encourage the development of Regional Groupings aimed at producing the same end pattern. Such regions as the South Atlantic, the Indian Ocean, South East Asia and the Pacific all lend themselves to such a plan.

Certainly at first there need not be any political content to these naval arrangements. But well publicised common exercises, the establishment (at first on a provisional basis) of various 'Standing Naval Forces' and the practising of such 'forces' in common operating procedures; a common regional command structure; all these are means to an end and however modest such a programme may seem it would I believe have a considerable political impact and would demonstrate that the High Seas are not yet a Soviet lake. Somehow, or so it seems to me, the US Navy and the Royal Navy and other friendly navies must soon start talking on these lines.

Bases

Many people still hold the view that bases around the world are an essential to the continual operation of a Fleet away from the Home Base. This concept in fact stems from two main requirements from which, increasingly, the US Navy and the Royal Navy are divorcing themselves.

(a) The need to clean boilers at set intervals inside and out. This is something that in smaller ships cannot always be done whilst remaining operational at sea.

(b) The need to dry-dock so that underwater valves and corrosion can be attended to.

Docking periods in both navies are no longer a significant factor. If and when, as is likely, both navies go to nuclear or gas turbine or diesel electric propulsion then the boiler problem will lose all significance.

There remains the problem of spare parts, repair by replacement, a reasonable policy of duplication both in machinery and weapon systems, the ability to carry enough ready-use spares, the increasingly precise estimates of 'mean time between failures', the ubiquity of commercial (or national) air transport, all these taken together make the provision of bases in the usual sense of the word totally irrelevant in peacetime for sophisticated navies such as the Royal Navy and even the much larger (and wider age span) US Navy.

The human, rather than the material factor is now the critical one and although Nelson kept his men at sea for years this is no longer a practical possibility. Ships are made to fight and there is a limit to the space which can be devoted to amenities for the crew, while anyone lucky enough to cruise even in a well appointed liner will admit that life on board palls and the sight of a port is welcome. So it is with navies and fleets. Periods alongside for relaxation and (only incidentally) for running repairs, are as essential for the Western as for the Soviet Fleets; accepting of course that the need inevitably becomes more pressing for those who normally enjoy a higher standard of living.

In periods of tension or actual alert the situation becomes more difficult because of the need to ensure the means of fuel, food and ammunition replenishment. Short of a world in flames none of these difficulties is insuperable, although each calls for considerable skill and expertise in the economic operation of warships and the husbanding of resources; skill in routeing of warships and support ships and, wherever possible friendly or neutral ports within the operating range of the Task Force. With nuclear powered task forces and more so if nuclear powered supply ships can be afforded and risked, these difficulties are reduced.

When Admiral Lord Fisher turned the Royal Navy from coal, an indigenous fuel, to oil which had to come from the Persian Gulf he gave as his prime reason the reinforcement of the British Fleet by the presence at sea of the 25% normally in harbour, coaling. This concept was neglected by the Royal Navy and it was the US Navy under Fleet Admiral King (who constantly proclaimed that mobility was a prime military asset) who in World War II retaught the Royal Navy this lesson. The techniques and expertise of operating without bases have since constantly been improved by both Navies. Although both still use bases (they now prefer to call them 'facilities') when these are available as, by so doing, it is possible to maximise the tempo of operations which both navies may have been required to undertake.

In the light of a capability to operate without bases the whole Western naval capability can be placed in three categories.

Ocean Going Navies

Primarily the Royal and US Navies, but this group could also include the Royal Netherlands Navy, the French Navy, the Old Commonwealth navies including the South African Navy and perhaps, eventually, the emerging Japanese Navy. All these have the ability if not always the means to be ocean going. The Italian, Greek and Turkish navies would be concentrated in the Mediterranean and Black Sea.

Seaward Defence Forces

Nations with such forces possess ocean going ships but their respective navies have neither the training, nor the means such as support ships (nor perhaps the wish), to deploy their fleets for prolonged periods away from the home base.

Coastal Defence Forces

This comprises a very large group of navies some of whom, in a small way and some more so, have concentrated on the exercise of power at sea only in the immediate and limited vicinity of their coasts and ports. Such ships are in no sense 'ocean going' but can perform useful tasks nevertheless.

If one considers that Admiral Moorer's concept of a series of Regional Naval organisations is a possibility and, bearing in mind the time it takes to design and build warships as well as the main thrust of the Soviet military threat, their submarine fleet and the political and psychological thrust of the uniquitous Soviet surface fleet, we must in the light of what I have said, now examine the West's defensive counters.

This could mean 'the mixture as before'. But given some agreement amongst the main elements of the suggested Western Naval Alliance some rationalisation leading to economy of effort by all participants could well produce an effective and global naval counter force.

Leaving aside the UK and US seaborne SSBN deterrent there are three main needs to be met:

(a) Enough warships from Western nations to provide the necessary 'density' of Western naval power worldwide as an anti-Soviet political deterrent.

(b) An airborne or submarine ability to strike the Soviet Surface Fleet. The airborne deterrent could be land based or, less preferably, carrier based or, best of all, nuclear submarine based.

(c) A world-wide comprehensive static, seaborne and airborne anti-submarine capability

Admiral of the Fleet Sir Varyl Begg, that very great First Sea Lord, when he was Vice-Chief of the Naval Staff and the present incumbent First Sea Lord, Admiral Sir Michael Le Fanu, always held that they were amongst the Founder members of the Soviet Maritime Threat Club and I was permitted to put my thoughts (often gleaned from their discussions) on paper and publish them in the *Journal of the RUSI* in 1962/3 and *Brassey's Annual*. But there was no government reaction. Preoccupation, fathered by the terror instilled into the continental nations of NATO by tales of Soviet atrocities against Germany and the recollection of the very real Soviet land threat in the late Forties and early Fifties continued to be the focus of Western political and British Parliamentary thinking. Meanwhile the Soviet Navy, with its merchant and fishing fleets, cast a noose around the Western World.

That is what we have to break out of. No nation alone, not even the United States can do this. Our effort for peace must embrace the whole maritime affair, warships of all sorts with some regional responsibilities; shipbuilding by those nations who have the means and experience; freighters under Western control carrying goods and if necessary subsidised; and fishing industries to help feed the accelerating millions facing starvation. Western Universities and think-tanks and Staff Colleges must bend their energies towards providing maritime answers.

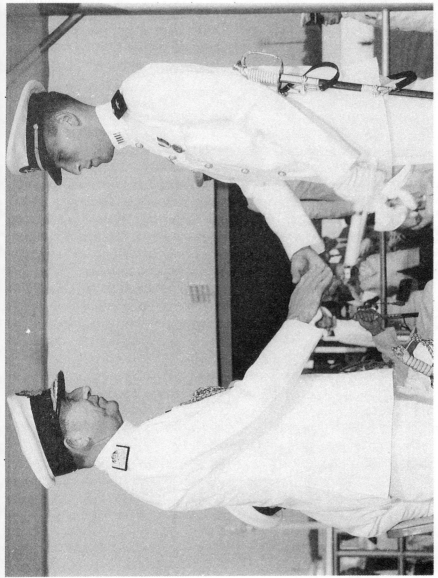

Class Leader Mr Fucci receives his Commission. (US Navy)

Left to Right: Admiral Thomas H Moorer, USN. (Chief of Naval Operations), Author, Sir Patrick Dean GCMG H.M. Ambassador, General Chapman, Commandant USMC. (US Navy photo)

THE BAND OF BROTHERS. 1968

Left to Right: Admiral Clarey, VCNO. Admiral Holmes, SACLANT. Admiral McCain, CINCPAC. Admiral Moorer, CNO. Admiral Galantin, Chief of Naval Materiel. Admiral Duncan, Chief of Naval Personnel. (US Navy Photo)

Mr Frank Barnett. President, National Strategy Information Center. (NSIC)

Author received at the 'Boot Camp' San Diego. The US Navy was receiving 200,000 new recruits anually. (US Navy Photo)

Author presents BRITANNIA TROPHY to Lieutenant Cunningham USN. Top US Navy pilot. 1968

Other Ranks birthday party and Picnic. US Naval Air Station, Meridien, Mississippi.

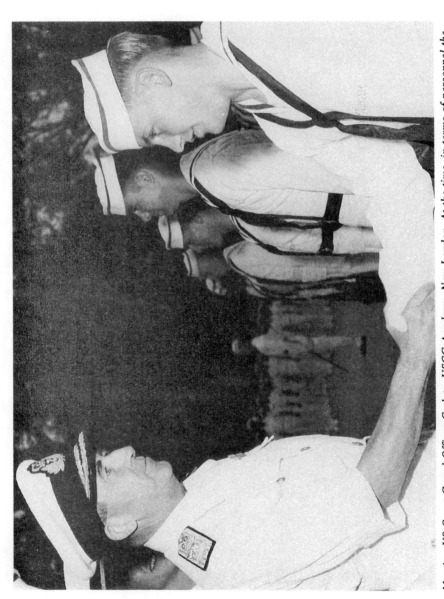

Meeting US Coast Guard Officer Cadets. USCG Academy. New London. At the time, in terms of personnel the USCG was the 3rd largest Navy in the world. (USCG Photo)

NAVAL REORGANISATION

THE MANSERGH COMMITTEE

Evidence from Commander (E) L. E. S. H.
Le Bailly. May 1954

As I have recounted in 'The Man Around the Engine' and 'From Fisher to the Falklands', at the end of the Pacific campaign I was invited by the Commander in Chief and his Staff to write a 'worm's eye' view of why the British Fleet was so much less mobile than the US navy; and subsequently, on the way home, to produce some views on the training of Engineer Officers and ratings. Those reports have gone forever. However they were still extant in 1954 and I was appointed to the office of the Extra Naval Assistant to the Second Sea Lord, inter alia, to give my views to the Mansergh Committee on a future officer structure for the Royal Navy. The result was a long and rather tedious memorandum which, so Admiral Sir Aubrey Mansergh told me later, had an impact on the committee in several respects.

Clearly they found my suggestion that the Supply Branch should have its own avenue to the Fourth Sea Lord responsible for Supplies and Transport and that the Royal Marines should take over the Fleet Air Arm, quite unacceptable. But my concept of a 'General List' was not otherwise so very different to that which emerged from their cogitations. The idea, cribbed from the Butler Education Act that Dartmouth should give a secondary general education to a large intake, from which only 50% should enter the Navy also defeated the Committee.

While in limbo from the department of the Engineer in Chief between 1946–49 I had visited 80 Independent Schools and spent a year at Birmingham University and the idea of making Dartmouth somewhat akin to the Citadel at Charleston, South Carolina or the Virginia Military Institute was not original but was largely as a result of discussions with headmasters and professors; while National Service seemed to me also to make it an appropriate idea.

Because the report was so long I have reproduced here only the synopsis which preceded the full text. Because of my experience before, during and particularly after the war I was particularly worried that the 'gap' between engineers and deck officers, sometimes wide though perhaps beginning to close in the immediate pre-war days and noticeably closer during the war, was once again beginning to recur due to the changing shape of the post-war Royal Navy and the reduction in opportunities for Sea Command for executive officers. Deprived of the chance of Sea Command as many inevitably were they were more than usually anxious to hold on to their privileged position in the Naval hierarchy which for so long has been assumed by the seaman executive branch.

That is the reason for the appendix to my evidence labelled 'Fifty Years Ago. Plus ça change. Plus c'est la même chose.'

SYNOPSIS

1. I mean no disrespect when I say that the Committee's task has been likened to that facing a body of Cardinals charged with preventing the dissolution of Christendom by the admission of Noncomformist and Anglican Divines to the Holy College.

The simile is apt for though, as in the Church, the schisms which rend the Service are bridged every day by men of goodwill, they exist nevertheless.

2. Only a radical change in policy, steadily implemented for a period of twenty to thirty years, will finally close the divisions in the Navy which have occurred or been deliberately created but much can be done between now and then given a goal clearly defined by the committee: leadership, goodwill, patience and no war.

3. The sombre fact that officer entries have virtually ceased colours all my proposals. A dramatic change in the whole naval structure and outlook is needed if they are to revive.

4. The following broad principles underlie all my suggestions:

   (a) We are one Navy. Officers, whatever their function must be trained together, have approximately the same career prospects and, rank for rank, must be considered equal except when exercising operational command.

   (b) Higher command and direction, in whatever sphere, must be nurtured and sustained by seagoing experience.

(c) The numerical requirement for highly trained naval officers with superlative leadership skills and brain capacity is small and the country can afford to allow this requirement to be fully satisfied.

(d) The Navy will never procure the best entry if it does not offer a sound training and, to the great majority, a lifetime of satisfying service commensurate with their acknowledged ability.

(e) The Navy, to a far greater extent than the other Services, demands that the majority of those responsible for its higher direction should have a sound technological training and this fact in no way compromises the Navy's other requirement that its officers should be leaders.

(f) Fleet engagements of the Coral Sea or the Leyte variety are a thing of the past.

Whether or not the Fleet Air Arm includes Coastal Command, its function in the main and except for small anti-submarine carriers, will be carried out by land based aircraft – at any rate by the time the new officer structure materialises.

5. My conclusions are as follows:

(a) That there should be three officer entries to Dartmouth to be known as:

   (i) The General List Entry

   (ii) The Supply Entry

   (iii) The Royal Marine Entry

The General List Entry comprising all officers now entered into the Executive, Engineering and Electrical Branches, together with a very few Constructor Officers.

(b) That initial training should be to a widely recognised standard and that initial entry should allow for a 50% wastage of officers reaching that standard.

(c) That officers should be selected and trained for Sea Command after about five years of common training; that this avenue should lead to all subordinate operational commands and to the First Sea Lord.

(d) That the General List, depleted by the subtraction of those selected for Sea Command, should be divided at a later stage into those who will be responsible for the Personnel and Material Administration of the Navy who will follow avenues to the posts of Second and Third Sea Lords, and those responsible for Research and Development, who will provide the Technical Directors.

(e) The Supply Branch should have its own avenue of promotion to Fourth Sea Lord; with a transfer to general administration on the personnel side.

(f) The Fleet Air Arm has given the Navy indigestion. Whether or not it includes Coastal Command it should be a separate force under the Fifth Sea Lord who should be a Royal Marine.

(g) In addition to the officer structures already mentioned above there should be:
   (i) A Second Line Navy Structure complemented to fill the less active but vital posts.
   (ii) A broad based Branch List Structure.
   (iii) A Short Service Structure.

In the course of my evidence I quoted, as symptomatic of the outlook of a rising number of Executive officers mostly trained at Dartmouth (and Eaton Hall during the war) the words of Dean Swift:

> *We are God's chosen few,*
> *All others will be damned.*
> *There is no place in Heaven for you,*
> *We can't have Heaven crammed.*

While to end my evidence I wrote as follows and of course what I wrote should be read in the context of big ships with large Wardrooms and many Executive officers born to man the armament in war but, normally just watchkeepers in peace:

'The truth is that in peacetime the Executive Branch is overmanned and, as many will confess, lacks much to do. The technical branches are often hardworked and, in the case of the Engineering Branch, often consist of a bunch of the younger officers in the Wardroom who, because of their age, tend to gang up together.

'Status' is an occupational disease usually of the idle 'passed over' executive Lieutenant-Commander – the 'little man'. The young engineer officer, sometimes tired and cross after a day in overheated boiler-rooms, resents their outlook and delights to mock and goad – and the gulf widens.'

In the words of G. K. Chesterton:

> *If all the good people were clever,*
> *And all clever people were good,*

The world would be better than ever
We possibly thought that it should.

Yet, alas, it is seldom or never
That the two hit it off as they should,
For the good are so rude to the clever
And the clever so cruel to the good.

I don't suggest that the cap necessarily fits; but how much better if all officers were clever and good and received one training to that common end.

APPENDIX
Fifty Years Ago

Plus ça change. Plus c'est la même chose.
(I have included here only a selection of the 24 different quotations I listed.)

For years the Admiralty have been advised and entreated to deal with the engineering question in a broad, liberal and impartial spirit. But in the words of Mr Dugdale, 'they have by arrogant and egotistical opposition succeeded in making one of our most honourable and important professions the most unpopular in the whole Navy.'

Mr D. B. Morison

But futile will be the most brilliant tactics, if the floating mechanisms fail in the hour of trial.

Professor Weighton

It is necessary that Engineer Officers should exhibit to their men an example of courage and coolness for the preservation of discipline and the ensuring of prompt attention and obedience to orders. But it becomes difficult to exhibit these necessary qualities if the spirit of these officers is crushed by the continual repression and non-recognition by those in authority.

Mr Bedbrook. RN (Chief Inspector of Machinery)

Certain Admirals after retiring have been seized with an attack of virtue ... but what we want is that the Admirals who are in power on the Board at the present time, shall find salvation. These are the men, and these explosions of virtue which take place when the restrictions of active service are removed, are sure indications of the strength of the written and unwritten laws which bend in the Navy always to maintain the status quo.

Mr Bremner

The engine rooms of our ships are already under-officered and the number of ships is increasing out of all proportion to the number of engineer officers.

Unless the Service is made more attractive we cannot be expected, as headmasters, to send our best and most promising pupils to go through a long course of training for this Service; and if the Admiralty have to be content with inferior men and to resort to temporary expedients it will be at the expense of the efficiency of the Navy and the safety of the Empire.

Report of the Annual Meeting of the Incorporated Association of Headmasters. 1901

You ask about engineers? To those I concede you give one of the best technological educations in the country but, after the age of forty, you deny all of them any chance of fulfilling themselves and, as a result, you have a frustrated and embittered crowd of men, itching to leave the Service. I'll never dissuade a boy who is set on the Navy; but I would never encourage a waverer.

Mr Hallward, Headmaster of Clifton College, to the author 1947.

The proposed transfer, in our Navy, of the machinery associated with guns, shot hoists, torpedo firing, to Gunnery Lieutenants will be disastrous to the efficient upkeep of these details as well as to their ultimate use.

Mr W. C. Borrowman

I am of the opinion that a better plan would be to adopt a system of common entry for deck and engineer officers, and for the first two years to submit them all to the same course of training at a Naval university, afterwards allowing them to specialise in the various Branches of engineering and deck duties.

Mr Rollo Appleyard

Speed is as great a factor in Naval efficiency as is the armament.
D. S. Bigge (1902)

In spite of all fictions to the contrary the engineering personnel are combatants: they either sink or swim with the ship and their participation in the sinking process is attended by trials of morale of a very severe and exceptional character.
Mr Bremner

We are therefore of the opinion that engineer officers should in future be classed with the military or executive branch of the profession, among those who would not on any occasion succeed to command (of ships).
Admiral Sir Cooper Keys' Committee 1876

ADMIRALTY FLEET ORDER 1/56

This A.F.O. brought back Admiral Fisher's ideas for a technologically based navy by joining the naval engineering branch with the main stream of naval policy making. The abandoning of Fisher's ideas in the Twenties contributed to a Royal Navy technologically backward when it went to war in 1939.

I had been an assessor to Admiral Sir Aubrey Mansergh's Committee which wrought this great change, then I had been sent to the Royal Naval Engineering College in 1955 as Second in Command specifically to make sure that all young naval engineer officers under training were aware of the implications for their future roles in the design, production and operation of a technologically advanced Fleet.

The Seamen (Executive) Branch had been particularly upset at several elements of the Mansergh findings, particularly those recommending the incorporation of the Engineering and Supply Branches into a General List. In order to pacify these fairly massive objections there were included in the Mansergh Report some phrases which suggested that the newcomers would require 'militarising' and also were to be given training in boatwork. Such was the reason for including in my speech given below my own experience in Hong Kong in 1945 and the fact that naval engineers were well trained in small boat work. (Indeed I could have mentioned, but for some reason omitted the fact, that one young engineer had just completed the first solo voyage in a 25 foot folkboat from Plymouth to New Zealand).

The Second Sea Lord and Chief of Naval Personnel, who had himself served on the Mansergh Committee, had indicated that he would like to dine in the old College at Keyham on Trafalgar Night 1956 but would not wish himself to speak or to propose the toast 'To the Immortal Memory'.

It therefore fell to me to carry out this duty and to indicate also to Admiral Sir Deric Holland-Martin that there was a new spirit amongst young engineer officers as a result of the Committee's findings and the impact of their recommendations on the training of (E) officers both at the old College (in which we still lived) and, perhaps in the future, for ALL naval officers in the new College for which finally the Board had received approval to build, despite the nation's faltering economy.

TRAFALGAR NIGHT 1956. ROYAL NAVAL ENGINEERING COLLEGE, KEYHAM

In a Mess which embraces officers from eleven different nations it would be inappropriate perhaps if we remembered Admiral Lord Nelson only as the man who saved our own country. That having been said, we should not forget the words of that great American historian, Admiral Mahan when he wrote that it was 'Britain's far distant storm-beaten ships upon which Napoleon's grand army never looked which stood between that army and the dominion of the world.' It would not even be appropriate tonight to recall Nelson as a Vice Admiral of the White whose Ensign, in only slightly different forms, is common to the united Navies of our Commonwealth; for we have officers from countries other than the Commonwealth here tonight.

Perhaps instead we should remember Nelson as the officer whose sheer professional ability and personal leadership has set a standard for naval officers the world over.

By professional ability I don't mean his seamanship – if Codrington, one of his greatest admirers, is to be believed Nelson was no great seaman – by professional ability I don't mean his ability to handle a ship, he was excelled by many of his contemporaries in the possession of that delicate knack.

No, Nelson was a master of his trade, which was war and in particular war at sea. His professional reputation rested on wider issues. On duty – 'Duty', he once said, 'is the great business of a sea officer'. It rested on his fearlessness of responsibility, on his professional courage and on an intimate appreciation of the factors limiting the efficacy of his weapons.

Even today in peacetime manoeuvres, storing and provisioning, all the requirements of planned maintenance, are matters which test the ability, foresight and courage of our Admirals. When Nelson joined the Fleet before Trafalgar he found that Collingwood, with the knowledge that Villeneuve was in Cadiz and might come out, had failed to recognise the inevitable. In a few days or weeks at the most, the Fleet would be so short of provisions and out of water that it would have to lift the blockade.

Despite the fact that numbers were against him, despite his understanding of the world tragedy that would ensue if he was defeated, Nelson acted at once. Within hours a whole division of his Fleet under a furious Admiral Louis was sent to Tetuan to water, to provision and to return. As it then happened, just as Louis had passed beyond the point of recall, Villeneuve came out – and so Nelson fought the great Franco-Spanish Armada without a sizeable portion of his own Fleet.

As to his personal leadership, at this distance we can only read of the results. The years when he came to fame were years of naval mutiny, of bitter feelings between many officers and their crews, of sectional grievance, of a largely discredited monarchy and of political party controversy. The ships and fleets he commanded were largely manned by pressed men and the dregs of a dozen nations. Yet in each ship, in each squadron, in each fleet soon after he had taken command, the results were always the same. Discipline improved, health improved, fighting efficiency blossomed. Lord Montgomery has said that Man is the first weapon of war. Nelson and Nelson alone welded his officers and those motley crews into an unconquerable weapon.

Gentlemen, remembering this quality above all, I ask you to rise and drink 'To the Immortal Memory of Admiral Lord Nelson.'

And now gentlemen, to the present day. We have just drunk a toast to Nelson's memory as we do throughout the Navy on this night, so that we may not forget the lessons Nelson taught us.

Unhappily for a century after his death, except for one bright interval, the Navy did forget what Nelson taught and sank into a state of abject lethargy. That one bright period was when Hardy, in whose arms Nelson died, Captain of the *Victory* at Trafalgar, became First Sea Lord and, for a few years waged an unavailing battle from the Admiralty to improve naval gunnery, to hasten the introduction of steam in the face of an unimaginative civilian administration and an unimaginative and almost wholly over conservative fleet.

Where that lethargy might have led us in 1914 when Germany invaded Belgium had it not been broken and disposed of ten years or so before, no one will ever know. But the man who broke it was Admiral Lord Fisher, Jacky Fisher, who had entered the Navy on the nomination of Admiral Parker, the last survivor of Nelson's Captains at Trafalgar.

All his life Fisher looked to Nelson for his inspiration and even published a monograph about him, the proof copy of which, corrected in Fisher's own hand, I read last week.

There was hardly a single facet of naval life that Fisher left untouched. But one of the most significant was what he called 'Machinery Education for all.' Every officer was to be given some technical training, though Fisher qualified this by saying, when he seemed to be advocating an increase in naval uniformed Instructor officers as opposed to the civilians at Osborne, that what he did not want was 'an article in the Navy stuffed by patent cramming schoolmasters like a Strasburg goose.'

With that 'Machinery Education' he introduced also an entirely novel officer structure adopted since by the Japanese and US navies but largely discarded by our own Navy after the Great War. Fortunately, however, that new structure and Fisher's ideas lasted long enough to ensure that every officer from Vice-Admiral to senior Captain at the end of World War II had been subject to the Fisher scheme. The last First Sea Lord held an engine room watchkeeping certificate. The present one is well known for his scientific and engineering bent.

Our principal guest this evening is Admiral Sir Deric Holland-Martin, the Second Sea Lord and Chief of Naval Personnel. Before he assumed that important office he was one of a committee of war experienced officers, for he himself had seen much battle, tasked to examine the best officer structure for the future. They met under the chairmanship of Admiral Sir Aubrey Mansergh, another battle tested officer, who, at the behest of even more senior officers who had been trained under the Fisher scheme, (so wantonly abandoned in the twenties) sought to re-introduce it in the context of the Royal Navy of today, rather than of the Fisher era at the beginning of the century. They took much evidence and noted that when the chips were down, as for instance during the re-occupation of Hong Kong, young engineer officers could be just as military and provide equal leadership under fire as their executive counterparts.

The first Admiralty Fleet Order of 1956 was the result. So I suppose one could say that if Admiral Mansergh was the Chief Architect of the new look Navy, for it is nothing less, Sir Deric, if it's not impertinent Sir, is the Clerk of Works. For of course the Second Sea Lord carries the heavy responsibility for overseeing those vast and difficult changes that A.F.O. 1/56 has introduced for the whole Navy, not only of responsibility but also of the long held attitude of mind. In Drake's words which the committee used we are, as an officer corps, 'to be all of a company.'

That puts on all of us who now carry the honoured (E) after our name, and a purple stripe on our arms, a heavy responsibility. If I may quote the Dean when I was under training here in the mid-thirties: '(E) officers have to win the trust and affection of their executive counterparts, not by reacting to slights and ill-mannered snobbishness, but by showing they can equal or where possible, excel executive officers in every field of naval activity.' And that is what those who heard him a quarter of a century ago tried to do throughout the war.

Gentlemen, World War II effectively demonstrated that a professional engineering education need not, does not and indeed never has negated leadership, that quality towards which all naval officers must strive. Applied science, technology, engineering, call it what you wish, is taught here to enable (E) officers to be clear, logical and objective, to be able to interest people, to weigh up various views, to reach decisions on which lives will depend and to explain them to others. During the late war and in Korea (E) officers have shown these qualities in full from Lieutenant (E) John Boddy in HMS *Trinidad*, who lost his life and was awarded a posthumous Albert Medal when he slid down a rope into a burning messdeck to try to save his stokers, to those Lieutenants (E) leading armed platoons to overcome and kill the bandits who sought to loot and terrorise Hong Kong when we reoccupied it after the Japanese had surrendered, to those young air engineer officers and pilots who kept the serviceability rate of their aircraft so high in the Korean battle that it was the envy of the US Navy. And, if you regard boatwork as an essential, well it was a Captain (E) who won the first Sydney to Hobart race and after all we in this College have never failed to enter and sometimes nearly win the Fastnet Race. We should never forget either those war experienced young officers who are changing the engineering face of the Navy today by their professional skills and leadership of industry learnt here at Keyham. Leadership is a quality that all officers need and after which we all must strive. It is not the prerogative of one Branch or another, or indeed unique to any one Branch either.

On that note, Sir, I will end. But, as a Mess we are not only grateful to you for sparing the time to honour us with your presence on Trafalgar Night, but immensely grateful too for the trust you have shown in the (E) Branch that it will try faithfully to abide by the views expressed by Admiral Mansergh, and also by your part in seeking and obtaining approval for the great new College now being built at Manadon. Much as we love and respect our little Keyham, the new College one day perhaps, will greatly enhance the technical literacy of the whole naval officer corps to the great benefit of the Fleet.

CIVILIANISATION OF THE NAVAL 'TAIL'

Speech at the RN Engineering College, Keyham, on the occasion of a visit by Admiral Sir Dymock Watson, Fourth Sea Lord and Chief of Supplies and Transport. Summer 1957

This was a period when the Royal Navy was undergoing one of its frequent and massive reductions. There was strong pressure to civilianise all the naval design work and to send only non-professional technicians to sea to maintain and service propulsion machinery, weapons and aircraft. It was also a moment when the lure of civilian posts for navally trained engineer officers was at more than its usual high level and the temptations to get away from the absurdities of Defence Policy were therefore greater than ever.

Admiral Watson, as a Lieutenant-Commander had been a most popular torpedo officer and a friend to all in HMS Hood in 1937 and 1938. His was always a voice of sanity and like many torpedo officers he was always a friend of engineers.

I have omitted the beginning of this speech as it was at the end of term and there were many domestic goodbyes to be said. But this was a moment when the Admiralty was offering 'golden bowlers' of unprecedented size to those officers who would leave the Service voluntarily.

Admiral Watson told me later that our views had been of use to him as coming from the heart of the naval engineering profession; and while, for him, there was little new in what I said, it gave him the opportunity to quote what we at Keyham saw as the proper role for naval engineers (with

which he fully agreed) to his fellow Board members and to those others,
principally politicians, who sought to reduce the Navy's 'tail' by
civilianising it.

He also mentioned how difficult it was to demonstrate that the equation,
so often hawked around by the press, of Admirals versus numbers of ships,
was totally false. Often with a smaller Navy it needed men with greater,
not less experience and authority, to meet the political demands so often
thrown at it when resources had been cut.

In his formal reply at the dinner Admiral Watson stressed how much he
agreed with what was said; how essential it was that the emerging Col-
lege at Manadon should produce professional engineers able to hold their
place with industry and scientific advance and, who knows, become a
college where all officers at some time in their early career should serve
to absorb a degree of technical literacy which the war had shown to be
often so greatly lacking.

. . . And now at last I turn to our guest of honour, Admiral Sir Dymock
Watson, Fourth Sea Lord and Chief of Supplies and Transport to welcome
you, Sir, on behalf of HMS *Thunderer* Mess.

I think that those who have known you in the past will agree with me
that Naval engineers, as a body, have always been privileged to enjoy
your friendship. I recall twenty years ago that you were an honorary and
always welcome member of the Engineer's Office in the Hood and though
I am not sure that a bicycle can be classed as a 'mechanically propelled
vehicle' it is perhaps at least a 'mechanical contrivance' and you were
President, Chairman and Founder of the Hood 'Wheelers' Club.'

When you were Fleet Torpedo Officer designate to Admiral Sir Andrew
Cunningham in the worst days of the Mediterranean fighting you took
passage in a small cruiser in 1941 in the last convoy to pass from West to
East for at least another two years. But instead of standing on or near the
bridge during the almost non-stop bombing attacks you chose instead to
spend long hours in the engine and boiler rooms so that, as you said, 'you
would use the one opportunity ever likely to come your way of understanding what life was like in a machinery space in action; to what
pressures and strains stokers and artificers were subject.' That was something, as I can vouch, which that particular machinery department never
forgot.

Judging, Sir, from the enquiries my Captain has had from Admiralty
officers in the last few days and from reports we have had to write for the
Commander in Chief for transmission to the Admiralty, those who are

responsible are anxious to know the reactions of we who serve the Fleet to the recent announcements about the possible civilianisation of what is so glibly described by the naïve and ignorant as the 'Tail'.

It is impossible in the few moments I have to give a fully reasoned statement of our views. As we understand the many problems which the Board is facing the Royal Navy is confronting a series of crises far graver in every respect that those which brought on the mutinies at the Nore and Spithead or more recently at Invergordon. To solve those troubles the Boards of Admiralty of the time did not need much more than leadership, strength of purpose, common sense and a decisive attitude, however lacking such qualities they might have shown particularly at Invergordon. Today the Board needs more besides those essential qualities.

It needs to have the technical literacy at its disposal to overcome effectively the mirages which politicians so often believe they see.

At this distance from Whitehall we don't really know what is going on but we hear rumours and we meet officers from other specialisations or Admiralty civilians, civilians from industry or, as last week, the Press.

It is I think common ground that each side in this controversy concedes the words written by Fleet Admiral King USN to the US Congress are true and currently applicable. If I may remind you of them they were these: 'The Navy, more than any other of the Services, depends on a high quality of engineering skill and practice.' As we understand it the main problem you face is this: Shall there be civilian or naval control at all levels of naval design, procurement and production – at every level in fact except that of actual operation under peace or war conditions?

No one can deny the technological predominance of the US Navy in 1945. Now naval engineers are very busy people and for that reason are often given less credit than perhaps is their due for a wider educational and professional background. This quality which certainly some, but I would hold rather too few, actually achieve, is said to be the unique prerogative of the seaman. However, those of us who like myself have many helping hands, sometimes have the opportunity to look outside to the wider world. That technological predominance of the US Navy of which I spoke can I believe be traced back to the writings of that great American Admiral, Mahan. His reasons for the decay of the French Navy when he was writing were not only accepted implicitly in his own country and thus guarded against, but are just as relevant to our British problems today as they were then to the French Navy. He wrote this:

The immediate reason was that, to a Service of a very special character, involving special exigencies, calling for special aptitudes, and consequently demanding special knowledge of its requirements in order to deal wisely with them were applied the theories of men wholly ignorant of those requirements – men who did not even believe they existed. Entirely without experimental knowledge, or any other kind of knowledge of the conditions of sea life, they were unable to realise the obstacles to those processes by which they would build up their navy, and according to which they proposed to handle it. It would be foolish, because untrue, to say that these things were easy to see. They were easy to men of the profession; they were not at all easy to outsiders, apt to ignore difficulties of which they had neither experience nor conception.

However, even if we disregard Mahan, civilian professional control of naval material has two further implications. Firstly, and of immediate interest to us at this College, we would cease to produce fully trained engineering professionals. Some of those here tonight, Sir, towards the end of a term, would feel that to be a welcome release but if we were so released then a second fact emerges. The technological efficiency of the Navy would rapidly deteriorate to the same sad state as our Merchant Navy which, through this very policy, is now so technically bankrupt that it is finding it more and more difficult to operate on a competitive basis. Indeed so sad is the situation today that the shipowners and shipbuilders themselves are at last seeing the light and are coming to us, navally trained engineers, with the offer of princely salaries above anything the Government could provide, to take over the development and technical direction of their Merchant Fleets. Indeed several great manufacturing firms, with nothing to do with the sea, are following the same path.

You will easily appreciate, Sir, that we Staff Officers here carry a large measure of responsibility for the attitude and thinking of the Officers under Instruction.

If I may say so, Sir, we have a very experienced Staff here, many of us battle wise. We believe implicitly that the requirement for professional engineers, whether in the realms of ship propulsion, weapons or aircraft, is that they should be able to speak to industry and the scientist with that complete and unassailable assurance that can come only from experience at sea, can be sustained beyond all argument, as can the need for professional engineer officers in the highest Councils of our Navy. That is what we tell the officers here who are under instruction.

When they leave we quote something else to them too. We quote Abraham Lincoln's second Inaugural Address: 'The dogmas of the quiet past are inadequate to the stormy present . . . the occasion is piled high with difficulty and we must rise with the occasion.'

If it is not impertinent to say so it is because of such policies as those set out in A.F.O. 1/56, which brought engineers into the main stream of policy making, that many of us feel that the Board of Admiralty of which you are a member is rising with the occasion and that is why we continue to proclaim in very definite terms that there can be no question of mass civilianisation towards which the Board is being pressed and that the need for professional naval engineers is unquestionable. On the contrary we say to the young officers, as I say it to them again in your presence, that they must equip themselves to play an ever increasingly important role in the higher direction of our Service and help thereby to solve the critical material crisis now facing the Board.

Because we jointly proclaim this we believe that the majority of the Staff here, despite the many highly attractive offers they have received from industry, despite the views of (and not surprisingly), at least some of their wives, are unlikely to accept voluntarily the munificent gratuity that your Board is offering us and many of our contemporaries: and we live in hopes that the young officers under training will follow our example.

Knowing just a little of the weight you are personally carrying, Sir, and of your very busy life, I'm sure I speak for all when I say how much we appreciate your visit to see the old and new Royal Naval Engineering Colleges of which we are so proud and to hear our views as to how best we may, by our professional training, help to create a fighting Navy beyond compare.

THE MURRAY COMMITTEE (Lord Murray of Newhaven) 1958

In January 1958 I was sent to the Admiralty to prepare a memorandum about the early training of officers which, at the time, was considered to have several very unsatisfactory features. The purpose of the memorandum was first to brief the Board of Admiralty and secondly the mainly civilian committee which the Earl of Selkirk was intent on establishing with a remit to overhaul the entry and early training of officers.

A chapter of 'From Fisher to the Falklands' (Marine Holdings Ltd.) is devoted to the work of this committee and included therein is a list of the appendices to my covering letter submitted to the Deputy Chief of Naval Personnel. The covering letter read as follows:

Suite 559 (Bathroom)
ADMIRALTY,
Queen Anne's Mansions
14th March, 1958

Sir,

I have the honour to submit the attached Memorandum covering several aspects of officer training.

In composing it I have set myself two limits. Firstly, as nothing has yet been promulgated about the Dartmouth Review Team I have refrained from visiting the specialist schools to hear their views. Secondly, in formulating a new plan, I have tried to keep to the present broad pattern and duration of training at Dartmouth, whilst reducing the inordinate length of training for those known as technical officers.

Indeed the burden of my song, in which I only echo Lord Chatfield and others no less renowned, is that ALL Naval officers should be technical officers and that some, amongst them (E) (engineering) and (L) (electrical) officers, should be trained to a higher and a few to much higher standards of technology. Those who at first are not so trained being the officers from whom the Post List will be selected, and who must devote their (it is to be hoped) great talents to the study of tactics, the operation of weapons, navigation and the control of sea operations.

Always I have had in mind the increasingly troublesome officer/rating relationship in the Fleet and the sort of difficulties which young officers of today have to face, of which these two are typical examples known to me:

A young officer who went to a Gunroom to find his brother a (not very good) Steward in the Gunroom Pantry.

A young officer whose father refuses to have him home *because* he is 'an officer'.

These facts and such incidents as the *Modeste* mutiny convince me that an entirely new approach is needed to our training methods. In the pursuit of such an approach I have inserted in my proposals a period of rating training under special conditions. I have trebled the Humanities instruction and in order to give all officers a better technical training I have doubled the science instruction and raised the entry standards.

All this is only possible by increasing the tempo of the course, restricting leave and radically altering the routine and practices.

Few will believe this can or should be done – I am certain on both points. Unless the young officer can be 'wound up' at the start of his career to work and live with a sense of urgency, we shall never progress.

I was privileged to be an 'assessor' on Admiral Mansergh's Committee so that I hold steadfastly to the principles of 'Identical Training' wherever possible, 'Common Training' for as long as possible and a truly amalgamated General List.

I don't think my suggestion that officers wishing to be considered for higher technological training should offer a higher standard on entry is illogical. We have a well defined need for some officers to be trained to a high standard of technology and a moral duty to train those possessing such talents.

If more offer with these high qualities than are in fact needed for higher technological training I doubt if the Post List will suffer; such officers who are not selected for the Post List will be able to be cross-trained subsequently, without difficulty.

I have not dealt with 'Other Service experience'. We did it quite well on an ad hoc basis before the war and I see no reason why, if time permits, we should not revert to similar practices.

I am conscious that all this has been very hastily written. Taken in its entirety naval officer training is a big subject and my object has been to cover as many points as possible and, as an exercise, to draw up what I believe to be a more satisfactory plan.

While the opinions expressed are purely personal I have used the first person. Mostly this paper is a distillation of views expressed by many officers of all specialisations at Dartmouth, Manadon, in the Training Carrier (when it existed) and HMS *Excellent* and those officers from the Fleet with whom I have come into contact in the last 3 years.

I have the honour to be,

Sir,

Your obedient Servant,

Louis Le Bailly

Commander, Royal Navy

Rear-Admiral C. L. G. Evans CBE, DSO, DSC.
Deputy Chief of Naval Personnel (Officers)

ENGINEERING AND THE ROYAL NAVY

This very large conference was held in 1965 at the Civic Centre in Plymouth under the auspices of the Institution of Mechanical Engineers. As Deputy Director of Marine Engineering and with the help of Captain R. G. Raper and Captain K. J. Douglas-Morris we produced the first paper entitled 'Some Thoughts on Strategy and its effect on the Design and Maintenance of Propulsion Machinery' which had of course, like all the other papers, been already circulated to those attending.

It fell to me however to write and present the opening address aimed principally at the very numerous non Naval members of the audience. Mention is made in this opening address of what we called a 'Constabulary Concept' which we interpreted as a quick reaction force founded on small nuclear powered aircraft and troop carriers and submarines, together with conventionally powered surface escorts and a nuclear powered fleet train consisting of ammunition, food and fuel replenishment ships. We hazarded that its 'beat' should be the Aden, Bombay, Singapore, Darwin, Simonstown, Mombasa area which we believed would encompass the probable world trouble spots.

OPENING ADDRESS
IN THE PRESENCE OF THE PRESIDENT AND MEMBERS OF THE LEARNED INSTITUTIONS, REPRESENTATIVES OF THE NAVAL STAFF, SENIOR MANAGERS AND DIRECTORS FROM INDUSTRY AND THE WARSHIP BUILDERS AND MANY SENIOR CITIZENS OF PLYMOUTH.

Gentlemen, In accordance with my instructions and on behalf of my co-authors and myself, I have first to say that this paper is published with the permission of the Ministry of Defence but the responsibility for any statement of facts or opinions expressed therein rest entirely with the authors and such statements do not necessarily reflect Ministry of Defence policy.

Next I would say what a great privilege it is for three ex-students of the old R.N. Engineering College at Keyham to present a paper in the Civic Centre of Plymouth, one of the 'Three Towns' for which our time at the College gave us such a lasting affection. To which I should add admiration for what has arisen from the ashes of The Palm Court, the Globe*, the Athenaeum*, Nicholsons and the other hostelries we all knew so well. What feats of engineering might have been lost to the Royal Navy, indeed what an ordeal, gentlemen, you might have been spared this afternoon, if the citizenry and constabulary of this great city has been less tolerant of our escapades!

Lastly, on behalf of my co-authors and myself I must acknowledge the help we owe to the President of the Institution, Vice Admiral Sir Frank Mason for his Parsons Memorial Lecture in 1956 from which we clearly have had to draw extensively.

In attempting to analyse just a little of British maritime strategy and to draw from it any lessons we could apply to the design of propulsion machinery, we knew we were treading a thorny path. Strategy is not a subject in which, in the past, engineers in general or naval engineers in particular, have been encouraged to dabble.

This vast complex of dockyards and the wonderful training machine at Manadon, and much else, are all pointed at one factor – the putting of a fleet to sea with the most effective hardware, whether propulsion machinery or weapons, and giving the nation due return for its skilled manpower and money. We therefore felt a considerable sense of responsibility in presuming to assert how part of this task should be achieved. We were also up against time and it soon became obvious to us that anything but a most superficial judgement on the interplay between strategy and the mobility of the Fleet in the more distant past would require far deeper research than we were able to devote to it; whilst in the more immediate past the impact of thermonuclear war has made necessary a complete rethinking of strategy anyway.

True naval mobility, the ability to remain at sea for weeks or months or even years, as so many sea captains who sailed from this port in centuries

---

*Often placed out of bounds by the naval authorities and equally as often patronised by the students!

past knew it, is something we seem to have lost in the steam age; only now are we realising how far we have to go fully to regain it.

It was Fleet Admiral King in this report to the US Congress at the end of World War II, after that astonishing seaborne campaign in the Pacific, who wrote, 'Mobility is one of the prime military assets'. Perhaps in this country this doctrine of mobility in the shape of quick reaction time, of long range and endurance, high speed, the ability to remain at sea without return to base for replenishment or man or material maintenance is something which has until recently never received the close study it deserves. In postulating our 'Constabulary Concept' we hoped to draw attention to the way in which we feel true mobility, if this could be once more achieved, could be exploited on a truly integrated interservice basis in support of the kind of national strategy we believe to be evolving.

Time has insisted that we should side-step the details of surface and submarine nuclear propulsion, the hovership, the future of fuel cells and other equally fascinating exotica.

Therefore, in order to trace within our schedule the changing pace of machinery development, we have had to ration our efforts on our accompanying paper to a catalogue of events which have taken the Navy, in half a century, from one which met a North Sea Strategy with a fleet not really engined for far distant operations and which relied on the constant support and close proximity of Royal Dockyards at home and abroad, to an Ocean Strategy demanding from the Fleet almost unlimited range and endurance with little but afloat support to keep it going at the end of a long supply line until ships' eventual return, after months or years, to the home Royal Dockyards half a world or more away.

As we see it, though the Navy has done some sort of machinery testing at the Admiralty Fuel Experimental Station (AFES) since the early days of the century and at the Admiralty Engineering Laboratory (AEL) since the end of the first war (it could hardly be called research) it was not till 1944 that a number of steps were taken to put the development of the Navy's future propulsion machinery on a more rational footing. Efforts were made to interest the land turbine and boiler firms in naval machinery. The Admiralty embarked on a standard range of diesels to reduce the enormous logistic problem with landing craft. The work at AFES on combustion and at the AEL on diesel propulsion was stepped up very considerably.

In the post-war decade a wide variety of development contracts were placed with industry for steam, diesel and gas turbine projects ranging from a study of the best possible steam installation for immediate use in ships to a very ambitious development of a complex cycle gas turbine plant. Other forms of development contracts were aimed at improving methods of production, especially, for instance, gearing production. Committees were also set up to foster co-operation between the Admiralty and different industries. All this effort produced our modern steam machinery for frigates and destroyers, the Deltic Engine for patrol boats and minesweepers, the Admiralty Standard Range engine for submarines and frigates, the G2 and G6 gas turbines as boost engines. Then of course the hydrogen-peroxide fuelled submarines and the Rolls-Royce RM 60 gas turbines were also both highly successful projects. In steam, diesel and gas turbine fields a great effort also went into producing electricity generators and other auxiliary machinery.

It was at this moment that to some extent we became unstuck. The emphasis in the Naval Staff requirements was rightly on reducing weight, space and fuel consumption, which meant some tremendously ambitious designing well beyond the bounds of previous experience. The outbreak of the Korean war made hurry inevitable and the step from the drawing board to the operational warship was taken too quickly. For instance the Y 100 machinery design was started in 1949, the prototype set was delivered in 1951 and orders were placed for 8 frigates to be built as fast as possible. Much the same speed of design and delivery was applied to the diesel driven frigates.

The result was that when the early ships of these classes started trials there were many teething troubles. Because of the hurry to get the ships to sea it took in the end nearly six years fully to fit the modifications found necessary as a result of operational experience. Now this is done the Whitbys, Rothesays and Leanders all perform very reliably and are exceptionally easy to operate. The diesel frigates with four engines geared to each shaft suffered from serious clutch trouble between engines, but once this was cured, as it quickly was, these ships too became known for their reliability.

In the boost gas turbine frigates we had learnt our lesson. HMS *Ashanti* and *Devonshire* were both completed well ahead of the subsequent ships of these classes and did extensive evaluation trials. We found out that gas turbines only reveal their secret troubles one after the other and, throughout the years of apparently trouble free development, may keep a real stinker up their sleeve. During these evaluations at sea the snags were revealed and instead of subsequent ships of the classes enduring the same troubles, the Tribal and County Classes have been modified before completion and each ship has done better than her predecessor.

During this period too the Navy has got smaller, the ships more sophisticated and expensive, while a rising standard of living ashore has meant better habitability on board, only achievable by reducing the complement. We have managed, by design, to reduce the number of operators, and the numbers on board are now determined mainly by the maintenance and servicing task.

The Fleet today faces unmentionable threats from weapons of devastating power and extraordinary accuracy, which may be launched at it from near or far distant aircraft, from other surface ships or from the depths of the ocean. Answers to these threats have to be found, cost what they may. So fast is the progress of weapon technology that sometimes, in the span of a ship's life of twenty years or so, she will be partially or wholly rearmed at least once and perhaps twice.

Even more difficult almost than money or the prophesying of strategy and tactics and technical equipment is the striking of the correct manpower balance. Quantity versus quality and the search for the correct equation between numbers at sea and the numbers of uniformed and civilian technologists and technicians in the design and support echelons are all problems difficult to define with any precision. They are also matters of great public interest, often unhappily, uninformed interest, and rude references to 'teeth' versus 'tail'. What is the relationship between the capital cost of material built into a ship and the capital cost of manpower who design, put to work, operate and maintain the material? After all, many airborne weapons of unparallelled ferocity carry no men. Is the number of men actually at sea any yardstick to the effectiveness of the Navy?

In the past so much of the globe has always been coloured red and in that red there have always been available friendly ports and bases and fuel and ammunition depots. Life from the logistic and maintenance and manpower aspect has not presented the operational problems it does today. Naval engineers, we think, have often not understood or, more likely, have not been permitted to appreciate, these broad operational problems.

Indeed we, the authors of the first Paper, find it difficult to escape the conclusion (and perhaps we engineers have been to blame) that machinery in the past has tended always to be too much the exclusive business of the 'engineers flitting through their ruddy tinctured twilight' as one correspondent once described their role. Perhaps we have all been influenced too much by the apparent facility with which steam machinery can be tailored to fit the ship, instead of, as we should, regarding the propulsion machinery in particular as the most essential and vital military asset, as another weapon to be nurtured and bred from and developed fully to satisfy the operational environment and the operational reliability finally demanded of it. Perhaps we have all taken the machinery too much for granted.

The 'Fascinating Fifties' provided us with a great variety of warship propulsion systems and with these we acquired wide experience. Steam is still the only suitable plant for the really high powers required in large aircraft carriers. The development of the steam catapult, the very high demands for electric power, for air conditioning machinery and the heavy hotel services demand all favour large steam driven generators. The nuclear reactor is obviously a possibility for the future and is particularly suitable for a carrier where high power is required for flying on and off for a large percentage of the ship's seatime.

For smaller ships there is a choice of steam, diesel or gas turbines or a combination. Each case has to be studied and a gas turbine and one or other of the former two are under study.

It is clear that steam still has a future but compared to diesels or gas turbines, the maintenance task it presents in a ship with its problems of accumulating water and steam leaks, of the many minor adjustments, of the host of drains, vents and so on which are apt to give trouble, make us long for a concentrated development on one set of steam machinery. This would allow it to be engineered like an aero engine and its troubles eliminated and its successors bred from it, without everything being altered because of the differences in horsepower required and configuration of the next class of ship. We have no doubt that our steam machinery could be enormously improved for maintainability and reliability if the techniques now familiar in nuclear engineering for reducing leakages and for ensuring purity of water and above all, and we say this with all the emphasis we have, cleanliness in installation, were applied.

Our aim now must be to go 'nap' on the very minimum of such systems that will give the Naval Staff a sufficiently wide spectrum of performance to cover their minimal need. Furthermore, in going 'nap' we must ensure, unless there are formidable reasons for not doing so, that the machinery selected – this will apply particularly in the diesel and gas turbine field – is developed from a line for which there is a large production need and which therefore will have big industrial backing. Alternatively, as naval requirements are unique in the world of steam we may well have to develop one standard steam set right up from the drawing board (and pay for doing this properly) for naval purposes. By doing all this we shall not only concentrate the efforts of our technical manpower at HQ, which is good economic doctrine, but we should also be able so thoroughly to test and develop the small number of chosen machinery systems – steam, gas turbine, diesel or a combination, that though some ships may appear to be overpowered and some seem to be underpowered from the ideal demanded by the Naval Staff, the operational commander at least will be sure of what he has got is thoroughly reliable in terms of operational usage.

It was Mahan who said, 'The need for a Navy stems principally from the possession of a Merchant Fleet and the need to ensure the Merchant Ships unhampered passage over the sea routes of the world.' While Lord Fisher wrote that 'the Army is a projectile to be fired by the Navy.' Both these statements are equally true now and so in the context of the world today our philosophy must be that the Navy fights on and under and over the sea and also *from* the sea. The latter including attacks on hostile territory by sea-based missiles, sea-based aircraft and amphibious forces.

We then, the authors of the first paper, visualise the three Services, under the umbrella of the deterrent, more and more playing the 'Constabulary Role.' In General Sir John Hacketts' words,' the orderly application of armed force, . . . the management of violence.'

If such a concept is valid then clearly the fleet has to achieve a far higher degree of mobility than has ever before been considered possible in the steam age. Whether such mobility is above or below the surface is not really a relevant issue in this discussion.

With the fleet we possess today and in the interests of the fleet we shall possess tomorrow we must continue a relentless battle for the precise definition of the really troublesome areas of machinery defects and failures. This is the job of the newly created Fleet Maintenance Authority whose constant search for facts and constant querying of any departure from pattern, together with a sense of understanding by the whole fleet of the need for this sometimes painful probing, alone can give us the answer.

Constantly as we wrote and rewrote our original paper, and even more so as it has been discussed between ourselves and with our colleagues, it has been borne in on us how the high standard of design, development and manufacture, which the Navy has always demanded, is being pushed higher and higher by the pressure of technology applied to the limited war at sea in which we are now engaged. Failure to meet these demands will not be met by sudden death as it is in the air – but it costs the sweat and tears of many devoted engineer officers, artificers and mechanicians and mechanics who seem prepared to go to remarkable lengths to keep ships operational, their great responsibility and pride and, one might add, their great tradition also.

We, the authors, believe that it is because of the devotion of these men that we have got away with such low development costs in the past: but the past is catching up with us.

Once the Ship Maintenance Authority has defined the areas of unreliability then these must be systematically removed by post-design work and subsequent machinery modification by the Royal Dockyards.

For the future fleet, we reiterate once more, we need to conceive a minimum number of propulsion systems which, between them, will cover the broad spectrum of Naval Staff requirements in terms of speed, noise, endurance, manpower and so on; and once conceived the design of these systems must be standardised and developed and tested to a degree of reliability comparable to that of an aircraft engine.

This of course may, indeed will, mean money, but it is our judgement that with a proper concentration of technical effort on the combined problem of material and manpower, that the cost will be no more than that of our diffused efforts today. The final cost in terms of fleet mobility, of operational usage, may well be less.

To conclude may I repeat a paragraph from our paper which seems to us to be terribly important:

A strategy is a policy which, with the world moving at such a pace, can be changed, if not overnight, then certainly far more quickly than machinery can be designed and developed, and ships built and deployed. The thoughts and ideas of statesmen and governments can be translated into words so fast; the concepts of the scientist and engineer take years to see the light of day. Because of this it is vitally important that the scientists and engineers (who apply science) are in close touch with the strategists. Major new technological concepts must be grasped quickly, brought to the notice of the strategists and their evolution must not be delayed by preoccupation with minor details or by mere indecision. We naval engineers must ensure that the technical instruments of our maritime strategy are the right ones and are ready on the day. To do this we must constantly think about these things, know about them and discuss them. The balance between what is required strategically and what is practical technically and within our resources must be struck at an early stage; and we, the hardware men, have a tremendous responsibility at that moment.

MANNING AND KEEPING THE FLEET GOING

This is the final draft of a paper written probably in the mid-1960s sent to the Naval Staff explaining the material problems of keeping the Fleet running and emphasising the problems associated with 'Trickle Drafting'. This was the system then in force whereby sailors and officers were fed into ships 'willy-nilly' and as a result there was an excess of 'finger trouble' through ignorant maloperation.

It concluded with a proposal, first put forward by Admiral Sir William Fisher, 'The Tall Agrippa' as he was known and loved throughout the Mediterranean Fleet, in the wake of the Invergordon Mutiny, that the Navy should establish some form of Divisional and Battalion system as practised by the Army. This, Fisher held, would greatly improve relationships between officers and ratings. Whilst thoroughly agreeing with Admiral Fisher my main suggestion was that such a system would also do a great deal to assist material reliability.

The Naval Staff thought otherwise, although steps were taken to abolish 'trickle drafting'. Nevertheless (and in this case borrowed from the USN) alternate crews for SSBNs have been in operation since those submarines first went to sea, with enormous success.

It should be explained that when this was written there were still Sea Lords: Second responsible for personnel and the Third for all material. The reference to the 'Squirearchy of Lythes Hill' was a rude name for those hardworking officers and ratings, who dealt with the drafting of sailors and who lived in some state near Haslemere.

A period of neglect of seapower has always ensued after every great war and the reasons are well known. In numbers the Navy, compared to the other Services, is small and so, on demobilisation there is not that pervasive loyalty through the countryside for long enjoyed by the Army and in modern times also by the Royal Air Force. The Merchant Navy, that other essential element, suffers in peace from fragmentation in the shape of the different and competing shipping lines; whilst the shipbuilding industry and the fishing industry, like the Commonwealth, are suffering from a ministerial neglect rarely displayed since the days of Lord North. Happily there are signs that the climate is changing, as, eventually it has always changed; but in the case of the Royal Navy it would be idle to imagine that this brings with it a promise of anything but a marginal increase in the proportion of the gross national product available for the Navy Votes.

Instead we are faced with a rapidly increasing and largely uncontrollable rise in the prices of ships, weapons, aircraft, stores, spare gear, ammunition and fuel. Whilst the avalanche of technology is providing us with weapons and machinery of unbelievable complexity and incredible efficacy, *when they work*. Thus at a time when the task is tending to increase and the resources are remaining static, usage and availability of ships, the only means whereby the task can be met, are both tending to diminish.

Measured over a six year span each ship is probably at sea from a minimum of perhaps 20% to 25% up to a maximum of 50% of the time, and it is an opinion of Commanding Officers that an increase of much over 50% in peacetime, would cause an appreciable breakdown in morale.

The Royal Navy is faced therefore with two distinct problems:

(a) How to bring usage up to a maximum without interfering with morale.

(b) How to arrange matters so that given an appreciable increase in material usage over the maximum in (a), morale will not suffer.

At once we run into a problem that has bedevilled us for years and which can be roughly described as the difficulty in mating the departments under the superintendence of the Second and Third Sea Lords. For until this is brought about it is doubtful whether any solution will offer more than a passing palliative. This is not for any lack of effort or willingness on either side, for solutions and proposals for solutions, and committees and working parties there have been aplenty. Neither by 'mating' is meant the acquiring of any area of superintendence of one Sea Lord by the other, but simply after as short a period of gestation as possible the birth of a child which will really bring together, in the shape of ships more than ever continually at sea, the acute and terrible perplexing problems which confront all those 'on both sides of the house'. Most if not all the problems in both the material and personnel worlds have common roots, namely:

(a) The present avalanche of technology.
(b) The lack of money.
(c) People.

In the personnel world the principal difficulties arise from:

(a) A demand for a higher and higher academic standard of both officer and rating which, certainly in the case of ratings, is inappropriate to the standard of pay scale it is possible to offer. Happily in the case of officers a vocation still exists amongst many of them which allows the Navy to recruit and keep a good proportion of the all round top 1% of the community at a salary which by commercial scales (for the top 1%) is ludicrous.
(b) A demand for more and more (shore) training which is inconsistent with the Navy's manpower ceiling if the main task is to be met.
(c) A shortage of highly skilled technical ratings which results in less availability of ships and too much dependence on shore support.
(d) A constant battle between the increasing demands for better habitability and the prime purpose of a warship which is to move and fight.

In the material world the difficulties, if possible, are even more perplexing:

(a) A constant flow of expensive gleams in scientists' eyes and the extreme difficulty of backing the right horse which will do as well 'on the course' as on trial jumps.
(b) The constant demands of the Naval Staff to 'retrofit' every new weapon into every old ship so that the dockyards have now become 'modernisation and conversion' agencies rather than the helpful refit and repair garages they used to be, and have thereby thrown an intolerable burden on the Fleet, and utterly lost its sympathy.
(c) The rapidly mounting cost of weapons and aircraft and the apparent impossibility of forecasting the completion date of either.
(d) The increasing complexity of sophisticated weapons, propulsion equipment and (by old standards) their frightening unreliability.

There are of course many others but in the present context these all add up to a grim and forbidding situation.

Before proceeding it is necessary to dispose of those addlepates who proclaim all the time that fundamental changes are wrong, and dangerous to morale and that stability must be the watchword. Despite the efforts of Hardy and Collingwood and Cochrane these sorts of people had their day from Trafalgar until Sir John Fisher's influence began to tell; and even then despite all his efforts is it stretching the truth too far to suggest that the Royal Navy entered the First War still surrounded with the shibboleths of a century before, and that the addlepates nearly won! It is common knowledge how much opposition there was to the Mansergh reforms; perhaps not so well known were the impassioned pleas, overruled only by the constancy of the Board, 'that the tender roots' of Mansergh should not be torn up by the Murray Committee, which of course was created only to put right one minor, but vital miscalculation, in the greater and far wider Mansergh scheme.

Alfred Whitehead in his lectures 'Science and the Modern World' had this to say:

'We must expect, therefore, that the future will disclose dangers. It is the business of the future to be dangerous, and it is amongst the merits of science that it equips the future for its duties. The prosperous middle classes, who ruled the nineteenth century, placed an excessive value on placidity of existence. They refused to face the necessities for social reform imposed by the new industrial system, and they are now refusing to face the necessities for intellectual reform imposed by the new knowledge. The middle class pessimism over the future of the world comes from a confusion between civilisation and security. In the immediate future there will be less security than in the immediate past, less stability. It must be admitted that there is a degree of instability which is inconsistent with civilisation. But, on the whole, the great ages have been unstable ages.'

Is there perhaps this same attitude to change in Queen Anne's Mansions, (at that time a part of the Admiralty concerned with personnel), or is it that the shadow of Invergordon still haunts its corridors? The Report of the Committee on Rating Structure pursued so fruitlessly year after year by Mr. Willis in the Navy Debate has, perhaps rightly, disappeared from sight, having by its very complexity baffled every expert, even those who served on the Committee. The proposals for a radical reorientation of the Artificer structure have been dubbed 'revolutionary' and shelved; though the term 'Apprentice Mechanician' seems to have survived the wreckage. Master Rates fall always at the last hurdle and so we go on into an age of computers and nuclear power with a personnel arrangement better suited to the placid days of the thirties.

Where do we go from here? One fact is plain and is witnessed to by every honest seagoing Commanding Officer. Recommissioning is a process which not only destroys the ship as a fighting unit for a lengthy period but also carries with it a degree of physical damage to material which is a progressive handicap throughout succeeding commissions. To some extent this has always been so but the situation today is far worse because of:

(a) The vast amount of 'know-how' needed by complex weapon equipment.

(b) The sheer efficiency of the modern drafting system.

To the writer's knowledge there were Chief Petty Officers in H.M.S. *Hood* when she sank who in one rank or another had served in her for 15–20 years, key men who were quite indispensable. Don't ask how it was done. We all knew. But the ship benefited enormously and in the pre-war and wartime Navy these sorts of 'arrangements' were common. Now they rarely exist, though the need because of (a) above is far more pressing.

Trickle drafting has much to commend it; but perhaps much more against it. What else is there left? Together with others, who are far more able, the writer has explored this problem as it exists today and in the much more acute form in which it will exist by the end of the decade. He, at least, can conceive of only one answer and that involves an upheaval which would make even Mansergh or Nihill naval reorganisation committees seem like damp squibs. This change, in simple terms, would involve an adaptation of the Army battalion system and the functional employment of officers and ratings in specialised roles. Let us conceive a Drake Regiment with a 1st and 2nd Battalion. The 1st Battalion are manning all the Frigates from an Escort Group whilst the 2nd Battalion (recently relieved by the 1st) have taken over the duties at one of the functionalised Frigate Escort Group Training Schools (let us say H.M.S. *Mercury*) and are giving precommissioning training to 1st Battalion of the Blake Regiment soon to relieve its 2nd Battalion now at sea in another similar Escort Group.

The Fraser Regiment specialises in Guided Missile Destroyers and the 1st Battalion now at sea in H.M.S. *Devonshire* will soon perhaps relieve the 2nd Battalion ashore in H.M.S. *Sultan* and now engaged in training a recently raised battalion of the Jellicoe Regiment for service in H.M.S. *Kent*. In the submarine world that hardbitten Myers regiment, now

operating 4 'A' Class, are soon to be expanded and rearmed with Por-
poises; whilst the Hunter-Killer regiment is to take over *Valiant*.

The Heavy Brigade, the Boyd, The Vian, the Somervaille, the Ford, the
Berthon, the Bedale Regiments, six in all, would man the three operational carriers in turn; two regiments to each Carrier, one afloat and one
ashore training at the great new Carrier Schools at *Excellent* and *Vernon*
and, at the same time providing refitting assistance for the carrier in
dockyard hands.

Naval Officers often regard a Pongo (rude naval term for an Army
Officer) as a bit slow. But no Pongo in his worst moments would order
(say) the XV/XIX Hussars now equipped with armoured cars suddenly to
take over the operation and tactical use of Chieftain Tanks; the Hussars
being relieved in their armoured cars by an Infantry Regiment. Yet we, in
the Navy, do just this and our ships suffer, made to suffer because availability is less than it might be and, worst of all, the Navy and the country
suffer because, needlessly, ships are laid up.

Let us hope that the pundits of Queen Anne's, when they migrate as
they are soon to do, to Whitehall and to the Empress State Building will
come to regard ships in the same way as they were looked at in the
material departments after Nihill – namely as integrated weapon systems.
Furthermore as weapon systems which need to be driven, maintained and
fought by integrated, properly trained, and fully experienced teams of
men instead of a changing hotch potch put together to some inflexible
formula, though always with the greatest consideration and sympathy for
the seagoers, by the Squirearchy of Lythes Hill.

And what can the material departments do? Surely, in these days of a
continuous technological avalanche, they will give up 'Mods. and Cons'
in the dockyard; they will give up keeping frigates for 25 to 30 years; they
will give up putting new wine in old bottles.

The dockyards, by their enforced preoccupation with modernisations
and conversions, have been compelled utterly to neglect the running
Fleet. The continuous cobbling up of old ships and retrofitting of new
weapons into old ships keeps the Ship and Weapon Design Staffs so
heavily engaged that the design of new ships is neglected or ceases
altogether. Meanwhile the Shipbuilding Industry shudders to a standstill
for lack of orders.

Statistically, (on such statistics as can be culled from the corridors of
Foxhill ship design department in Bath), it seems likely that a '13 year
life' frigate with one good refit at the 6–7 year mark would give us an
active Fleet of far greater reliability than is now thought to be possible at

no more than our present total cost. If the Fleet was regarded as a series of weapon systems to be manned alternately by Battalions trained and skilled in the idiosyncrasies of the Ship Class concerned, then at last the country would be getting a large and highly efficient Fleet well worth the £400m a year we devote to it – and what is more – an up to date Fleet of constant high availability, manned by enthusiastic specialists.

Old Loves Return

ROYAL NAVAL ENGINEERING COLLEGE, MANADON, PLYMOUTH.

Site purchased 1939. Approval in principle for National Marine Sciences College, 1949. Stage 1 Building for naval purposes only and Foundation Stone laid by AOF Lord Mountbatten 1956. College opened by Her Majesty. 1958. Proposal to abandon 1993.

Projected Demand for Given Minerals to 1985 and 2000

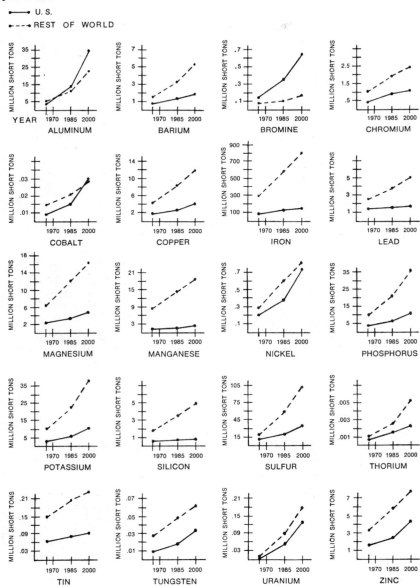

DATA SOURCE : Department of the Interior.

The Increasing Gap Between World Food Needs and Food Supply

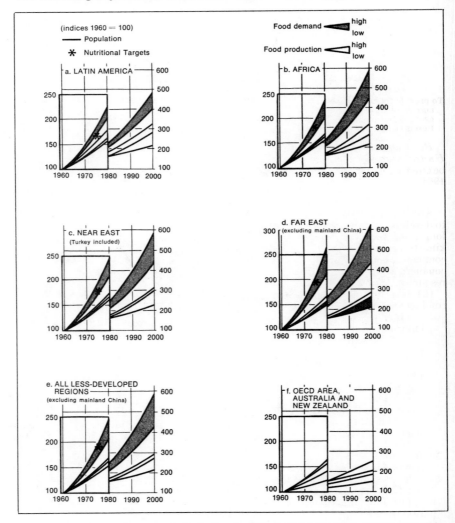

SOURCE: "The World Food Population: Its Implications for OECD Countries" *The OECD Observer*, June 1966, pp. 29–30.

Public Law 89–454

89th Congress, S. 944

June 17, 1966

𝔄𝔫 𝔄𝔠𝔱

To provide for a comprehensive, long-range, and coordinated national program in marine science, to establish a National Council on Marine Resources and Engineering Development, and a Commission on Marine Science, Engineering and Resources, and for other purposes.

Be it enacted by the Senate and House of Representatives of the United States of America in Congress assembled, That this Act may be cited as the "Marine Resources and Engineering Development Act of 1966".

Marine Resources and Engineering Development Act of 1966.

DECLARATION OF POLICY AND OBJECTIVES

SEC. 2. (a) It is hereby declared to be the policy of the United States to develop, encourage, and maintain a coordinated, comprehensive, and long-range national program in marine science for the benefit of mankind to assist in protection of health and property, enhancement of commerce, transportation, and national security, rehabilitation of our commercial fisheries, and increased utilization of these and other resources.

80 STAT. 203.
80 STAT. 204.

(b) The marine science activities of the United States should be conducted so as to contribute to the following objectives:

(1) The accelerated development of the resources of the marine environment.

(2) The expansion of human knowledge of the marine environment.

(3) The encouragement of private investment enterprise in exploration, technological development, marine commerce, and economic utilization of the resources of the marine environment.

(4) The preservation of the role of the United States as a leader in marine science and resource development.

(5) The advancement of educational and training in marine science.

(6) The development and improvement of the capabilities, performance, use, and efficiency of vehicles, equipment, and instruments for use in exploration, research, surveys, the recovery of resources, and the transmission of energy in the marine environment.

(7) The effective utilization of the scientific and engineering resources of the Nation, with close cooperation among all interested agencies, public and private, in order to avoid unnecessary duplication of effort, facilities, and equipment, or waste.

1966. The Vice-President, United States assumes responsibility for the exploration and development of AQUASPACE.

THE MANAGEMENT OF WARSHIP DESIGN

Controller's Conference at
Weston-Super-Mare
March 1967

In the late Fifties the design and maintenance of warships was brought together by the Controller under three Directors General, Ships, Weapons and Dockyards. Nevertheless quite quickly the accelerating sophistication and price inflation of machinery and weapons and the difficulties of accurately estimating the likely building cost of new designs of warships to meet the established threat, as well as the comprehensive task of actual design, suggested that further changes were urgently needed.

Messrs. Urwick Orr, the well known Management Consultants, were brought in and produced a very useful series of recommendations. These, however, were not acceptable to a number of professional ship designers, especially some of the most senior elements of the Royal Corps of Naval Constructors and it was on the Royal Corps that there always fell the main burden of creating designs from the multiplicity of often contradictory requirements and the physical laws governing stability and the capacity to operate a warship in any climate. Further to explore the practicality of the Urwick Orr recommendations and to determine precisely what immediate action could be contemplated, an inter-disciplinary working party was convened, consisting of the deputy directors of naval construction, marine and electrical engineering, under the chairmanship of the senior administrative civil servant in Bath, Mr Turner, and with a brilliant Principal as secretary, Mr Richard Lloyd-Jones, (now Permanent Secretary to the Welsh Office).

In due course their report created much the same schism and in desperation the Permanent Secretary to the Board of Admiralty and (by then) a new Controller (Third Sea Lord) arranged a weekend at a conference centre near Weston-Super-Mare with the aim of thrashing out some action. Broadly the Turner report had two recommendations. First it agreed with Urwick Orr that the management of the Ship Department should be divided amongst the different technological disciplines and related directly to the different functions concerned with design and building rather than on strictly disciplinary lines as prevailed at that time. The argument against this change was almost unanswerable as it was such an arrangement that had produced the first nuclear submarine, was in successful use at the Yarrow Admiralty Research Department and was already set to be used in the design and building of the Polaris Fleet. However it was resisted by the Deputy Director of Naval Construction who produced a minority report. Much more contentious was the proposal for a small, largely graduate manned inter-disciplinary Forward Design and Resources Directorate. This was a new concept designed to avoid as far as possible the difficulties of resource estimation which had contributed to the (mainly political) decision to cancel the large aircraft carrier programme, as described in 'From Fisher to the Falklands' (Marine Holdings Ltd.).

Mr Turner decided that he would himself present the Functionalisation of the Ship Department to the Conference and that, before leaving to take up the post of Naval Attaché in Washington DC, I should present the (amongst some) highly unpopular concept of a Forward Design and Resources Directorate which had become the focal point for the opposition.

In the course of the next few years and despite initial opposition both recommendations were implemented with the addition of some cosmetic changes to make them more acceptable.

My presentation as agreed by the majority of the Turner Working party is given below.

The Need for a Forward Design and Resources Directorate

Gentlemen, it is my unhappy task, unhappy only because it is Gold Cup Day at Cheltenham, to present to you the need for what our Director-General calls 'The Queer Directorate'; although in my view the only thing queer about it is that we have gone so long without such a group in the Controller's department. Perhaps that is why the Navy is in such a mess today.

What I propose to do is to talk about the two really big issues which face the Controller's organisation and how the majority of us on Mr Turner's working party believe The Forward Design and Resources Directorate will help and where we believe, inevitably, we must go in the next two or three years.

Now that I have passed my half century I am learning today, from my own feelings and inclinations, that there is nothing so dug in and super-conservative as 'the old pro', the old professional. We have to do things in the way we understand. We talk glibly about 'experience counting', when we mean we are too lazy to get up to date. I've been concerned, as I know others have, that there has been a tendency here tonight to raise the barricades on the old professional frontiers. I noticed in one of the summaries being read to us by an engineer (I quote); 'he was afraid of being hull dominated.' What he meant was 'Constructor dominated' . . . and there have been other examples.

We have in the Ship Department a considerable body of tough, enlightened and very competent young men, civilian and naval. It has been my privilege to know a lot of them, constructors and engineers, during my five years in all on the staff at Keyham and Manadon. They understand computers and hanker after modern management techniques; they cry out for systematic analysis and other modern decision making processes. They are disturbed at our apparent passivity and the civilians amongst us I believe, are hoping for a lot from the next twenty-four hours. I think we must remember this because, if the young constructors and engineers are tempted into industry (and when the shipbuilding Board gets going there'll be some first rate jobs offered them) they'll be off. And with just we oldies left I don't think there will be much of a ship department.

But the second reason is equally important. The problem at the end of the war was the contempt and distrust, in the fleet, for the design departments. Today this is a little better – one of the Director-General's achievements. Nevertheless it could hardly be said that the dockyards are happy with our designs: and the present maintenance load for weapon systems must call into question their serviceability under active operational conditions. The problem with which we are faced today is far more difficult, and much more profound. Let me try and explain it.

There is a feeling among politicians of both political parties, among people who study defence both in the press and media, and in the universities and places like the International Institute for Strategic Studies; among what was referred to last week in *The Times* as the 'Sanhedrin' of Permanent Secretaries; among top industrialists and among many Americans that, since the last war, and particularly in the last decade, the Royal Navy has failed to produce a credible concept of maritime operations or of the types of aircraft, submarines or surface ships to go with any such concept. Nor does there seem to have been any attempt to set such a concept within a realistic parameter covering money, naval and headquarters manpower and support manpower. We have in fact (to use an old skiing term when we ran violently downhill) just 'gadarened' without any clear indication of where we are going. I know it is easy to quote the new guided missile destroyers, but I think most people feel that a capital cost of £200M and a running cost of £3–£4M per week is quite a bit to spend on deploying just three seaslug missile launchers around the world. Our weapon costs have been prodigious; our armoury and order of battle in military, as well as in cost effective terms, are unimpressive.

The question we have to consider tonight therefore, is not whether the ship and weapon departments and the naval staff have altogether lost the confidence of the Board of Admiralty. No, it is whether or not the Royal Navy has lost – or is losing – the confidence of the country. And if, as in my judgement it is, what can we do to help restore matters.

When Lord Murray's committee on officer entry and training met the First Sea Lord, they asked what he was expecting from the General List. If Sir Michael Cary (the PUS) will look up the minutes he would find that the following was Lord Mountbatten's answer:

> We have, probably, the best engineers in the country in the Naval service. The trouble is that they are like children in the affairs of Whitehall and so the Board never gets the quality of advice or the broad advice it seeks. It is one of the paradoxes in any technical organisation that the qualities required to reach the top are not necessarily those needed at the top. Technical administration below the top is a matter of making technical decisions from deep professional knowledge. Policy making, the job of those at the top, is concerned with developing a sense of direction and a sense of purpose; and this means looking at other things besides the strictly professional criteria; and this is what our engineers are so often unable to do.

I submit that even if we do have men at the top who understand their proper role, they must be assisted to plot the right course. The Controller's organisation today, in my view, utterly lacks any machinery to help develop that essential sense of purpose and direction. The last Controller and his predecessor both saw the need; thoughts in those days led to a well equipped and properly managed Controller's 'control room' and a dynamic Controller's management team. Both, for various reasons, have not produced the answer and so the Controller's organisation still lacks a sense of direction and purpose.

The Director-General (Ships) is the *primus inter pares* amongst the Controller's Directors-General. This is not by divine right because he is Head of the Royal Corps of Naval Constructors but because the Ship Department, over which he presides, is the heart of the Controller's organisation. The Director-General (Ships) has two distinct tasks. He is in charge of a Hull and Power Agency just as the Director-General (Weapons) is in charge of a Weapons Agency. But, importantly, the Director-General (Ships) is also the Controller's warship design and production manager.

In any design problem from Noah's Ark to the anti-missile missile there must always be tremendous tensions, incredibly imprecise statements of requirements, mistrust of anything new, demands for things too new, lack of accord among management. And all this can lead to stifling indecision, pressure from those on top for quick results, and arbitrary, often disastrous, decisions. The Controller must have someone in direct charge to manage all this.

The DG Ships therefore has to be able:

(a) To define the ship design problem.
(b) To find the most suitable means of solving it.
(c) To make it possible to solve it on time and within an agreed budget.

As I see it, what the Board of Admiralty needs from a Controller, before it invites political approval for a design, is what is called a Project Definition. One of our major problems is that we have for far too long adhered slavishly to phrases and definitions such as design study and sketch design which, however well understood by designers, are obscure to the Board.

In crude terms I suggest Project Definition means that enough work has been done on a design to enable the Board to put forward proposals to the First Lord and his Cabinet colleagues in terms of time, money, manpower and performance, which are sufficiently accurate to ensure that subsequent changes are minimal and never of an order of magnitude that would make the Board look ridiculous and lose the confidence of Ministers.

To establish the machinery to do just this is the prime purpose of the Forward Design and Resources Directorate which the majority of the Turner working party recommend.

If we don't accept something on the lines our working party suggests, if we don't employ every modern aid and technique to assist management, if we don't stop dividing ourselves into professional camps and deploying our frontiersmen with bayonets fixed, then most of our young men will leave and we'll finish up like the Ministry of Technology, as the haven for all the sloths of industry. Only a ship that never moves can do without a rudder. A ship that needs to move very fast (as we should be doing) needs a good rudder, such as the majority of the Turner Working Party propose in the shape of The Forward Design and Resources Directorate.

The days of grandiose maritime strategies and great fleets steaming the oceans are gone.

What the Secretary of State and the Board need, and what I submit they are not getting, is a Controller's organisation with a sound Ship Department heart which can produce for the Board a catalogue of warship designs. These should be accurately costed in terms of time, manpower and money for the different mixes of weapons and machinery which are practical options over the next five to ten years.

There should be a second list, obviously less accurate, with best estimated costs for the next ten to fifteen years.

Lastly a gaze into the future of possible warship and weapon options, and an order of cost for twenty years ahead.

There will be a price to pay. We need to persuade industry to establish perhaps a couple more design agencies besides the Yarrow-Admiralty Research Department (Y-ARD), of comparable competence so that there can be competition for export markets.

What must be avoided at all costs is to listen to the faint hearts who will surely say there are not enough naval architects and constructors to man up such agencies. Let us recall that Mr Leonard Baker R.C.N.C. and one young Royal Canadian Navy constructor, followed later by Mr Mason R.C.N.C. and Commander (E) E.B. Good RN and one Chinese gentleman, were established on loan to Canada two years after the design process of the Whitby class of frigates had commenced in the U.K. In six years they designed the similar St. Laurent Class, organised the Canadian shipyards, built the factories in Canada for marine machinery, and finally commissioned the first ship eighteen months ahead of the first of the Whitby Class in the U.K.

That perhaps could be construed as the measure of our incompetence.

THE BRITISH MARITIME PROBLEM
7th November 1967

I was asked in November 1967 by H.M. Ambassador in Washington to let him have an unclassified view of the British maritime problems in their broadest aspects, so that he could have these views as a background, wherever relevant, to some of the many speeches he had to make.

This paper also provided a very useful tool in the preparation of the many speeches I found I had to make in the States and provided a background to many discussions with the 'Think-Tanks' which so abounded.

I felt then, as I believe today, that the massive Soviet shock armies in Eastern Germany and on the borders of NATO, certainly with contingency plans (since discovered) for a massive nuclear/conventional thrust across the German Plain were there more to terrify and to occupy the attention of Western nations rather than actually to invade, while the Soviet Navy certainly rich in quantity if not always in quality of the instruments of sea power, slowly cast a maritime noose, a potential blockade, around the developed nations of the world.

Modern Warfare

However effective good diplomacy may be, warfare, acts of organised violence, although their pattern may be difficult to predict, will almost certainly occur and these the UK will often have to do something about. The Navy's task, with that of the other Services, is the management and containment of violence so that diplomacy can be given time and a better climate in which to work; so that total war can be avoided.

Military Power

The military power available today, to any country, is derived directly from the difference between, on the one hand the product of the country's

191

total population, individual effort and indigenous natural resources and, on the other, the proportion of those two devoted to establishing or improving a modern national infrastructure and to the provision of individual welfare.

However, the vast cost and wide variety of instruments of military power make the task of selection one which needs the most modern and sophisticated approach, a wrong selection in terms of quantity or quality can be just as prejudicial to the national interest as the making of no military preparations at all.

Capital Investment in Military Establishment

In terms of actual long term committed capital investment navies are built very much to last. The life of a total warship weapon system is generally 20–30 years, although individual weapons and equipment may be changed during this period. As the gestation period for a warship is anything from 5–10 years we are always looking 20–30 years ahead; and this is one of the major problems when money (as always) is at a premium and a 'bad bet' can run away with so much. Air Forces are not conceived for such a long span and civil air transport (at present) often benefits much more from military development than sea transport does from naval shipbuilding. Armies constitute a comparatively short term military investment, though becoming longer as battlefield equipment becomes more sophisticated, although in terms of manpower they too are increasingly expensive.

It is thus essential in all cases, but especially in the building of navies, that the vast amount of national treasure expended is, wherever possible and applicable, directed also towards the improvement of nationally useful industrial techniques and to more economic and efficient production. Such an outlook has been noticeably absent in successive governments throughout the years and some share of the blame for their lack of imagination, and therefore our out of date and inefficient shipbuilding and shipping industry must rest with the Admiralty. The Board of Admiralty was responsible for the sponsorship of the shipbuilding industry until 1961 when the Ministry of Transport took over that responsibility until it was recently transferred to the Ministry of Technology.

Modern Sea Power

Although probably not yet fully accepted in UK naval circles (and far less in most political circles, the media and the public) traditional ideas of seapower as set out in the Eyre Crowe memorandum and in the works of Mahan are largely out of date.

Only two countries, the USA and the USSR can afford fleets in the old traditional sense of the word, consisting of the whole inventory of maritime weapons and, with such fleets, the capability to fight from the sea as well as over, on and under the sea. Other nations have got to make their choice in the sure and certain knowledge that there can be no sudden 'change of course'. (It is of course arguable whether advanced nations other than these two can afford traditional type armies in view of the extraordinary increase in the subversive and guerrilla skills of small nations.) Air forces too, because of the increasingly extreme sophistication of modern military aircraft, are apt to run out of money so that the attainment of the quantity needed for minimum effective deployment is becoming as difficult as the provision of an optimum number of warships.

The Maritime Problem
This can conveniently be divided into three elements: the USSR, other navies and the problems of the sea bed.

A. THE USSR.
(1) Except during the days of Peter the Great, Russia (now the USSR) has always been a land animal. In the last war her navy was regarded only as a support on the flanks of her army. As we found to our dismay in the Forties she was not ready to send her ships or submarines far from her territorial waters.

(2) For these reasons when NATO was set up the Soviet Navy was not considered a threat to our sea communications and so, although land and air forces were put directly under the command of SACEUR, initially no forces were put under command of SACLANT.

(3) Now we have to accept that the USSR has become a great maritime power, second only today to the United States and indeed in some aspects, leading the United States.

(4) The USSR has progressed nuclear propulsion at sea and leads all other countries by years in the production of sea-borne missiles (despite Polaris), she is building helicopter carriers and, in my view, we shall soon see the start of large aircraft carriers. The USSR has an immense, sophisticated and versatile submarine force and the Soviet Navy has its own shore based maritime airforce and, probably, leads all other countries in certain types of communications.

(5) The USSR is rapidly learning how to co-ordinate maritime forces which operate on the surface with those operating in the air or under the

sea. The operational range of all ships has been increased by their ability to replenish with weapons, fuel and stores at sea when underway. The Soviet Navy now appears in all oceans of the world and can remain on station for long periods, self-supporting.

(6) The USSR has a mighty fleet of specially equipped trawlers which for many years have been monitoring our radar and radio transmissions throughout the world, while inserting themselves unwanted and unasked into the West's maritime exercises. She has the largest fishing fleet in the world directed by the Soviet Admiralty employing at least 100,000 men, spread all over the Atlantic, bringing in the fish protein and acting also as antennae and spies when the occasion demands. The USSR is known to have extensive knowledge, greater perhaps than any other nation, of oceanography.

(7) The USSR is spreading her maritime influence all over the world, partly by providing the ships and equipment for some of the smaller navies, partly by financing port facilities in various countries and above all by building a large and efficient merchant marine which, unlike most of the merchant navies of the democracies can quickly be transformed to various sorts of military use.

All this is taking place in a country which, although every man counts, because of its wartime casualties and temporarily reduced manpower for agriculture and industry, is still ready to keep a Navy of 450,000 men.

In September 1966 Admiral Kazatonov, the great submarine expert, who for the last three years has operated the Soviet Navy, in an unguarded moment at a dinner at Moscow, expressed his frustration that he was not as yet able to emulate the ability of the United States 6th Fleet to influence political events in the Mediterranean by virtue of that fleet's deployment in that area. In April this year (1967) Brezhnev, speaking in Czecho-Slovakia, demanded that the Americans should stop their maritime forces from operating in the waters he described as 'lapping the southern shores of Europe'. A few weeks later in June, just after the Israeli/Arab war of this year and just before he went to the United Nations, Kosygin accused the United States and the UK, by the presence of their Carrier forces off Aden and in the Mediterranean, of influencing affairs in the Middle East and encouraging the Israelis to take the initiative against the Arabs.

To sum up, the Soviets seem not only to have built up a great maritime force but they are now embarking on a policy of using it in peace to obtain political ends and are groping to outflank NATO by the use of maritime power which, because it can operate in the oceans of the world which belong to no one, is able to disregard the sovereign rights of other nations.

B. OTHER NAVIES

(1) With more than two thirds of the world's surface covered by sea, more than half of it 10,000 ft. deep or more and with a hundred or so sovereign states possessing coastlines, military activity of one sort or another will surely continue at sea. But modern technology has produced such flexible weapon systems, so far ranging in their effects, that power at sea need not necessarily be exercised from warships. Each country, and more so countries such as ours, now have to argue the case for warships against a wider range of alternatives than ever before.

(2) The whole context of seapower has changed. Budget limitations, especially for countries like the UK which have created a nuclear deterrent force, make it necessary to ask, and to answer, what steps in the ladder of maritime escalation can we afford to 'buy into', but also where will be the 'cut off' point when it would be wiser to forsake conventional military preparations and rely only upon the deterrent (and hence decisive) nuclear weapons. In the case of the UK too it is necessary to ask and answer the question of where the RAF conventional strike capability should come on the escalation ladder. Most of the smaller navies operate from bases susceptible to much bombing and provided the range was achievable, in the event of hostilities the RAF alone could render a smaller navy inoperable.

(3) The optimum size of these smaller navies and the choice of individual maritime weapon systems, now so complex and at an increasingly inflationary cost, is already a problem far more difficult than ever before and indeed is as yet hardly understood. In the context of underwater exploration, now actually taking place, the next decade is going to produce far more difficulties still.

C. THE CONTINENTAL SHELF

(1) The strongly held view in US naval circles, with which I agree, is that a less well understood aspect of the future maritime military problem, that of the Continental Shelf, is likely to become one of the principal political issues and sources of conflict in the near future. The Continental Shelf is the sea bed which extends round most of the land masses and which varies from 600–3000 feet down before the ooze drops over underwater cliffs to the abyssal depths of 10,000 feet and beyond. On this 'shelf' there are vast supplies of minerals, oil and gas, diamonds, tin, iron,

sulphur already being brought to the surface. Many of the most prolific fishery grounds and an enormous supply of protein needed to feed a world population exploding at the rate of 200 (net) births over deaths per minute, are all there too.

(2) Diving bell work can now proceed at 500 feet and man is going deeper. It is possible today to buy submarine vehicles which crawl about the ocean floor to inspect the 2,500 oil rigs in the Gulf of Mexico. So work at an ever increasing depth will now proceed as the years go by and the rapidly increasing interest makes it likely that clashes and conflict will occur.

(3) The 1958 Geneva Convention on the Continental Shelf which defined the proprietary rights out to the 600 feet depth and (less clearly) beyond contains the seeds of disharmony. The biggest area of possible conflict is in South East Asia with its large number of populous, expanding, ill-developed states, chronically hungry and conflict prone. There is great mineral wealth there and the fishing rights are already in dispute. There is nothing in International Law at present to prevent any nation staking out a claim to the underwater rights beyond the territorial limits. Half a dozen nations now claim rights out to 100–200 miles and these underwater claims could very well also include the right of innocent passage over the area of water/sea bed claimed.

(4) The British/Icelandic 'Cod war' (in my view) is only the prelude to a vast over fishing of the oceans already well under way by predominantly Soviet fishing vessels. The supply of protein is just not keeping up with the expanding world population and increasingly sophisticated methods of stunning and netting fish will soon reach crisis proportions.

British Naval Thinking

(1) Naval thinking, often rather sterile and unimaginative, has been undergoing a cataclysmic change over the last few years although no real consensus has yet emerged. Nevertheless there are some clear indicators accepted by many.

(2) The surface ship (including surface ships engaged in amphibious operations) is being progressively squeezed between air or space reconnaissance and missiles from above, and underwater detection and underwater weapons of one sort or another, from below. Therefore, to enable the surface ship to operate in a hostile air or missile environment requires control of the accompanying tactical air and underwater assets out to hostile airborne or seaborne (torpedo) missile range. Given adjacent and friendly airfields for the RAF or Carriers, the first is difficult and,

conceivably, depending on the opponent, impossible. On the other hand, given nuclear powered submarines some control of the underwater situation can be obtained but this would be vastly improved by surface ships (however vulnerable) fitted with helicopters and steadily improving sonar. So surface ships, almost essential as anti-submarine helicopter platforms and for overall tactical control, may be too easily targeted by remote fast moving airborne missile dispensers. However nuclear submarines adequately armed with underwater to surface or underwater to anti-air (the latter as yet not developed) weapons can also help to dominate both surface and underwater, so denying surface attack from an opponent.

(3) Thus if money is short (as it is in the UK), and so insufficient for a Carrier Force as well as a nuclear submarine force (given the need to buy a Polaris force as well) the choice points towards submarines which could deny the surface to an opponent rather than Carriers who could not themselves operate without nuclear submarine escort which, if the Carriers were bought could not be afforded!

The Shipbuilding Industry

There are two problems. One of these affecting the whole industry and the other that part devoted to warship building.

(1) The Industry in its two essential echelons, design and actual building, is run-down, out of date in its philosophy and very inefficient.

The Patton and Geddes Committees have pointed the way for the shipbuilding industry. Dramatic mergers on the Clyde and Tyne and a closure of many yards followed by the specialising of others in the designing and building of individual types of merchant ship are now in train. There is however a long way to go before the essential graduate entry will start coming forward in numbers sufficient to give the industry the new and up to date look it deserves. It is still being run by the (over conservative) hammer and chisel men; there are apparently intractable union and demarcation problems to be solved. At least however a modest start has been made, though 'modest' is the operative word.

(2) The intelligence/operational requirements/material management (in brief the 'weapon platform/weapon' choosing and selection machinery) of the MOD (N) is not yet properly tailored to solving the problems of conceiving, designing and building future threat defeating warships with the very minimal skilled sea experienced or naval experienced in-house graduate design resources now available; and with the wide variety of threats requiring different types of hull to counter.

Four major problems confront the MOD (N) in trying to cope with (2) above. These are:

(i) A lack of adequate arrangements (and in some cases a lack of willingness to contemplate such arrangements) to establish a reasonably precise definition of the threat and then to derive from it the best possible answers within the money available.

(ii) The need for advanced management techniques, so very necessary in the present economic climate, is not widely understood in the MOD (N) outside the nuclear submarine building operation In particular (again with the above exception) there is a general lack of a 'Systems Approach' which looks at a warship as a single integrated fighting system.

(iii) There is still an Olde Worlde attitude to HQ personnel management both civilian and naval; too much emphasis on the traditional brand of stentorian 'leadership' and too little on objective and dispassionate judgement, so essential today with the increasingly educated civilian and naval personnel. The US Navy are a little better than we are (other than the RN submarine service which sets an example) and, with that exception, both navies have a long way to go.

My own view is that the RN made a giant step forward by the recommendations of Admiral Mansergh's and Lord Murray's committees. With luck and a certain staunchness not always apparent on the part of the Board of Admiralty the rising generations of naval officers will be better equipped technologically to cope with the personnel and material problems of an increasingly technological age. Unlike some of my engineering colleagues I do not advocate a graduate engineering training for *all* naval officers but I do most strongly advocate an engineering training relevant to their particular specialisation for all executive (seamen) officers and a graduate professional engineering degree for a proportion of engineering specialist officers. This, in my view, will save the Navy from sometimes accepting too readily the dreams of scientists and permit a better type of leadership. This is now apparent in the submarine service which understands (to put it crudely) that today it is as useless to shout at men as it is to shout at machinery, when either falls down on the task.

The Shipping Industry

Many of the troubles of the shipbuilding industry stem from the highly conservative structure and composition of the shipping industry which, from time immemorial has been content, without question, to accept from the shipbuilders uneconomic practices and out of date machinery and equipment. Its system of discipline and labour relations is archaic although things are moving slowly forwards after the 1966 strike.

All this results in a merchant fleet, rebuilt at considerable profit to the builders in the post-war decade, whose operating standards are markedly inferior to our trading opponents. Again, as in the shipbuilding industry, things are beginning to move as the younger men now taking control (Geddes – P & O Tankers, Cayzer – Union Castle, Smallpiece – Cunard) start to understand the problem. There is a long way to go.

THE EXPLOITING OF THE SEA AND SEA BED
February 1968

During my first few months as Naval Attaché in the United States I became more and more concerned that the UK was falling behind in the exploration and exploiting of the sea and the sea bed. Taking the opportunity of a visit by Lord Mountbatten, at his request I put my views on paper and he sent them to Sir Solly (later Lord) Zuckerman to pass to the Prime Minister, Mr Harold Wilson. These things take time to wander round bureaucracy and unfortunately the Government fell just as the matter was beginning to warm up and the Conservatives' eyes, as they are today, were fixed on Europe to the complete neglect of our maritime heritage.

I had an opportunity later that year, when the Vice President as a member of the Washington St David's Society came on board HMS Glamorgan on a Sunday to sing Welsh Hymns, of discussing the possibilities of Aquaspace with him; and this discussion reinforced my view that we in the UK were in danger of 'missing the boat'.

THE AIM

This Paper seeks briefly to set out some of the facts about the sea bed in general and the Continental Shelf in particular. It concludes by suggesting some names for a small but powerful 'task-force' which might, with authority, report to the Prime Minister on the need for initiating and directing a national effort, in the interests of the human race and to the manifest advantage of the UK, towards the exploiting of the food and mineral resources so clearly and so readily available in the world's oceans.

THE SEA BED

This consists of the Continental Shelf and the abyssal depths to which it finally drops.

THE CONTINENTAL SHELF

The Continental Shelf is that part of the sea bed which surrounds the world's land mass to a depth of about 600'. The shelf belongs to the adjacent country and, by the Geneva Convention of 1958, that country holds sovereign rights over its use and, out to the depths of practicable exploitation, beyond it.

LEGAL AND GEOGRAPHICAL IMPLICATIONS

Granted some truth in forecast technology the geographical boundaries and perhaps the legal relations between states will manifestly be changed. The right to exert sovereignty over the entire adjacent sea bed by one nation or another has now already received tacit approval. It is also clear that the law of the sea bed will be quite different from the law of the sea. Underwater frontiers will meet. Islands will cease to be islands. New borders will be, and indeed in the North Sea, already have been created between nations.

FOUR MAJOR INTERNATIONAL PROBLEMS

  (a) **The Increase in World Population**. It seems generally to be agreed that over the next thirty years the population of the world will double and the food consumption per capita will decrease, starvation becoming even more widespread.

  Two thirds of the world's population live in countries where malnutrition is endemic. Protein deficiency is the greatest killer of children of pre-school age. The gap between the 'haves' and the 'have-nots' will widen. Starvation is a powerful stimulus to action. Desperation recognises no frontiers.

  (b) **World Communism**. The main strategy of the USSR effectively to spread world communism may now no longer be primarily a military one. Instead, on the evidence of the education programme which is now believed to be turning out graduates in excess of the Free World by a factor of 10:1 in the related fields of naval architecture, marine engineering, ocean engineering, geophysics etc., the new Soviet strategy appears to have as its aim the domination of all available areas of the sea bed and the sea above it. Such a strategy can be construed in a favourable light as being one which will allow the USSR to do more than any other country to meet the needs of the doubling world population and to prevent war. Communism will be swallowed with the proteins.

(c) **The Sea Bed as a Source of Conflict**. If the geographical and legal complications already referred to are accepted, then in the present state of human and international relationships a further source of political issue and even conflict has already been added. Plainly the problem of dividing up an area three times the size of the present land mass, containing all the riches required by future generations will soon be with us.

(d) **The Sea as a Source of Conflict**. Already the breadth of territorial seas over which sovereignty is claimed is now rapidly increasing as strong national aspirations take hold. From the traditional range of a cannon shot (3 miles) still adhered to by the UK and USA, Guinea has advanced her claims to 130 miles and Chile, Costa Rica, Ecuador, Honduras, San Salvador and Peru out to 200 miles. A large number of states claim a 12 mile limit and the recent UK 'Fish War' with Iceland could well recur as small navies proliferate or small countries with adjacent seaboards indulge in conflict. The problem of the Right of Free Passage through Straits was vividly highlighted last year in the Israeli-Arab war.

TECHNOLOGICAL POSSIBILITIES

In the U.S. it is estimated (optimistically) that the economic use of the Continental Shelf and beyond, to a depth of 3000' is virtually assured in the next decade. For the further area down to 8000' it should be possible to work with submersibles and to build installations on the sea bed.

WEALTH FROM THE SEA

Estimates vary but a very conservative one suggests that the sea can provide at least sixteen times the future world requirement of animal protein provided the danger of over-fishing (now in some areas happening to a critical extent) is recognised and dealt with. Other areas have as yet not been touched. Modern fishing techniques are being developed. A new look is being taken at the design of fishing trawlers. Aquaculture in various forms is now well established in many parts of the world.

There are vast mineral resources not over-difficult to exploit and, once brought to the surface, extremely easy to transport.

There is power in the shape of oil and gas deposits which, with present engineering skills, can effectively be harnessed. At the moment only 6%

of the world's oil supply comes from under the sea and current US predictions are that within a decade a quarter of the world's oil requirements will have to be met in this way.

Fresh water for drinking is something that, with the rapidly expanding world population, is becoming progressively more scarce. Very soon the West Coast of America will largely be supplied with water distilled from the sea, while in certain areas of the oceans fresh water springs on the sea bed are being tapped to supply the adjacent land mass.

98% of the world's goods are still transported by water and this proportion is unlikely to change. Indeed with the inevitably increasing industrialisation of developing countries sea transport, in the total, will also increase year by year. Merchant shipping and the application of modern technology to its production and operation will be an essential factor in the maintenance of world peace and the establishing of an all round better standard of living.

The industrial development and expertise needed to utilise the wealth of the sea bed and the techniques necessary to harvest the sea, to achieve an output of fish protein concentrate to help reduce world starvation and the increasing and far more sophisticated and manpower economic developments in sea transport would all seem to be in the classic British pioneering, technological and indeed, humanitarian tradition.

ACTION NOW STARTING IN THE US, UK AND USSR

In the context of the wealth of food and mineral resources now becoming available as a result of the new ocean technologies all the problems are magnified immeasurably and the actions in hand are now examined.

(a) **The United States**.

(i) It is only about two years since the USA really woke up to what is happening and there are still many doubters. The fact is that the skills needed to exploit the sea and the sea bed are so diverse that there is difficulty in bringing all these together. In the case of the USA this has been done by putting the Vice-President in charge of a steering committee established by an Act of Congress in order that marine resources and the development of ocean engineering should be progressed to the fullest extent possible with the Government money ('The Wet N.A.S.A. Programme – $515M in fiscal year 1969 budget).

(ii) Many Colleges have established courses in Ocean Engineering; learned societies have been created to guide and collate the literature. The US Navy has been playing a leading part (because of its expertise in marine science and technology) in making it clear that the maritime problem is not solely a naval one, but concerns also the merchant marine, the fishing fleets, diving technology and the various oceanographic agencies. At the same time a highly advanced nuclear propelled deep submergence vehicle is being built.

There has been the rush, usual in the USA, to 'get in on the act' and, although the development of the sea bed is not just a matter of building a fleet of submersibles, vast sums are being expended by shipbuilding and aerospace firms on hardware. The latter firms especially are beginning to understand that space exploration has very little in the shape of commercial return once satellite communication has been perfected. As a result of all this there are now over 30 US submersibles, some of them designed for depths up to 8000'. The problems of designing such vehicles for use beyond a depth of 10,000' have been found greatly to increase the expense. Much of the research and development into really deep diving vehicles has been done at the instance of the US Navy as a result of the US S/M *Thresher* disaster.

(b) **The United Kingdom**

(i) The position in the UK appears to be similar to that in the USA two or three years ago, except that the Royal Navy, with its many difficulties and problems of the last few years, has not taken the same powerful lead to alert the Government and the country to the benefits of exploiting the sea bed and the sea. As in the USA there are a great number of agencies of one sort or another concerned in the matter (The Atomic Energy Authority is officially the lead agency) and a small step forward was taken in the autumn of 1967 when the Ministry of Technology and the AEA held a conference on the technology needed for sea bed exploration. That conference, however, was at far too low a level and was in no position to grip at high level, as is essential, all the different aspects of this problem mentioned in this memorandum. More is hoped from a forthcoming conference between the RN and the AEA due to take place in March 1968 at Greenwich.

(ii) One small submersible has recently been built by Lintotts in Sussex and Vickers shipbuilding has fabricated parts for a Canadian submersible which is being used by Canadian and US agencies. Although the AEA has been charged with responsibility for the development of submersibles there seems to have been little or no co-ordination between their endeavours and the wide range of submarine expertise existing in the Ministry of Defence.

(c) **The USSR**

On the evidence of the educational programme, of her widespread fishing fleet and of the Soviet Union's price cutting war in sea transportation of oil and goods and of her world-wide naval activity, the USSR is set on dominating the majority of that two thirds of the world area covered by sea, to which at the moment, only on the fringes, are there any strong national claims.

LIKELY ADVANCES IN DEEP SEA TECHNOLOGY

Apart from merchant shipping and fishing vessels there are three main developing technological means whereby the sea bed and the sea can be better exploited. These are:

(a) Deep Diving Techniques. It is now possible by means of saturation diving, whereby the diver breathes a helium/nitrogen/oxygen mixture, for man to exist in 'habitats' and as a free swimmer, and to work at depths of 800'–1000'. Within a decade these techniques will have been perfected and on an experimental basis man will be going much deeper. In the distant but foreseeable future the use of an appropriate fluid which will fill the lungs but which contains oxygen to sustain life is envisaged. The difficulty with this type of technique at the moment is that the support for deep sea diving still has to be on the surface and thus is susceptible to storms and bad weather.

(b) There are now submersibles with air locks through which men can enter the sea and return to these mobile 'bases'. These, being underwater and able so to return to harbour, do not require surface support as in (a) above. Prolonged 'saturation' diving such as in (a) above from submarines is, at the moment, difficult because of decompression problems. However there are already seemingly practicable schemes for a combination of (a) and (b) involving fixed 'habitats' on the sea floor and 'transfer capsules' which could be attached to mobile submarines which would largely obviate both decompression and weather problems.

(c) The third developing technology is the production of battery or nuclear powered submersible vehicles which, through the use of powerful lights, sonar and remotely operated arms and grabs, can perform a great many of the activities normal to man. Such types of vehicles are necessarily very complicated especially when designed for depths below 1000' which, generally speaking is the limit of present experience.

To sum up, the development of permanent 'habitats' devoted to sea bed exploitation and farming as well as mining, by Cousteau in France and the US Navy has shown that man can tolerate prolonged exposure at depths. More convenient means of transport to and from the surface are now being developed.

Further and deeper experiments with Royal Navy help are in train for next year (1968). The US Government and industrial technologists are developing materials suitable for these 'habitats' which, in the future, could include nuclear power stations set on the sea bed to provide essential warmth and light.

PARLIAMENT

From various conversations I have had before and since leaving the UK, even MPs of all parties responsible for shipbuilding constituencies and others higher in the ministerial (and Opposition) chain, seem to believe that shipbuilding is 'Old Hat' to be undertaken only by Third World countries and that aerospace is the best destiny for a 'sophisticated' (though some would question that adjective) industrial country such as the UK. Somehow a programme must be contrived to convince MPs that it is from the exploiting of 'Aquaspace' rather than 'Aerospace' that a more prosperous Britain could emerge.

CONCLUSION

Vice President Humphrey's Committee has been found an essential tool even in the United States, where already there seems to be a far greater appreciation than in the United Kingdom of the political possibilities of approaching world starvation and the realities stemming from the spread of Soviet maritime power.

The five elements already referred to, warships, merchant ships, fishing ships, oceanographic ships and the ship design and building industry, all have clear cut but closely related missions. It is already evident from the grand design of Soviet strategy that each of these elements is being systematically used to fill gaps which the 'Free World' has abandoned or which have existed and the 'Free World' has failed to fill. I do not question the need for our land and air defences in Western Europe, but I cannot see, except as a last resort, any possibility of a Soviet thrust across the German Plain. Soviet strategy is far more long term and, if possible, free of the threat of a nuclear exchange.

There needs to be a clearer understanding in the United States of the implications of the many new mini-navies which have evolved since the war. These provide their owners with a considerable temptation to claim (and defend their claim) greater areas of national territorial waters either because of the implications of the 1958 Geneva Convention or more likely because of the particular predilection of the various countries concerned.

Nationally Britain possesses a very good Navy indeed (except in numbers) by either Soviet or US standards, a badly neglected Merchant Navy (by Soviet standards), a rapidly decaying fishing fleet, practically no oceanographic ships and a run-down but slowly improving ship design and ship building industry. However, in advanced diving techniques the UK is only just being surpassed by the USN and the National Institute of Oceanography, and British Hydrography has already undertaken invaluable oceanic surveys.

It seems crystal clear to me that a British 'task force' analogous to Vice President Humphrey's committee is needed and it is for consideration that the issues at stake are so important that it should have direct access to the Prime Minister. Such a task force would require naval representation, but equally, if not more important, it needs people to serve on it who are sufficiently well known to ensure that their findings on the wide variety of interlocking problems can carry enough weight to provoke the development of a national effort. A less than comprehensive list of possible names is given at annex.

Last of all the sea is surely still an emotive issue to the people of Britain at a moment in history when they lack any issue to which they are inclined to respond. If any government of the left or right could only play these cards effectively then our maritime heritage might once more be awakened. If that happened then the nation would reap a considerable dividend, not only from the material benefits that would accrue, but also from the sense of creative and united purpose which any such endeavour might well provoke.

ANNEX

Names of some who, should the 'task force' proposed in this memorandum become established, it would seem worthwhile inviting to serve:

Messrs. Deacon & Fleming. National Institute of Oceanography
Rear-Admiral Ritchie. Hydrographer of the Navy

Mr Basil Lythall. Chief Scientist (RN) and one time Director of the Underwater Warfare Establishment

Mr Hempleman. Superintendent, RN Physiological Laboratory which is looked on by the USN with envy and admiration. It may be that its equal in expertise and equipment exists in the Soviet Union, but it certainly has no equal in the Western World.

Lord Caldecote. A naval architect by upbringing who knows the potential of British aircraft industry and might easily be made aware of the latter's relevance to aquaspace.

Professor Laurence Martin. Woodrow Wilson Professor of International Politics at Aberystwyth whose recent study *The Sea in Modern Strategy* has provoked much thought into the implications of the ownership and exploitation of the sea bed.

THE ROYAL NAVAL ENGINEERING COLLEGE, MANADON, 1960

This piece was written when the new RN Engineering College at Manadon was taking shape under the Government approved plans for the move from the old, small and much loved but inadequate College at Keynham in Devonport.

The new College was completed about 2 years later.

The first permanent establishment of Engineer Officers, all appointed by warrant, came into being in 1837, and rather grudging commissions were achieved by a few, some ten years later. On the eve of the Crimean War they numbered 79 in all: in 1939 there were 1,200 commissioned and warrant officers and by the middle of 1961, after the amalgamation of the engineering and electrical branches, the combined total was 3,000.

The Royal Naval Engineering College was established at Keyham, in Devonport, in 1880, and here the great majority of the Navy's professional engineers were trained until, sadly, the College, by then the oldest Officers' Mess in the Navy, was closed in 1958. During the whole of this period, except for one short break, a training structure evolved under the guidance and control of the navy's engineers designed specifically to produce a breed of officer dedicated to preserving that most vital attribute of the Royal Navy, its mobility.

It is perhaps of interest that the only break in the training of Engineer Officers occurred during the First World War, when those cadets who had left Osborne, but were not yet aged 16, were sent to Keyham until they achieved that ripe age at which it was considered appropriate to send them to sea in war time. Among them was the present Chief of the Defence Staff, Admiral of the Fleet Earl Mountbatten of Burma, now the senior serving life member of the Officers' Mess of the Royal Naval Engineering College at Manadon. This estate, noted in the Domesday Book, was bought by the Admiralty in 1939, when it was realised that Keyham could no longer house either the number of officers or the comprehensive equipment needed to match technology in the future Navy.

This is not the place to discuss the details of training of technical officers in the Navy but rather to define the part which it is hoped that Manadon will play in the training that will fit technical officers to play their full part in the Navy of the last half of this century. This year two members of the Board of Admiralty will have completed 45 years of service in the Royal Navy. It is as sobering a thought to realise that a few of those who join the Navy in the next year or so will be in similar positions at the end of the century, as it is to consider the engineering techniques at that date which will be at the disposal of those who are about to undergo their naval engineering training. Before attempting to describe the objects of this training it is essential to spare a moment of time to try to clear our minds on one of the most fundamental decisions affecting the training of officers, which was taken quite recently by the Admiralty.

Lord Moran has written: 'The Senior Service has long occupied in the hearts of Englishmen the place reserved in Germany for their army. Where so much is slipshod and even humiliating, here, against a background of the rough sea, is a breed of men, doing a man's job about as well as it can be done.

'. . . That a boy has set his heart on this tough service goes for something. He has initiative; he is a cut above the ordinary. Long before the Hitler youth was thought of, the Navy caught him young and soaked him in the pride and joy of a great tradition . . . but more than anything else it is the influence of the machine which keeps the Navy from going to seed in peace. Every rating is a mechanic, there is purpose in each day.'

With the helter-skelter technological advance of today, the Admiralty has been under the greatest pressure, both from educationists and from engineers, to arrange for all officers to read for an engineering degree or at the very least for them to read a course of engineering study approximating to degree standard. The Americans do it; the Canadians do it; the Russians do it; and to say the least, there is considerable logic in the proposal.

Two streams of officers

Yet, the Board of Admiralty has most firmly resisted it and has decreed that the training of officers, after a common two years' apprenticeship, spent mostly at sea, should be divided into two streams. In effect the Board has ruled that, in all the functions of an officer, in powers of leadership, in self-discipline, in behaviour, in example, these two streams shall be identical, only in one way shall they differ: one stream shall wield the weapon the nation entrusts to its care, the other shall help to forge it and shall go down to the sea to keep it sharp.

The propriety of this decision is above all question, if the lessons of recent history, the hard economic facts affecting the country's existence and what Lord Moran calls, 'the background of the rough sea', are all properly appreciated. If we are to ensure the free passage of our merchant fleets throughout the world, our Navy, already so diminished, will be stretched to the limit and, if the occasion arises, will have to fight as it has so often had to fight, against the heaviest of odds.

This is nothing new to us and if we look back no further than the last world war there are examples aplenty where superior tactical handling and the innate quality of our weapons gave us victory against all apparent probability. Harwood, at the River Plate, Vian, at Sirte, Sherbrooke, in the Barents Sea, Walker, in the Atlantic, Wanklyn, in his *Upholder*, Hichens, of Coastal Forces, all showed the way and there were scores of others well known to historians.

In one of those postscripts after the 9 o'clock news about one such engagement, it was said: 'In this sort of fighting, there are men who combine those particular qualities of cool leadership and complete knowledge of the technical side of the job so perfectly that their battles are successful where others fail.' It is with this aim in view that the first stream will be trained. But the one stream is complimentary to the other; without the other, either would fail.

Fleet Admiral King, in his report to Congress at the end of the Second World War had this to say: 'The Navy, perhaps more than any other of the services, is dependent on a high quality of engineering skill and practice. All our ships and planes, the establishment which designs and builds them, and the equipment which operates and arms them could not exist without the engineer and the technical expert – each technician aboard ship must learn not only his own particular part of its machinery, he must also learn how to operate it so that it will contribute most to the efficiency of the ship as a unit. There is no better example of the necessity of teamwork than a modern man of war.'

Perhaps it is possible to appreciate from this statement the role of the other stream who must help to forge the weapon and who are destined to go to sea and keep it sharp and to be trained for both these functions at the Royal Naval Engineering College at Manadon.

We mentioned earlier the pressure on the Admiralty to allow all officers to read for a degree and to the resulting decision which has, in effect, produced two streams, those who go to sea to wield the weapon and who do not read for a degree, and those who have to design and maintain the Fleet and in whose training for this function there is an opportunity to read for a degree course.

There is not space here to probe too far back into history but mention has already been made of the R.N. Engineering College at Keyham and we must dwell for a moment on the training given there and, until this very year, at Manadon. The purpose was strictly naval and the syllabus was a blend of mechanical and electrical engineering derived directly from the Cambridge Mechanical Sciences Tripos and Naval Marine Engineering theory and practice translated from the needs of the Fleet, together with substantial practical workshop training.

In all, including the period of practical watchkeeping training at sea the period required, even under the fairly intensive regime which was followed, was about 4½ to 5 years, and the result of success was recognised, after a further period of responsibility, by the Institution of Mechanical Engineers as being sufficient to merit the award of Associate Membership. But, in fact, and no one was more surprised then Naval engineers themselves, the training between the wars and during the 1939–45 period produced a breed who have made an impact on the engineering life of the country quite out of proportion to their numbers, which were insignificant.

In an analysis this is perhaps not so surprising. Entry to the Navy in those days was always difficult; those who achieved it were already in the top bracket academically; if the training was good, as it was, and the opportunity to practise a wide diversity of engineering present, as it most certainly was, the results should have been good. It may also be of interest to note one other factor which counted for much. Keyham, certainly from the 1920s onward, had an Engineer-Captain at its head, but perhaps most important of all, the Dean was a selected Commander of the engineering specialisation; straight from sea, and under him as his professors and lecturers, he had a mixed bag of Naval Engineer Officers, civilian professors and lecturers and a small and highly select body of Naval Instructor Officers who spent the majority of their service life at Keyham.

Many of the latter had fought at sea or in the trenches or had flown in the First World War and all of them were great personalities in the truest sense of the word. Indeed, since their inevitable retirement from the Navy for age (but inexplicable for any other reason), they seem to this day to be found lecturing at Sandhurst, at Greenwich and as principals and professors at technical colleges up and down the country. To these great teachers, for that and more they were, the engineering branch and the Navy owe a great debt. It is good to know at least that, just before it was closed, they came to Keyham, the place they had served so well, to dine once more as the guests of the engineers who had been their pupils. Now that is all in the past and we look to the future at Manadon.

When the Board took the decision to divide the officer stream in two, there were two other subsidiary decisions required. The first was to amalgamate the old engineering branch, to which this article has so far referred, with the electrical branch, now in the second decade of its life; and the second was to decide the type of training for the amalgamated branch. This is not the place to consider all the arguments which have led eventually to the recognition of Manadon by the University of London as being an establishment at which suitably qualified students can read for an external degree in mechanical or electrical engineering, and to a selected few of both specialisations being sent to Cambridge to read for the mechanical sciences tripos. Such a decision has meant a fairly radical reorientation of the training policy at Manadon to some extent away from that which might at first sight seem to be a strictly naval need.

To concede this, however, involves shutting the eyes both to national changes taking place today, and to an even greater extent, tomorrow. The raising of the standard of entry is an essential step towards the convincing of parents and masters that a career in the Navy is a worthy pursuit for boys of high intelligence, and apart from the argument that the Navy has no right to good calibre minds that it is not prepared to educate further, a decision on this important question requires judgment on the nature of the responsibilities likely to be carried by these officers in the future Navy.

Whilst the needs of the Royal Navy over the next twenty or thirty years cannot be determined precisely, there are two clear pointers, the level of education, both general and vocational amongst ratings, is rising; and even more apparent perhaps, all aspects of life are becoming increasingly complex technologically, whilst the developments in the equipment and methods of naval warfare are such as to make basic scientific and engineering knowledge a rapidly appreciating asset.

This tying of the syllabus to an entirely external and less obviously naval yardstick has meant several changes in the organisation of the College, not least the replacement of a practising seagoing Naval Engineer by an Instructor Officer as Dean and Director of Studies, and a less obviously naval curriculum at least for the first three years of the course of study. No one who has experienced Oxford or Cambridge or other universities since the war would concede any noticeable increase in the cloistered calm of university life. The fact that most undergraduates are without private means, that competition for entry is fierce and that, as never before, a career depends on the results achieved, has meant a tremendous increase in the tempo of work, approved by some, regretted by others.

At Manadon the very reverse could be true. The officers have already chosen their profession, are in receipt of an adequate wage and the temptation quietly to jog along and just to pass the necessary examinations is a formidable one. Such an attitude of mind is of course quite incompatible with the needs of the Naval service and the problem of how to maintain the initial enthusiasm of these officers for the Navy whilst they undergo their academic slog is a very real one.

> 'Keep then the sea about in special
> Which of England is the round wall
> As though England were likened to a city
> And the wall environ were the sea
> Keep the sea which is the wall of England
> And then is England kept by God's hand.'

So said the Libel of English Policy, five centuries ago.

> 'Throughout our long history there have been periods in which the gifts of the sea have been flouted, entailing in some cases a swift Nemesis. Political conditions, oblivion of the teaching of war, or the perverse counsels of individuals in authority, have induced neglect of the national navy, and encouraged reliance upon subordinate – and for Great Britain – wholly ineffectual measures of defence. War has thus found the country unprepared, and heavy losses, easily avoided, have been entailed. So soon as stern necessity has arisen, the rehabilitation of the Fleet has forced itself upon the nation as the one indispensable means of guaranteeing territorial integrity at home and abroad, and of giving effect to the national will.'

So wrote Clarke and Thursfield at the turn of the century.

Britain today has certain inescapable commitments and at the same time if we are to survive the penury to which we have reduced ourselves in the defence of civilisation in two world wars only a small proportion of the gross national product remains for investment in the relatively unproductive fighting services. Throughout history, sometimes through the neglect of statesmen, sometimes, as now, because of the hard economic facts of life, the size of our Navy has unnecessarily or necessarily, declined. To the Technical Officer, above all officers, this inescapable fact poses a challenge of the utmost severity. To meet this challenge the Technical Officer finds himself called upon to serve the Navy in three well defined roles.

The primary role of the young engineer, whether mechanically or electrically trained, is to keep the greatest possible proportion of the Fleet and naval aircraft ready for war and available at sea. All else pales into insignificance before the importance of making the best use of the weapons with which the nation has entrusted us.

The second role, in which necessarily the Naval engineer works with the Admiralty trained civilian technologists, whether he is a member of the Royal Corps of Naval Constructors or an Admiralty civilian electrical or mechanical engineer, is in the Royal Docklands or the Aircraft Repair Yards to which the Fleet or Naval aircraft return for periodical major refits, for the fitting of newly developed weapon systems or for other modification.

Lastly, in conjunction with civilians or Admiralty civilians, including those mentioned above, and members of the Royal Naval Scientific Service, Naval engineers can influence and approve design. Here their role is to provide a nucleus of sea experienced aeronautical, electrical and mechanical engineers who can act as planks between the Navy and industry and over which there can flow two streams of traffic: seagoing naval needs in one direction and developments in industry likely to be of use to the Navy, in the other.

Thus today the Navy is endeavouring to make good the lack of quantity, which throughout history it has endured, by a supreme emphasis on quality in operation, in repair and in design. In this battle the Royal Naval Engineering College at Manadon plays the key role, for it is there that the young Technical Officers are trained and it is from there that they will go to sea to play perhaps their most vital role; as it is the seagoing officer who will keep the weapon sharp in these critical years that lie just ahead and it is his sea experience which in the future must be used to ensure swift and sure repair and the design of warships best suited to the strategic needs of tomorrow.

RENDCOMB COLLEGE

PASTORAL CARE AND CHARACTER
RENDCOMB COLLEGE

Anyone who dares to expound on the teaching of leadership is treading on dangerous ground. But, after 5 years as Chairman of Governors of a school where primary schoolchildren aged 11 (whose fees were mostly paid for them) were deliberately mixed at age 13 with an equal number of preparatory school children with a different background (whose fees were met by rather more well off parents) I determined to leave my views for my successor. The early Eighties were troublesome days for all sorts of education, private and state, and many of the problems in the inner cities particularly and in rural areas to an increasing extent, seemed to me not only attributable to the type of training in vogue for some years, given to teachers, but also to a lack of parental (and those at schools in loco parentis) responsibility. In an Independent Boarding School problems of teacher standards were probably far less because of the selective powers of headmasters; and certainly in my experience because of the rather better emoluments for possibly far more actual, but certainly more satisfying, work.

In many ways Rendcomb was (and is) unique. Founded by a rich man who had been unhappy at his Public (Independent) School but supremely happy at Magdalen College, Oxford, and who deplored a 'class conscious' society, Noel Wills in the 'English Review' of June 1924 laid down the principle that has continued to direct educational policy at Rendcomb:

'THE TRUE ARISTOCRACY AMONG MEN IS IN REALITY SIMPLY THE ARISTOCRACY OF BRAINS AND CHARACTER.

The mixture between those who received a free education (due to the Wills family and until lately Gloucestershire County Council) and those who paid fees, produced a social mixture which, in those days was and

219

to a great extent still is unique amongst educational establishments. Noel Wills' belief was that many of the greatest benefactors to the human race appeared to owe little or nothing to wealth; and from this he came to understand, perhaps well ahead of his era, the power of opportunity and environment. It was the latter two that Noel Wills sought to provide.

In a Government Report of 40 years ago with which I was brought into contact at the time there appeared the following passage:

> 'In the last resort the sound upbringing of young people depends neither on the State and its instruments, nor on the voluntary organisations and institutions, but on the adults who are in contact with or concerned with young people in their daily lives. From this it follows that anything which impairs the adult's personal sense of responsibility prejudices the upbringing of young people . . . for at any given time each boy and girl in the country is in fact looking for guidance to an adult, be they parents, teachers, trades union officials, or officers in the forces of the Crown. And because the evidence laid before us suggests that in recent years there has been some weakening in the sense of personal and parental responsibility it is not to organisations or institutions, but to individual men and women that we address this report.
>
> Interwoven with, and inseparable from this first theme, is a second . . . the expression of a conviction that the road back to responsibility is the road back to Christian principles. Here again our working party are at one. They believe that for us in Britain the revival and renewal on a much larger scale of such an attitude to life among young people is essential . . . We are convinced that the best hope for the future lies in an acceptance of the Christian ethic in its broadest sense.'

It is generally held that an officer in the Forces of the Crown has some unimpeachable authority deriving from (in the case of the Navy) the Naval Discipline Act. Although this Act may provide the shadow, the substance largely disappeared after the mutiny at Invergordon nearly 60 years ago. Thereafter discipline assumed a new look. Officers had been brought face to face with the prevailing spirit of the times. This was (and still is) usually roughly described as 'democracy', but to a large extent it means a disinclination to accept any form of restraint, and a desire for unrestricted freedom of life and action.

In a human society so complex as that of a fighting service friction and misunderstanding are bound to arise when there is any doubt as to who is in charge, who must lead, and who must follow. And so bodily or mechanical discipline, which has its place in service training, has been switched, certainly in the Navy, to something less obvious and tangible but more real and deeply ingrained.

Management skills can be taught and learnt but it is this infusion of personal leadership which is so badly needed on the British industrial scene today.

A few people are leaders by instinct and need only to have those instincts channelled in the right direction for them to grow up to be influences for good. Others take the wrong road and civilisation suffers. But for most people during adolescence the instinct to be a leader is muffled by an innate reserve or shyness, or indolence, or up-bringing. Just a few fizz, like a champagne bottle newly opened, while a few have no instinct for leadership and are content always to remain as cabbages, just to grow and to fructify and play their humble part in God's Garden. It is the 70%–75% between the champagne and the cabbage whose interest adults, whatever their role, must try to engage.

What is Leadership?

Today the term is often used in a rather derogatory sense. And the relationship between leadership and the law needs to be examined. The formal definition of law, as propounded by nineteenth century writers on jurisprudence (Law is the command of the Ruler) differs little, if at all, from Hitler's *'Das ist Recht was dem Fuhrer gefallt'* Both lead, as they do in the Soviet Union today, to the gas chamber, the concentration camp or the pseudo-psychiatric clinic.

Professor Dunstan in his book *The Artifice of Ethics* considers the relationship between law and morality and he quotes some paragraphs from Lord Justice Devlin's Maccabaean Lecture on *Morals and the Criminal Law*, as follows:

I have spoken of the criminal law as dealing with the minimum standards of human conduct and the moral law with the maximum. The instrument of the criminal law is punishment: those of the moral law are teaching, training and exhortation. If the whole dead weight of sin were ever to be allowed to fall upon the law, it could not take the strain. If at any time there is a lack of clear and convincing moral teaching the law will fail.

And as Professor Dunstan remarks, Lord Devlin's Lecture ends with the words, 'Without the help of Christian teaching the law will fail.'

Lord Moran in his book *The Anatomy of Courage* makes the same point in a slightly different context. Of the events in Germany and in the Democracies between World Wars I and II he writes:

> One of the causes of their defeat, the Germans asserted, was that the minds of their youth had not been prepared in peace, for the trials of war. There was a veritable toilet of the mind . . . even their schoolbooks were doctored . . . to inculcate into the whole German Nation the prized qualities of the soldier. Happily no democracy can be prepared, in the German sense, for war . . . we are of course paying in full for this freedom of the mind . . . but it should and can be prepared to fight evil; a free people is only ready to resist aggression when the Christian virtues flourish, for a man of character in peace is a man of courage in war.

In an attempt to draw this together therefore, it seems to me that in a democracy whether in the context of a citizen 'Service' or a citizen 'Workforce' true leadership, except in moments of extreme urgency, should never have to rely on the law of the land. Instead those who aspire to lead must try to do so through their character and personality and moral courage, based principally on Christian teaching, as well as the moral control exercised through various institutions developed in society, for which Professor Dunstan suggests the term 'Conventions'. Aspiring leaders should be taught the reasons for maintaining these 'conventions' which Professor Dunstan explains as follows:

> My hope is that when we recognise a little more clearly the moral imperatives by which, without much explicit or self-conscious use of moral language, we live together, we shall realise more the importance of these imperatives in the life of the community and may indeed wish to strengthen them.

But the real art of leadership seems to be the art of dealing with human nature in whatever may be its state of development at the time. Until fairly recently men could be governed through their hearts.

Shakespeare caught the fashion of the Middle Ages:

> For he today that sheds his blood with me
> Shall be my brother; be he ne'er so vile
> This day shall gentle his condition:
> And gentlemen in England, now abed
> Shall think themselves accursed they were not here,
> And hold their manhood cheap whiles any speaks
> That fought with us upon St Crispin's Day.

'England expects that every man will do his duty', signalled Nelson before Trafalgar.

'Stick it out. We must not let the Army down,' signalled Admiral Cunningham, as ship after ship was damaged or sunk in the Battle of Crete.

Yet I suspect that any such signal from Admiral Woodward during the Carlos Bay Battle, as ships were damaged and sunk in the age of the missile, would not have done much to inspire men to even greater feats of courage and fortitude than they were already showing; and Woodward was much nearer the actual fighting than Cunningham.

Today in the Services, no less than on the assembly line, man has to be governed not only through his heart but also through his head. In the prosaic language of our age Lord Murray of Newhaven told the Board of Admiralty in 1958 when recommending a new schedule of training for Naval Officers:

> The needs of the Royal Navy over the next twenty to thirty years cannot be determined precisely at the present time, but there is a clear pointer. The level of education, both general and vocational, among ratings, is rising, while changes in society continuously erode the ordered class supremacy of officers. In the Navy of the future leadership is likely to come to require in addition to personality a higher level of technological knowledge.

Because I was the Committee's co-secretary I know it was their judgement (all but two classically educated) that the paragraph applied equally to other walks of life and that the British educational system was proving remarkably obdurate in not accepting what, to the committee, seemed the unmistakable pattern of the future.

Leadership today therefore seems to depend as never before, not only on the development of character and personality but also on an education which will help to illuminate those particular technological elements within the 90% of all human knowledge acquired in the last forty years, essential to the peaceful development of a rapidly burgeoning world population.

What then is the role of Rendcomb College in all this?

From the principle that 'he who pays the piper calls the tune' the curriculum at Rendcomb has to be slanted towards the achieving by the pupil of those types of academic success which the parents regard as an adequate return for their very considerable expenditure. In plain terms most parents spend a lot of money to ensure their children's academic success and are less concerned about the development of personality and character, provided a certain minimum standard of behaviour is assured.

In a remarkable speech entirely composed on his own, when responding to the principal speaker on Founder's Day, the Head Prefect, (a Foundationer – that is to say from a family too poor to pay the fees) had this to say:

> To have the opportunity to spend one's most formative years in such agreeable surroundings and to have experienced the atmosphere of friendship and loyalty, which I believe to be unique to Rendcomb, is undoubtedly a privilege.
>
> To be a Rendcombian is to be distinctive. For at Rendcomb an individual develops freely while learning a sense of responsibility, of service to the community and the importance of fellowship. It is these qualities which the school will consistently instil in its pupils because that is the spirit of Rendcomb. Any school must be capable of reconciling traditional values with the needs of modern Society and while the school must not stray from the ideals of its Founder, whom we remember especially today, Rendcomb cannot and will not estrange itself from the outside world, remaining sufficiently flexible to meet its challenges.

But the excellent young man was the Head Prefect and so should anyway have been head and shoulders above his peers. What I find so difficult to establish is how far down does such a degree of excellence penetrate in any of the yearly groupings of 40 or so adolescents. So often in schools as in youth clubs it is the bright and lively boys and girls who receive attention while the apparently really bad ones get expelled. But in between there is a mass who are perhaps developing more slowly and who need a guide of some sort to show them the right path.

Experienced and worldly wise schoolmasters will say that young boys and girls have not changed in the last four hundred years, let alone the last forty and that may well be so. But I shall try to argue the need for more resources, more care and more skill to be devoted to pastoral care, not only because that is what our Founder would have wished, not because of the traditional flowering of the adolescent urge, but rather on the grounds of the gross materialism which now pervades society, on the far more, at least superficially, attractive means of sublimating that adolescent urge available today, and thirdly on the lowering of those once primary defences which we of an older generation generally enjoyed and which Professor Dunstan terms 'conventions' – those conventions which society has traditionally provided in the past as regulators of behaviour and conduct.

The role of Rendcomb, as I see it, is to develop as far as possible in the human material which the Headmaster admits to the College, those qualities which go to make up what is generally called 'The Whole Man or Woman'. This I think I would characterise as the 'morality of love', the going of just that little bit further than natural morality would enjoin. But 'Love' is far too hackneyed a word these days. One has to go back to the Greek *Agape* or the Latin *Caritas*, 'the art of being a dear' as Lord Hailsham translates it and which St. Paul so succinctly sets out in his Epistle to the Corinthians, at least in the Authorised Version. *Agape* is more than conventional love, it includes invariable respect for people's personalities as well as a liking for them.

A young officer of the Royal Air Force, writing to his widowed mother a few days before he was killed in action in the blue skies over England in 1940, had left a letter to be delivered to her if he ever failed to return from a mission. This is just a part:

> Today we are faced with the greatest organised challenge to Christianity and civilisation that the world has ever seen, and I count myself lucky and honoured to be the right age and fully trained to throw my full weight into the scale . . . Those who serve England must expect nothing from her . . . You must not grieve for me, for if you really believe in religion and all that it entails that would be hypocrisy. I have no fear of death, only a queer elation . . . the universe is so vast and so ageless that the life of one man can only be justified by the measure of his sacrifice. We

are sent into this world to acquire a personality and a character to take with us that can never be taken from us . . . Thus at my early age my earthly mission is already fulfilled . . . but you will live in peace and freedom and I shall have contributed to that.

I believe that in his upbringing by his parents, his school and the Royal Air Force, Flying Officer Rosewarne was what I would describe as a 'whole man' and because, despite the carnage of the First World War there were still many like him in our country in 1939, civilisation survived.

What then are the difficulties facing Rendcomb in accomplishing the task for which parents pay?

I would place these in two categories: External and Internal.

Amongst the main external difficulties I would place the following:

(a) Drugs, Drinking, Smoking, Pornography
(b) The current incoherence of Christian teaching
(c) Marxist-Leninist ideology

Whilst the internal difficulties might be:

(d) The pressure of the academic curriculum and the essential physical programme.
(e) Some in-breeding in the teaching profession.
(f) The lack at Rendcomb for historical and geographical reasons of a vertical 'House' system whereby a Master and his wife and senior pupils can more easily give pastoral care and set an example.

Drugs

The problem outside Rendcomb is rapidly growing. For less than £5 it is possible to buy a 'fix' of cocaine or heroin in most amusement arcades in any city; or alternatively several 'fixes' of cannabis.

Boys who have recently left Rendcomb have reported that cannabis smoking in university Halls of Residence is commonplace. All drugs come in small packets and are easily concealed. Early stages of addiction are sometimes difficult to spot until it is too late, whilst a 'hangover' from drink is usually all too obvious.

Cheltenham has a fairly notorious 'Drugs' scene.

Drink

Easily obtainable, but its effects are more immediately discernible and its concealment rather more difficult; and alcohol addiction takes quite a time to achieve. So College defences against drugs are likely to be reasonably successful against drink.

Smoking

Most boys and girls smoke more often as a 'dare' than from any conscious desire. In most schools it is the 'done thing', perhaps a formal initiation into 'seniority'. In some schools pipe smoking is permitted for VIth Formers and a smoking room provided. The price to be paid by them is to enlist their aid in outlawing smoking among juniors.

Pornography

Easily available and encouraging of 'teenage' sex. But see below.

When boys and girls are educated together sexual experimentation and calf love are inevitable. It is up to the adults, the teaching staff, constantly to exchange information so that whichever adult happens to be charged with the responsibility for the boy or girl concerned is aware of how far the inevitable 'love-ins' are progressing and perhaps reaching danger point.

I once wrote an instruction for my officers in a training establishment. It strikes me this could apply equally to schoolmasters.

It should always be remembered that the best officers are those who possess powers of observation and, having those powers *know how to use them*. It is the smart, quick and if possible cheery voice that gets the work well done. Nothing is too trifling to take notice of; for although a small thing may signify but little in itself, it is the accumulation of such, when left unchecked, that goes so quickly to show the want of supervision which spells a slack ship.

Discipline in a ship, 'tone' in a school. There is surely very little difference. But it is from the adults with whom the young come into contact that the 'tone' or discipline derives.

The Incoherence of Christian Teaching

By this I mean particularly the recent changes in the liturgy. It seems to me entirely just that the Alternative Prayer Book which I have read carefully can be termed 'a lapse from a picture to a diagram. A graceless, imageless diagram, a mere caricature of symbolic affirmation.' But it is not only the damage that has been perpetrated in the liturgical field that is now driving the young away. I wrote to *The Times* nearly seven years ago seeking to halt (as happily it did) a peculiarly useless and, to ordinary folk, entirely confusing, doctrinal argument and I put my views thus. My hundred plus replies were, the Editor told me, quite exceptional.

As Prelate calls to Prelate and Canons exchange gunfire of excru-
ciating wisdom; as the Synod embarks on another session of
infinite irrelevance; as our ancient liturgy is destroyed and the
grand old hymn tunes replaced, many of us, with our loved and
loving children, become repelled by the sheer banality of the
Church's preaching. So may one humble seeker state briefly what
he is looking for.

On one side of the chasm seem to stand those who hold that
Man is just a tool-making animal, a chance coming together of
atoms, matter, molecules, muscle, bones and fat, with no hope
beyond the grave; that any means justify the end; that the only
end is the inevitable progression of socialism towards world communism; and that the only sin is to impede (or fail to accelerate)
this process. In a nutshell that Manpower, which can be rationally
controlled, will always prevail over Heaven-power which palpably cannot.

On this side there are those who were brought up as Christians,
who were led to believe that there was a progression and purpose
in life; that we live under a transcendental moral law handed
down by the Old Testament prophets, pointed back to its true
meaning by Jesus and adapted by Paul to instal the foundations of
our Christian heritage, on which our great, though vastly imperfect, Western civilisation has been built. With us (I suppose) can
be counted those of the ancient Jewish Faith, the warriors of
Islam, those who follow Hinduism with its indestructible vitality
and the gentle Buddhists with their cyclical belief in rebirth, now
being ruthlessly exterminated by the Hanoi socialists.

In a world of genetic engineering, amazing technological advance, population explosion and a rising tempest of violence it is
no wonder that Christian leaders, generally ignorant of engineering and science, find it difficult to interpret to us the second order
rules by which we should live, from the first order principles of
the Kingdom of God. But rather than marching in processions in
their glorious robes or wrestling with each other over doctrinal
trivia, cannot they proclaim, for His sake if not for ours, in words
so clear that ordinary folk can understand, on which side of the
chasm they are?

The Dean of Peterhouse in his recent Reith Lectures put my problem
rather more succinctly:

Both in daily life and in the worship of the Church, the prevailing emphasis upon the transformation of the material world has robbed men of their bridge to Eternity. Around them, as in every age, they hear the clatter of disintegrating structures and the shouts of outraged humanity. But the priest in his sanctuary no longer speaks to them of the evidence of the unseen world, discovered amongst the rubble of this present one. He refers them instead, to intellectualised interpretations of the wrong social practices and political principles which have, in the view of conventional wisdom, brought suffering to the society of men.

It seems to me in the years ahead that Rendcomb must somehow acquire more distinct 'Houses' where designated and carefully selected Masters and Mistresses can set an example that adolescents will delight to follow, who will give that pastoral care that in the present arrangement, despite enormous and usually well directed effort, may sometimes be lacking for the 'in-betweeners'. (Thanks to the Dulverton Trust these have now been provided.) Nothing however must detract from that loyalty to Rendcomb, as opposed to a particular House, which is such a notable feature in the present regime which echoes so well the ideas of the Founder.

The College has recently started training for the Duke of Edinburgh's Award, building on the enviable reputation which, thanks to one Master, the College already possesses in the field of rock climbing and mountaineering. Adventurous Training, as it is called in the Services, can contribute greatly to character and courage. The recent inauguration of a Parent's Association is a great step forward because, too often I fear, the 'conventions' derived from Rendcomb tend to disappear during the holidays due to the quite understandable difficulties of parental supervision. Masters and Mistresses need relaxation and rest as well. If some can be found in the holidays to supervise mountaineering expeditions of various degrees of difficulty, or sailing, and if the cash needed can somehow be found, then much will be gained.

RENDCOMB COLLEGE
REMEMBRANCE SUNDAY 1981

One of the greatest and most academically and sportingly successful but least known small Independent Schools in the UK is Rendcomb College, Cirencester. Established in the early Twenties by Mr Noel Wills it enters 20 boys and now girls from Gloucestershire Primary schools at age 11, largely paid for by the Wills family or by the Gloucestershire Education Authority or endowed scholarships. A further 20 at age 13 for whom scholarships are also available are entered annually from fee paying preparatory schools and the two groups are merged for a year before being distributed amongst three Houses. There are some 30 girls in the Sixth Form.

I was privileged to become Chairman of Governors at a fairly critical moment in the life of the College and was asked to preach a sermon on Remembrance Sunday. The Parish Church at Rendcomb is small and, as the local British Legion also attended, I had to preach twice, once to the over and once to the under 13s. But in what follows (the 13-18 version) I was constantly aware of the British Legion in the front rows, some with World War 1 medals, and the Headmaster and senior staff, all regarding me with beady eyes.

When I first went to school in Oakley Hall on the other side of Cirencester, the Memorial Chapel had just been built by the parents in memory of the many Old Boys who had died in the First World War. On what we then called Armistice Day, for the war had ended at 11.00 a.m. on 11th November 1918, we used to go into the Chapel and after the two minutes silence at 11:00 a.m. the Headmaster read out the many names inscribed on the Chapel walls.

Now, there is yet another list of names cut into the Cotswold stone and I knew nearly all of them and several were my close friends. So for my generation there are a lot of Remembrance Days.

In midsummer I remember the brave little Oakley Hall scrum half who lived at Minchinhampton and who was killed in his Spitfire in those blue skies over southern England in 1940. In August I remember Tom Sadleir who lived over the hill from here at Througham and with whom I had so many happy days playing cricket at our Rendcomb Founder's home, Miserden Park. If you ever pass Bisley cemetery you will see Tom's initials on the wrought iron gates, put there by his father when Tom was brought back to lie quietly in the Gloucestershire countryside he loved so well, after he had been killed fighting for all he cherished in a fierce Motor Gunboat action off the east coast.

Then there was my closest friend at Dartmouth, Captain of a one-way petrol filled fireship which, like the battle against the Armada, would have been sent into Calais at Churchill's express order had Hitler not called off the invasion of England from the sea. Then he was lent as a navigator to our hard pressed Royal Air Force and finally he too was killed when his ship was torpedoed one dark November night off Tobruk.

And last my beloved cousin with whom I had climbed peaks in the Alps and Dolomites. I saw him for a fleeting moment just before he took his squadron of tanks over the beaches on D-Day, June 6th 1944. He fought without leave right through to Germany, refusing a Staff Course that he might stay with his soldiers to the end in that bitter winter – and the end came for him just before Germany's surrender when a sniper killed him.

All those four, like you, had had a good education and knew what they were fighting for. They understood what Hitler was doing in Europe and were ready to lay down their lives to stop him, but there were many others, no less brave, but perhaps with less understanding of why they were putting their lives at risk. To show you what I mean I recall from amongst the many I knew who lost their lives, just four humble stokers in a small cruiser called HMS *Naiad* in which I served and which was sunk by torpedo one night after a whole day of continuous action. All of them had left school when they were just 14 and, like most of their comrades who died that night, they had never had much of a life.

There was Leading Stoker Lambkin who looked after the steering gear. In action he was under 4" of armour which could only be opened from the outside and when he was on watch there were always four thundering propellers only a foot or so outside the steel hull walls. When the sea was rough as it so often was he would be going up and down 15' to 20' with each wave as it passed. But Lambkin gave to that steering gear all the love and affection and care he would so much rather have been giving to his little family to whom he sent all his pay and who were living in a tenement in much bombed Sheffield. The only answer to the German dive bombers was a sudden acceleration and a quick turn after the bombs had left the aircraft. Because our steering gear under Lambkin's care worked so well, our lives were saved. I have no doubt that when, eventually we were torpedoed and sank too quickly by the stern, Lambkin was still there with his steering gear – and there he lies now, his duty done.

Then there was Stoker Harrison. A country boy whose father worked on a farm not far from Rendcomb. Perhaps because I was brought up near here too he became my messenger in action and we spent many hundreds of hours sweating it out in the engine room. He had one problem. Every now and then his sweat glands would stop working and as you can imagine his body temperature went up and up and he had to be taken to sickbay, given drugs and packed in ice. Sometimes he had to be sent to hospital when we entered harbour but, like a moth to the flame, he always wangled his way back. So, as he was a very intelligent lad, we trained him as a dynamo watchkeeper looking after one quarter of the ship's vital power supply, because the dynamo rooms were well ventilated and comparatively cool – and there he was, well and happy – and there he died.

And so to Stoker Storey. Bred from a long line of Durham miners his body had adapted to the hewing of coal in those small tunnels that go out for a couple of miles under the sea. His legs were short even for his small frame and his arms were long, while his face had those heavy pockmarks that sometimes come from lack of vitamins and near starvation. His childhood in Jarrow had been grim. There was no work for his father, no money and no food except that from the soup kitchens. Because he was not very clever we gave him the job of brewing up the tea and taking it round to the boiler and engine rooms. Every hour, on the hour, he would start his rounds, come bombs or shells or rough weather. The hatch above our heads would fly open and Storey would descend the vertical ladder without spilling a drop. When he reached the engine room platform his ugly face would break into what I can only describe as a heavenly smile of triumph. He had just delivered the tea when the torpedo came into the Forward Engine Room.

Lastly there was old Stoker Petty Officer West. Brought back from a well earned retirement at the age of 50 after more than 22 years in the Navy, he was nearly twice my age. But he was so staunch and apparently unafraid and so cheerful that I gave him the youngest and most inexperienced stokers for his boiler room crew. When he and his crew were off watch from their boiler room they provided the fire and repair party near my cabin. Because I never used my cabin at sea I let him stretch his weary legs on my bunk when we were not in action and nothing was happening.

One day after we had been badly bombed and there were many splinter holes I found him lying on his back with a sick berth attendant trying to staunch a terrible wound in his side. I asked why he was on the deck and, before anyone could answer, he opened his eyes and said, 'I've picked up a little puncture Sir, I don't want to mess up your blankets.' So we lifted him onto my bunk and there a few hours later he died.

Now we have to ask ourselves two questions. The first is unique to my generation. Why were so many good men taken and why were we left? 'Duty' Winston Churchill used to say, 'is the rent we pay for life.' Those who were killed paid a heavy rent as they did their duty for a very short life. It has always seemed to me that the charge on those of us who were left should be just as high, if not higher. So often duty clashes with our convenience or our wishes. 'England expects that every man will do his duty' Nelson signalled before Trafalgar.

> So nigh is grandeur to our dust,
> So near is God to man,
> When duty whispers low, THOU MUST,
> The youth replies, I CAN.

wrote the poet Ralph Waldo Emerson.

But the second question confronts us all and particularly you who are younger. What was it that gave to the Lambkins and the Harrisons and the Storeys in their hundreds and thousands, in and out of the forces, the courage and fortitude and endurance and cheerfulness to go on? Many, if not most, had been starved and neglected in the onrush of the industrial revolution and owed their country little. I don't suppose many of them had ever considered, deeply, the causes of the terrible war in which they found themselves embroiled. But they had a latent faith in their country and way of life, grossly imperfect though it may often have seemed. They sensed that the coercion and tyranny which National Socialism had brought to Germany was totally wrong. And most of them today I believe would have the same feeling about that far more subtly packaged ideology, Communism.

So this is the moment, as I see it, where you come in. Because from those to whom much is given, and much is given you here at Rendcomb, much is expected. The talents your parents gave you which got you here, if you develop them, can be of the greatest help to those with whom you will come in contact in the fields or factories, in the office or mine or fighting service or police or wherever your destiny may take you.

I went round the world once one way and twice the other in my last five years before retirement. I've seen the glitter and the froth, the poverty and the squalor, but I know of no country more than ours which seems to have rooted in its ordinary folk what I would call a natural morality. Forever truth is better than falsehood, beauty than ugliness, justice than injustice, kindness than cruelty. That has been the strength of our nation in the past. That is the sure foundation on which you must build to give our nation the same strength in the future.

Don't kid yourselves that it will be easy. Leaving aside the fact that we are confronted by the greatest armed might the world has seen, let us, this morning, concentrate on the spiritual and moral assault for which the lines of attack are equally apparent.

Alongside the potential for military assault there are those who are being brought up to believe that Man is just a chance coming together of atoms, matter, molecules, muscles, bone and fat with no hope beyond the grave; that any means however dishonest or brutal always justify the end and the only end is the inevitable move towards world communism; and the only sin is in any way to impede or even fail to accelerate this process.

However bad we may be as practising Christians I think most of us believe that there is a progression and purpose in life; that we have to live under a transcendent moral law, handed down by the Old Testament Prophets; pointed back to its true meaning by Jesus and adapted by Paul to lay the foundations of our Christian heritage, on which our great though still vastly imperfect Western civilisation has been built.

I said earlier, this is where you come in. While you are at Rendcomb and before you go out into the hum and roar and clatter of the world, you have a chance here to establish foundations of Faith. 'Faith,' St. Paul said, 'is the substance of things hoped for, the evidence of things not seen.' Although I vaguely understand what St. Paul meant I prefer what a naval chaplain once said to me, 'Faith is reason standing on tiptoe.' I find it easier to visualise myself with such few scattered wits as I have left, standing on tiptoe and trying to peer over the wall of disbelief which the world so delights in building around one.

But you have a dedicated Chaplain and a very talented Staff to help you. Somehow, before you leave Rendcomb, you have to try to accept, quite unreservedly, with your head and your heart, the historical fact that Jesus existed and all that flows from that fact. You have to learn the full history of freedom within the law which is your priceless heritage and you have to reject intellectually the Marxist doctrine that Man is but a tool-making animal.

If you can move someway down this road by the time you leave Rendcomb then you will have done much to armour yourselves against the moral and spiritual assault which confronts us all and you will have started to equip yourselves to help others to fight those assaults also. Furthermore you will find you have the courage to confront any military assault should it ever come upon us.

On a lonely hillside between Burma and India there lie a great many young men from the armies and air forces of the old British Empire and Commonwealth who fought the (until then) all-conquering Japanese to a standstill as they sought to sweep on into India and then threw them back.

Amongst them is a great stone and on it is written these words:

> You that go home,
> Tell them of us and say,
> For your tomorrow
> We gave our today.

Now we can live in what should have been their 'tomorrow'. Instead it is your 'today'.

It is more than that. It is Remembrance Day.

RENDCOMB COLLEGE as purchased in 1920 by Mr Noel Wills. There are now 5 Boarding Houses, a swimming pool, Sports Centre, Concert Hall, Art Block, 3 Rugger pitches and 3 hockey pitches besides a 10 acre sports field and small golf course. (All provided by the Wills Family and Dulverton Trust). (Rendcomb College Photo)

Rendcomb Parish Church and College Chapel, on Remembrance Day.

HMS NAIAD. Sunk March 11th 1942

Survivors on board HMS JERVIS AM 12th March 1942 after many hours in the water and before being sent at once to replace casualties in other ships of the Mediterranean Fleet. (Photo from author's collection)

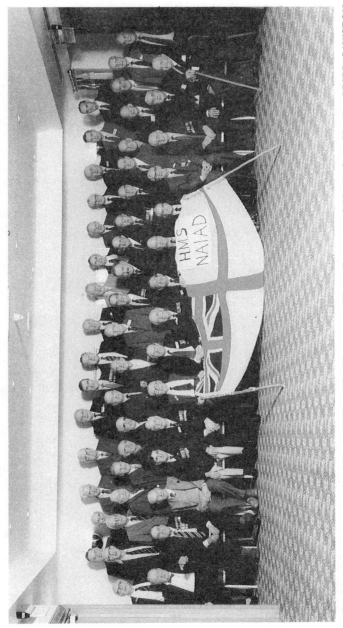

HMS NAIAD survivors 11th March 1992. Fifty Years on. (Photo Courtesy of Mr Andrew Martin. LBIPP SAWSTON, CAMBRIDGE)

THE FUTURE

CONFERENCE ON STRATEGIC DIRECTIONS
Chicago, February 18th 1979

Mr Copley, the owner and editor of 'Defence and Foreign Affairs Digest' asked me to give the opening keynote speech to this large conference and exhibition.

Though from my time in Washington DC in the late 1960s I was aware of the potential of 'SMART' weapons, at that time they had been clothed in secrecy. At this conference Dr Cotter not only described their potential but went far beyond in describing their application to any war in Europe. Most of the attachés in Washington except, strangely, the British, were at the conference. In view of their absence I took tapes of all the presentations, including Dr Cotter's, back to the UK for Marshal of the Royal Air Force, Sir Neil (later Lord) Cameron the then CDS. A meeting was set up but sadly, at the very last moment, Dr Cotter (for reasons I have never established) was forbidden by the US authorities to meet the Chiefs of Staff and the meeting had to be cancelled.

The problems of a hole in the ozone layer were then still unknown to me, otherwise I should have included them and neither had I heard of AIDS. Because the Conference had been well advertised there was a large crowd of anti-war protesters who invaded the hotel and from whom we had to be protected on our way to the conference hall by a large force of well armed police. Nevertheless I had a chance to talk to some of them and I hope convinced a few that we too were against war.

DEFENCE TECHNOLOGY '79
CONFERENCE ON STRATEGIC DIRECTIONS

Mr Chairman, Ladies and Gentlemen. When I read the list of famous names around me I find it difficult to understand why I have been chosen to address you, unless it is for the very obvious reason that you want to get the worst over first.

As Daniel Webster once said, 'I might well have desired that so weighty a task should have fallen into other and abler hands. I could have wished that it should have been executed by one of those whose character and experience give weight and influence to their opinions such as cannot possibly belong to mine.'

I must emphasise that my remarks bear no official imprimatur. I have entered no government office nor had any communication with any of them except the Inland Revenue since I retired 3 years ago. I am however a member of the Institute for the Study of Conflict and I owe much, in my further education, to the Chairman, Professor Leonard Schapiro, to Mr Brian Crozier, Director-General, and to Professor Hugh Seton-Watson as well as to my many wise and learned colleagues on its Council whose help I gratefully acknowledge.

I am here by courtesy of Mr Copley, of *Defence and Foreign Affairs Digest* and he has asked me to look at the world strategic outlook as I see it developing.

With things moving at such a pace what one sets down one day may well be out of date the next and this has added to my difficulties in trying to meet Mr Copley's remit.

Mr Chairman, when the last world war ended for me I was in my third ship, 20,000 miles from home. On the evening of that day on which we, in the British Flagship, had watched through our binoculars, the surrender on board the great U.S.S. *Missouri*, our Commander in Chief ordered the full naval sunset ceremony.

So, as Fujiyama's snowcapped peak glowed pink and the Royal Marine Band played the evening hymn, 'The day Thou gavest Lord is ended, The darkness falls at Thy behest', interspersed with the clear shrill notes of the 'Sunset Call' as only the Royal Marines can sound it, our White Ensign, flown throughout the war, by day and by night, was lowered for the first time in six long years less a day.

Some were in tears and many were near to tears. As I thought of my first two ships, one with her shattered remains lying on the sea bed in the cold Denmark Straits and the other off Tobruk with many close friends inside them, I was sure I was not alone in demanding that this must not happen again.

This feeling was reinforced when, soon after, we saw what had once been Hiroshima and helped to bury the poor calcined bones of some of my countrymen who had ended their lives in a prisoner of war camp nigh to Nagasaki.

All of us, on whichever side we had fought, who had seen at first hand the sombre useless slaughter of war, felt that we must try to build a bridge to peace.

But as the years went by and I found myself in a humble position helping to place some of the foundations on which NATO was built, I came to see, as anyone who studies the scroll of history must endorse, that a pattern still persists.

From man's recorded beginnings physical force seems to have been applied incessantly to the resolution of social problems . . .

'Go, tell the Spartans, thou who passest by,
That here obedient to their laws we lie.'

. . . Simonides' couplet telling of the men who plugged the Pass at Thermopylae was succeeded twenty-four centuries later by those other sad words on the field of Kohima where in 1944 the 2nd British Division barred the gate to India . . .

'When you go home
Tell them of us and say,
For your tomorrow
We gave our today.'

But those of us lucky enough to get home will always carry another memory besides that of the carnage of war – the unforgettable sight of the hungry, the neglected, the poor, the downtrodden and the weary – and so we came to understand the truth of Walt Whitman's words, 'Now mark me well, it is written in the essential nature of things that from any fruition of success, however full, shall come forth something to make a greater struggle necessary'.

Ladies and Gentlemen, it is to a few aspects of this greater struggle that I shall now try to direct your thoughts.

Last year, in Brighton, England, at a rather smaller conference than this I spoke of the burgeoning millions in the world giving us a net increase of

100 million a year; not only 200 extra mouths to be fed but, in the future, 200 extra aspirations to be met, for every minute I keep talking to you.

I spoke too of science and technology. Wars seem to have fanned the wings of science, and science has brought mankind a thousand blessings, a thousand problems and ten thousand perils. The technology of communication alone can now show that half of the world, who have not yet raised their demands on its resources above those of the Neolithic Age, wonders they never dreamed of. And where, I asked too at Brighton, is genetic engineering leading us?

I spoke briefly also of the world's resources – or what is left of them. If you are sceptical of figures and conservatively minded and assume only a steady population but a slowly increasing standard of life for that Neolithic half of the world, or equally conservatively, you accept the 200 mouths a minute and a slower rate of industrialisation and production that the experts confidently predict, you reach the same answer. The energy flow derived from either scenario will exhaust the reachable and the near-reachable conventional fuels, in our children's or our grandchildren's lifetime. That is, of course, unless a man-made holocaust or the Super Germs of which we are beginning to hear reduce the world's population catastrophically.

I spoke too of the general loss of faith in some of the great world civilisations, principally, I now believe, in the Christian World. I tried to draw a picture of that Mountain of Ultimate Reality around which man, down through the ages, be he Buddhist or Hindu or Muslim or Jew or Christian has camped; all of them looking at the mountain from a different viewpoint and arguing amongst themselves as to what they see.

I mentioned that increasing throng which seems to include so many of the multiplying young who, due to the temptations of a materialistic ideology and the failings of their respective priesthoods, are turning their backs on the mountain and marching out into the desert towards the mirages they think they see but never reach.

Two halves of one world: the first in which starvation and poverty are putting hate in place of hope; the second in which comparative affluence is the norm, but in which hope has been beaten down by the fear of war or of a coming catastrophe resulting from the profligate use of our resources and neglect of the environment.

Time does not permit me to read it all to you but here are the last few lines of a poem written by a young officer of great promise who died in the Western Desert in 1942:

'A thousand soldiers are lying dead
(Splutter the gun, and the bombers drone
Deafeningly, drummingly overhead);
But a white moon rises, the sun sets red,
The sea rolls restless about her bed,
Man tramples his laws alone.'

'Man tramples his laws alone' – do we not all feel the same developing sense of helplessness stealing numbingly over our minds as the current of destiny sweeps us along?

Where, within the parameters of burgeoning population, exploding technology, loss of Faith, and indiscriminate consumption of resources should we seek the shore? Where, in these last few years of the Twentieth Century, perhaps indeed in the last few years of the type of civilisation we have evolved, should we seek for landmarks, as we ride the flood?

My own generation has been pounded and battered by a rising tempest of violence and in the few years left us we have to encourage our children to examine the state of their spiritual resources. Political problems are essentially moral problems and unless our children can regain the hope that so many have lost, then there is no future.

Let us try and show them they are wrong when they say, as some do:

'Oh what shall I be at fifty,
Should nature keep me alive
If I find the world so bitter,
When I am but twenty-five.'

We must say to them, 'Your choice is anarchy or order. Do not let specious plans for a new world divert your energies from saving what is left of the old. Time has nearly run out.'

The young should be saying with Wordsworth:

'Bliss was it in that dawn to be alive
But to be young was very heaven.'

From here we must go on to relight the essential Beliefs of our Western Civilisation. We share much with the animals, too much some would say, but one thing no animal shares with man is the power to reflect, to know that he knows. Man has a memory and from memory derives a knowledge of history, and a knowledge of its history is fundamental to our civilisation.

Thus we have to rid ourselves of the idea that our age is altogether unique; that the past is not worth remembering and that only the present and the future should occupy our attention. Solzhenitzyn tells us that the much greater material power we have today makes us a much greater danger to ourselves. Of course it does. The explosion of technology is on an unprecedented scale. But all the great ages have been dangerous. It is the function of technology to equip us to face the future secure in a knowledge of our past. Our task, in the almost sublime words of the Charter of the great Institution of Civil Engineers is 'to direct the great services of power in nature for the use and convenience of man'.

We engineers are certainly not blameless for what has happened, but somewhere, somehow, we, in the West, appear to have failed. There seems to be a lack of widely educated engineers so that the direction of our affairs, and very often I'm afraid the misdirection of our affairs, is in the hands of men and women who know about people but who have no understanding of technology, or of fundamental scientists whose unconscious attitude is to treat people as if they were the cells, atoms or elements to which they are used, rather than human beings.

Engineering, properly taught, represents a philosophy, as I understand it, the ability to see a particular field of knowledge in all its human relations, and engineers have to deal with human problems, often in the most difficult circumstances, all their lives.

Let us therefore now turn to the Slough of Despond through which we have to trudge. For our prayers and the replies of our leaders, both temporal and spiritual, can be summed up, I'm afraid, in the words of the reprise from that old post World War II musical, *Paint Your Wagon*:

> Where are you going? We don't know.
> What are you doing? We can't say.

So let me say where I think we are going.

First Russia. In rather simplistic terms it may be said that the Soviet Empire consists of three main elements, the Russians, the vassal states of Central Europe and the Asian Republics while Soviet colonialism is abroad in Africa.

Central Europe has been under Soviet hegemony for nearly 30 years, some of it under direct Soviet occupation and all of it under Soviet institutions. Yet with the exception of Bulgaria which traditionally has always had a high respect for the Russians, there has been practically no assimilation and Russian domination has quite failed to touch the life blood and souls of the remainder. The Czechs, Hungarians, Poles, East Germans, Romanians, although perhaps at different speeds, would not find it difficult today to turn liberation into liberalisation. Whether Catholic or Protestant or Eastern Orthodox, these countries regard themselves as culturally superior to the Russians and resentment against an alien imposed regime is still widespread and wholehearted; so they will continue to be indigestible for the Soviet Union and they will remain un-Russified.

Rather different considerations apply as you move towards the Caucasus and Central Asia. Here the Muslims have scored two successes. Their rate of natural increase is now about twice that of the Russians and, at a conservative estimate, by the year 2000, one third of the whole population of the USSR will be Muslim. Further they have managed to preserve their cultural and social 'separateness'. As soon as they get home from work they close the door and they are in a world where there are no Russians. It is certainly true that Russia, and colloquy with the Russians, provides a key to the outside world; a key which Islam, until now rather backward looking and antediluvian, has not really provided. But it is a key which is in charge of the Muslim population, not of the Russians.

In the Middle East, in Iran and on the African littoral, no less than in the Philippines, there is the phenomenon known as Islamic Marxism (which is a contradiction in terms), and this resurgence of militant Islam seems in fact to be a revolt against the national, but westernised élites, which have come to power in recent years.

Perhaps one day not too far ahead we shall see this activism spreading to Central Asia and with it will come into play The Law of Colonial Ingratitude, to which I shall return in a moment.

The Russian people seem to have a tremendous capacity for civilisation.

They have produced writers and musicians and great scientists and thinkers whose ability to probe and stimulate and explain the mysterious depths of the human mind put them in the top league. But this tremendous capacity has been and is still inhibited from its full flowering by the persistent armour plated barbarism of their ruling autocrats and bureaucrats which has been demonstrated over a period which stretches back for five hundreds years or more.

It has perhaps been made easier too by a specific national defect which seems to recur century after century, namely an inability to stand up to tyranny from their rulers or (on the few occasions when a new élite has shaken off the old by force) the ability only to rule anew in a tyrannical way. It is as if one vertebra is missing from the spinal column of the whole nation.

Momentarily (in a historical sense) this defect may have a considerable impact in the African context. The influence of Western civilisation dedicated as it is to individual values, even after a comparatively short spell of western colonialism, has brought some internal struggle between those men and women in Africa who see the intrinsic worth of individualism and the large number who still adhere to the ideas of a tribal society which is necessarily more general and collective.

And, it seems to me, that there is some sort of convergence between this form of collective society and the type of political society which constantly seems to emerge in Russia.

However, we have ample proof that better conditions do not diminish but rather increase discontent in multi-national empires and very soon what Professor Hugh Seton-Watson (from whom I have learnt so much) has aptly called 'The Law of Colonial Ingratitude' will start to operate.

Surely it is flying in the face of historical experience to suggest that the Soviet Union will be exempt from this Law. It will certainly start to operate again in Africa where the different nations have not thrown off one type of colonialism to welcome another. In time, and who can say when, it will start to operate in Central Asia; while for rather different reasons the same sort of turmoil is not far below the surface of Central Europe.

The fact is Marxism-Leninism has to go forward to survive. It cannot retreat. Expansionism is inherent to it. It is all very well for Brezhnev* to speak of, I quote, 'A great brotherhood of working people, united irrespective of their national origins, by a community of class interests and aims . . . with relations between them with no equal in history, so that they have every right to call such relationship "the Leninist friendship of peoples".'

The facts which I think are pretty plain, are really quite different. The Soviet Union is facing the same problem that Spain, Portugal, France, Belgium, Holland and not least my own Country have long left behind. And the problem is, 'How to shed an empire?' The great danger for us all today is that the leaders of the Soviet Empire seem not to recognise that they have this problem at all. What then *is* the perception of the world held by these leaders? We can only guess. First, of course, there is a justifiable determination that never again will a would-be conqueror

---

* 21 December 1972

knock on the doors of Moscow or tread the soil of Mother Russia. But beyond this they surely perceive that industrialisation is not only fundamental to their ideology but also to the pursuit of the overwhelming military power as a means of political power which is now their aim. Thus as the price of energy needed to extract and utilise energy constantly rises, so they perceive that they must reinsure themselves as best they can and this, they assess they can do in two ways.

Firstly, as conventional energy begins to get scarcer and the cost mounts, steps must be taken to ensure that the Soviet Union, of all nations in the world, shall be the last to feel the pinch. Secondly, as the technologies of more infinite energy than that of fossil fuels develop, the minerals and precious metals on which many such technologies depend must be within the overall political control of the Soviet Union. This, it seems to me, is the rational explanation for many of the Soviet moves in the Middle East over the last decade or so; for the wooing and political control of the African states as well as (now that the industrialisation of Central Asia has gone ahead) for the revival of Mackinder's 'Great Game' and the drive for a direct route from Tashkent to the Coast, from the Oxus to the Arabian Sea.

So, to sum up, I see two great thrusts towards world turmoil developing out of the Soviet Union: the thrust to get her hands on the cheapest sources of energy which she can make use of in the immediate future, not only to sustain her great military panoply but to increase industrialisation in Russia itself, in the Central European States and in the Asian Empire and of course to resell for foreign exchange; from this thrust emanates a drive to control those materials which will contribute to the technology of more infinite energy resources in the future. The second great thrust is the internal struggle which I see building up within the Soviet Empire; and this will put her neighbours in the Western Alliance in the same great peril as it will put her Chinese neighbours in the East.

And so to China, but before discussing that vast country let me say that I see no inevitable clash between our two societies provided we each acknowledge the differences and recognise our common interest in peace.

After all China was civilised, in the fullest sense of the word, when our ancestors dressed in skins and lived in caves. Perhaps soon, who knows, we may see another flowering of that civilisation which will give to China a new and more coherent expression in world affairs.

But what is Western Civilisation? I remember reading somewhere that the real demarcation between Europe and China was no chain of mountains, no natural frontiers, but a system of beliefs and ideas. In the rich pattern of this culture there are many strands; the Hebrew belief in God;

the Christian message of compassion and redemption; the Greek love of truth, beauty and goodness; the Roman genius for law. Europe, the begetter of Western civilisation, is a spiritual conception and if we Western men cease to hold that conception in our minds, if we cease to feel its worth in our hearts, it will die. When the Legions went back to Rome and Europe dropped into a dark age it was those same strands, hidden in monasteries and other isolated pockets, and preserved within a shrinking Byzantine Empire, that kept the embers of Western civilisation smouldering, until once more they could be fanned into flame.

There are many here who have visited China more recently than I have but I think it would be true to say that within living memory the country was torn by civil war. The peasants starved in a state of feudalism. Corruption and disease were rife. In the last three decades well organised food production has been the first priority. The peasantry, working with increasing efficiency for themselves and the State have improved output dramatically. The starvation I saw thirty years ago seems to have largely disappeared, and so have the rags, although the fashions four years ago were hardly Fifth Avenue style. The whole system seems to be geared to parallel development of the city and countryside, to technology and agriculture; and above all to self reliance and to making do with the tools at one's disposal.

There is a disturbing side of course; the continuous repetition of revolutionary themes idealising war and destruction of capitalism. Everyone from the moment he can read has some form of military training; morse code, marksmanship, acupuncture for use on the battlefield. All this and the constant refrain, ' Dig tunnels deep; store grain everywhere. Do not seek hegemony' is excused by the imminence (as China sees it) of a Soviet assault.

Everyone has a place, a home, a job from which he cannot move without permission, and few wish to unless it is to go to a university or the People's Liberation Army or perhaps as a pioneer to a far distant commune, probably never to return. Everyone reports to and is responsible to someone else. To us in the West all this implies a denial of freedom. To the Chinese the economic realities of today, compared with those of yesterday, spell security and well being. Our freedom they regard as anarchy.

But what hits the visitor so forcefully is the tremendous sense of national participation. I found it interesting too, to see how this was being spread through the Institute for Minorities where 7500 or so potential leaders from the 50 or more ethnic groups from the Borders learning

Mandarin, Marxism-Leninism and the culture and history of their predecessors, were being trained to lead new communes to be built up in the
undeveloped lands.

The great enigma, in my view, and I am afraid the signs are not good, is
whether or not the Chinese will be able to maintain the right balance
between agriculture and industry. Will the technocrats opt (and all the
signs are that they will) for the breakneck industrialisation which has
made both Russia and Japan so powerful, albeit in different ways, in such
a short time? I so well remember pleading with a young enthusiast on a
commune walking behind his motor driven plough, not to look forward to
the huge tractor which he proudly told me his commune was soon to
acquire. One of the great problems, and almost wholly unrecognised until
too late by the West, has been the impaction of the soil by heavy tractors
to the extent that the natural drainage of the land has been destroyed and
the movement of nutrients impeded. As a result more and more fertiliser,
at a cost of more and more energy and more and more pollution, is needed
only just to maintain the present harvests.

We can all understand the feelings of most Chinese that China must
possess power in the modern sense. If you have been kicked around by
Russians, and Japanese and Americans and Europeans, and if you feel you
are daily threatened by a great power it is almost impossible to react
otherwise. But I have hope. I do not myself believe that the Confucian
tradition of moderation and balance, of filial piety, of the family as a
microcosm of society, is far beneath the skin of most Chinese.

So China stands at the crossroads. If she settles for a balanced industrialisation and manages to maintain the present sense of national participation then I believe she will set an example to us all. But if a quarter of the
world's present population goes at breakneck speed for a fully industrialised society on the Japanese model, then the ensuing pollution and the
acceleration in the world energy flow, will only, in its turn, accelerate the
final world catastrophe.

It seems to me that Dr Kissinger spoke yet another of his so often
profound truths when he said, 'I think it is in our interest that it is not easy
to overrun China'.

If China comes to feel that she is not alone in staunchly confronting the
coming turmoil then she may be more inclined to look at the longer term
threat of world catastrophe from a resource and energy famine, as well as
the short term military threat which she anticipates.

Gentlemen, if I can try to sum up there seems to me to be a few facts we
can discern clearly:

Technology is growing faster than the teachability of human nature.

A small proportion of the world's population is using up the earth's non-replenishable resources at a rate which, in the interest of posterity, has to be reduced.

Given that there is some evidence that the present Soviet Leadership, (while always ready to exploit targets of opportunity) on the whole prefers a stable relationship with the West, they are also captives of events over which they have little control.

THUS, reaction within the Soviet regime to pressures within its Empire seems likely to imperil peace in the East and West.

THUS, Soviet fear of falling even further behind the West and Japan, economically and technologically is causing her to adopt a Foreign Policy which will (A) bring cheap energy resources under her political control and (B) ensure that the means of developing less finite energy resources for the future are secured to her now.

Western politicians too, desperately striving for votes in their democracies, either to gain power or to stay in power, always under fire by demagogues and pressure groups and a free Press, continue to promise their constituents a better standard of life, well knowing that the available energy flow, given rising demand in the rest of the world, is almost certainly inadequate.

Further, in seeking to sustain or increase the present level of Western industrial activity the politicians have started to subsidise the Soviet Union. Thus it too has become dependent on the West technically, economically, industrially and agriculturally; and this dependence allows the Soviet Union either to conserve its indigenous resources or to use them to create the massive military power needed to keep its colonies and dependencies in vassallage for years to come or, if it may appear expedient, to exert pressure on or even to assault the West.

In short, both sides of the Iron Curtain are on a roller coaster from which, quite clearly, they do not know how to get off.

Now to consider the Developing World. It was I think in a conversation between two historians, Arnold Toynbee and G.R. Urban, that Toynbee, in pointing out that Spain and Portugal once obtained the whole overseas world by a papal award conditional on promoting the Christian faith in the newly discovered territories, mentioned that Lin Piao produced the parallel claim that the Chinese are the appointed trustees of the underdeveloped world. How far is this true?

As of today we can answer only like this. It will depend on two trends, clearly identifiable but not yet quantifiable.

Firstly, to what extent in the next decade will the West and Japan and the Soviet Union, heading as I have suggested for turmoil or worse, be able instead to solve the problems of mutual destruction, of unemployment, pollution, over population, the profligate expenditure of irreplaceable resources?

The other element in the equation will be China herself. Will puritanism, frugality and the need to maintain a labour intensive society and the present ubiquitous sense of national participation, persuade the leadership away from embracing, too fast, the full scale and total industrialisation which must appear to them, from many aspects, to be so attractive?

If China manages to create a new and more balanced civilisation, and if the developing countries are more willing to learn from the mistakes of the developed countries than the developed countries have been willing to learn from their own mistakes, then indeed the poor, worldwide, may become the wards of the Middle Kingdom: and this is one more goad to the militants in the Kremlin to move in quickly to Africa and elsewhere.

Mr Chairman, Ladies and Gentlemen. When I lived in this country I fell in love with California. Who wouldn't? And I recall once reading a book about the State and at the end of an early chapter there was a couplet that went like this:

> 'All Hail, thou western world. By Heaven designed.
> The example bright to renovate mankind.'

But a few chapters later there were these perceptive lines by Richard Armour:

> 'So leap with joy, be bright and gay,
> Or weep my friends with sorrow.
> What California is today
> The world could be tomorrow.'

It was Oscar Wilde who wrote, 'It seems to me we all look at nature too much and live with her too little. We call ours a utilitarian age and we do not know the uses of any single thing.'

So, Mr Chairman, we should perhaps stop listening to those dreamers who try to persuade us all the time towards a softer and an easier life and we should recall instead that old proverb of the man who walked into a well from gazing at the stars.

The only thing, *the only thing that matters* if our free and pluralistic society is to weather the tempest that now assaults it is that we should 'Be Strong and of a Good Courage'. And do you remember the next phrase in Joshua, Chapter 1, 'Be not afraid, neither be thou dismayed'.

Sir, I must end. If I could borrow again from America's greatest orator in his *Reply to Hayne*, I would say, 'I have met this occasion: not sought it: and I have stated my own sentiments without challenging for them any particular regard.'

But in my own words, Sir, I cannot conceal from you my deep pessimism for the future.

How can the West and the Soviet Union get off the roller coaster on which they seem to have embarked?

How can Russia be brought, peacefully, to shed her Empire?

How can China be persuaded to deny herself, for the sake of the future of all mankind, the full fruits of industrialisation, which if she garners them, will so quickly wither?

How can the living standards of the Third World be quickly improved, or indeed improved at all?

How can human nature be brought to sustain rather than to destroy the resources of nature?

These, Sir, it seems to me, are the questions to which our world leaders, temporal and spiritual, from all countries, should be addressing themselves, if there is to be any future for those who come after us.

All this, Sir, should be the background to our discussions in the next three days but one thing we must constantly recall: 'To work for peace from weakness and fear will spell ruin. To work for peace from courage and strength may be salvation.'

And above all, Sir, there must be *hope*. For *hope* is the one sure rock on which our Western Civilisation has been built.

We all of us peer through a glass darkly, but when it gets too opaque I take comfort from the words of America's greatest Ambassador in this modern age, which I heard him use at the end of a speech when, uniquely, after being dined by The Pilgrims in London, David Bruce was rightly honoured also by The Pilgrims in his own country in New York. He said this:

'When optimism falters, one can do worse than recall the inscription placed by a ruined Royalist over the doorway of a little Leicestershire Church in the bitter aftermath of the English Civil War. It ran as follows: . . . 'In the year 1653, when all things sacred throughout the land were either demolished or defaced, Sir Robert Shirley, Baronet, founded this Church. His singular praise it is to have done the best things in the worse times and hoped them in the most calamitous'.'

Mr Chairman, Ladies and Gentlemen, Thank you for listening so patiently.

A LETTER TO THE DIRECTOR OF THE ROYAL INSTITUTE FOR INTER- NATIONAL AFFAIRS

It was towards the end of 1988, just over 30 years after I had joined the Council of a Naval publication, that I resigned to make room for someone younger and more in touch with Naval current affairs.

In my letter of resignation to the Chairman, later published under the title. 'Valedictory', I confessed a feeling of pessimism as to our future national heritage of seapower in all its different aspects. In his reply, the Chairman, at that time Director of the Royal Institute for International Affairs (Chatham House) saw a different and happier future and a 'New World Order' developing.

As his reply so greatly broadened our discussion I felt it necessary to reply yet again putting the more global reasons why I found it difficult to agree with him.

In some ways the ensuing three years have shown us both to be on the right lines. The Soviet Union has collapsed as we were both anti- cipating, but a better world which he foresaw seems to me to be as far away as ever. In particular I regret the fact that no statesman realises the contribution that a combined maritime strategy between Europe and America could make to a world suffering from conflict and starvation.

There is no articulate sailor or engineer in Parliament and certainly not amongst Ministers on either side of the House of Commons. The rest of the EEC statesmen and even the Dutch, Spanish and Portuguese are now land animals, and Senators and Congressmen across the Atlantic far too in- volved in the 'pork barrel' politics necessary to maintain their seats. Only, as I see it, by the adoption by the world powers of a maritime influence, of a general return to Faith in some Ultimate Reality at least by Europe and America, and the acceptance that the role of engineers is to

'harness the great services of power in nature for the use and convenience of Man', none of which seems remotely probable, do I see any likelihood of a better and more disciplined WORLD ORDER.
    That is what I try to establish in my 'REPLY TO A REPLY'

PART 1

You have greatly widened the field in your reply to my admittedly pessimistic resignation note in which I tried only to concentrate on the future of the Royal Navy. It is certainly true that my family often throw at me the term 'Gaskell Gloom' after my ancestor, a notably gloomy lady. But in broadening the discussion as you have, from the eminence in which you regard the world scene, I fear you have only added to my anxieties; and so herewith is my return salvo.

I think the fundamental difference between us is in our respective judgements as to where the Soviet Union may be heading. Some believe that perestroika has gone so far that it can never be reversed. The history of Russia over the last several hundred years persuades me that another dictatorship, should it occur as well it might, could quickly reverse any move towards liberalisation, as for instance occurred in Russia at the beginning of the century. Gorbachev is only mortal. Perhaps because I saw a little of the Great War, lived through the period of appeasement, fought throughout the Second War, saw what was left of Tokyo, Hiroshima and Nagasaki, I take a more sceptical view of what you term 'the processes of change' and any emerging sense of a 'new world order'.

In keynote speeches delivered with MOD permission at two big conferences, one in Chicago and one in Brighton over a decade ago, both founded on lectures and discussions at various Staff Colleges, and information coming to me while serving, I made certain suggestions as to the parameters within which we all have to try to find a way to exist. Because I find it impossible, at present, to discern any recognition by world statesmen, or the many 'Think Tanks', of three out of the four of these immutable boundaries, there lies, I think, the basis for my pessimism for the future.

The exception is the 'Green Factor', which some governments are now beginning to take seriously. But the other three factors are equally catastrophic though less comprehensible to ordinary folk. I list them all, though in no particular order.

1. **Technology**.

The onrush of information technology and, in particular, the influence of TV, is providing the masses with what an old Instructor Captain used scornfully to deride as 'wisdom while you wait.' Snippets of hastily produced, ill-digested and usually wholly superficial opinion, coupled all too frequently to untrue facts, compounded to an increasing extent in many transmissions by subliminal techniques, are profoundly altering public attitudes, and not for the better. Technology today can show the peasant tilling the land, the starving refugee or the beggar in an urban slum, worlds which, until now, they never knew existed. Expectations everywhere are being aroused faster than they can possibly be satisfied by any human agency. In the more developed countries the situation is equally bad or worse. On a typical day in the UK 38 million people watch TV on an average for 2–3 hours. We are catching up fast with the USA where the average child by the time he or she has reached 16 has watched TV for 10,000–15,000 hours, over 20% of its waking life.

Can you really regard with optimism, this apparently unstoppable electronic avalanche of mayhem; or advice as to 'how to avoid bad breath and keep the body beautiful' and thus to achieve some sort of dubious salvation? I find it difficult.

2. **Population**.

The burgeoning world birth rate (about 200 net increase over deaths each minute) and the onrush of genetic engineering are combining to lead mankind into a dark and horrific tunnel, with no perceptible light at the end. Our new found ability to alter the arrangement of genes and the developing science of cloning and in vitro fertilisation, leading to multiple births, is putting into the hands of mankind an uncontrollable weapon of unprecedented power for evil. And even if somehow, such activity could be put under reasonably effective international control (which is very doubtful) what if some artificially created mutations of humanity-destructive micro-organisms managed to escape?

Is this a future which can be regarded with optimism? Again I find it difficult.

3. **Ecology**.

Mankind has already lit the fuses of a whole series of ecological timebombs. Fossil fuels and precious minerals are being used up and can never be replaced. Rivers have caught fire and burnt their bridges. Fertile lands are becoming dust bowls. Deserts are on the march. Inshore seas are cesspits and the oceans are in peril. The destruction of the rain forests and animal species is accelerating. The heating of the atmosphere by fossil fuel effluents and the attack on the ozone layer are producing climatic changes which cannot accurately be foreseen. And though there has been some movement lately to acknowledge all this I still find grounds for optimism difficult to spot.

4. Faith.

At some period between the beginning of recorded history and the time, millions of years before, when the great rains slackened and the world was covered in primaeval ooze, the half-man half-ape we call a hominid somehow developed the ability which set him apart from the animals. 'The ability to think and reflect; not only to know but to know that he knows.'

Since then in countless civilisations that have arisen, prospered, declined and disappeared, it is possible to discern through the mists of time, certain common factors. Mankind and the elements in nature have always inter-reacted. This was first to achieve self-preservation and, when opportunity offered, to search for those extra dimensions such as beauty, utility, safety and in all these mankind had to innovate. From the very dawn of pre-history, as mankind fought against the elements, there was a certain inevitability in his life. The sun rose and set. The moon waxed and waned. The rains came and the snow; the wind and the frost; the flood and the drought; birth and death. There was no turning away from the earth at his feet or the sky above. Inevitably, as perception developed, so did a sense of fear and of awe. Here were great forces he could never match, on which he relied for food and for warmth, but which constantly assailed him for reasons he could not comprehend.

Is it any wonder then that mankind sought to placate, to mollify, perchance to pray? So systems of belief came into the world, some transient, some fanciful, some evil, many more mere chimeras. But just a few have remained. All of them supportful of some Ultimate Reality, linked to Revelation and anchored by Faith.

2000 years of Christianity and 6000 of the Jewish faith from which Christianity sprang have helped, on the whole, despite occasional terrible steps backwards, towards what we call 'civilisation', to an extent that none of the other great religions have quite managed. Now, suddenly, the picture has changed. In the last hundred years and, with a staggering acceleration in the last forty, the power, extent and depth of mankind's intervention into Nature has produced a revolutionary epoch in human history. Men and women, on a planetary scale, seem to be substituting the controlled for the uncontrolled, the fabricated for the unworked, the planned for the random. As Gustave Thibon has written, 'powerfully aided by modern technology, the individual has been torn away from the cosmic and social continuities, the earth, the craft, the family, the normal setting of human lives.'

'Faith is Reason standing on tiptoe,' or so I was taught by a great Naval Chaplain. I suggest we have reached one of those awful backward moving phases in the general advancement of our Faith that have occasionally occurred throughout the centuries. Western men and women can no longer, even on tiptoe, peer over the wall of Unbelief that we have erected around us. The general stagnation and often imprisonment of the Orthodox Churches, the abandonment of its liturgy by the majority of the Church of England and the apostasy of some of its bishops; the almost total dissension within the worldwide Anglican communion; militant Zionism and the often violently differing varieties of Judaism; theological schism and administrative chaos in the Church of Rome; these together are now threatening to destroy all that has been achieved in the Judaeo-Christian era. We seem indeed to be on the verge of another Dark Age such as engulfed Christendom 1600 years ago.

Thus the way lies open for gentle Buddhism or, I fear, much more probably and as I have proclaimed for two decades, the spread of Islamic Fundamentalism. As the Dean of Peterhouse has written:

> 'Both in daily life and in the worship of the Church the prevailing emphasis upon the transformation of the material world has robbed men of their bridge to Eternity . . . Around them, as in every age, they hear the clatter of disintegrating structures and the shouts of outraged humanity. But the priest in his sanctuary no longer speaks to them of the evidences of the unseen world, discovered amongst the rubble of the present one. . .'

Conclusion

These four parameters provide the background for my pessimism and why I believe that a 'New World Order' to which you look forward is as far away as it ever was. Indeed now that the true socialist pattern of economic management is increasingly recognised as a failure (as it is even by Gorbachev though not yet by most of his colleagues) your 'New World Order' under the continuing influence of Marxist inclined atheist ideology and the continuing retreat of the Judaeo-Christian ethic, seems to me to take quite a different line to that to which you adhere.

If the continuing Arab disunity actually inhibits the spread of militant Islam (although surely not its terrorist manifestations) then the increasingly Western drug orientated society (now probably unstoppable) seems to me more likely to develop on the lines of Aldous Huxley's *Brave New World*.

It is therefore against this sombre background that I now turn to the future of Europe on which, in the years ahead, the future peace of the world will depend.

PART II

EUROPE

In looking at Europe in 1989 there are three countries, besides Britain, and beyond the rest, to be considered: the Soviet Union, Germany and France. It is, in my view, wrong to ascribe all the potential changes we think we discern in the Soviet Union to Gorbachev. Every General Secretary has disavowed his predecessor and Gorbachev, like all of us is mortal. It is absurd to think, as some do, that Gorbachev has come along and ended 70 years of communist history. In every change of government in Russia over the last 500 years the incoming élite has always, in the end, reverted to a kind of armour plated barbarism, operated by its ruling autocrats and bureaucrats. However benign you judge Gorbachev's present personal intentions you must take into account Russian history.

The Soviet Union Today

Gorbachev recognises the failure of socialist economic dogma and he is driven forward into perestroika by that recognition. He well understands that further aggressive Soviet policy, on the lines his predecessors adopted, would only more firmly cement the surrounding countries (West and East) against a Soviet Empire heading (if it has not already got there) for economic chaos.

So, in terms of Marxist orthodoxy Gorbachev has inherited an almost no win situation. To continue the policies of his predecessors would finally destroy the Soviet Empire economically; to make perestroika work may well destroy him and those remaining dinosaurs amongst the 10% of the population who constitute the Communist Party. The risk is that in the that last dying orgasm, massive violence will cross borders and engulf us all.

Behind the rhetoric Gorbachev is pushing forward two policies. He is seeking to separate Western Europe from America and to make Moscow part of Europe.

Germany was born out of war, into a nation state, only in 1871. In the following sixty years she managed to provoke two World Wars. After the first one, Dr Bruening in the late twenties started to sort out Germany's economic problems and managed, with help from the West, partially to revise some of the worst aspects of the Treaty of Versailles. But Hindenburg dismissed him and opened the gates to Hitler. The 'reign' of Adenauer was curiously similar. He needed to rebuild the rubble left by World War II. Apart from these two periods, the German State had never had any alliances with the West. On the contrary it is the Bismarckian doctrine to which Germany seems to be returning: 'that whenever good relations existed between Germany and Russia, both countries flourished. But whenever the links between them weakened, both countries would suffer'.

I mixed with many young Germans in the Thirties and they had a strange romantic streak. None of them that I met, like me, had any idea of the very secret military liaison between Germany and Russia, where the German shadow army trained. But this romanticism was very evident amongst the *wandervogel*, bronzed and very fit, singing those haunting melodies around their camp fires. They idolised Hitler for the way he had pulled the Reich out of the Weimar chaos of inflation and unemployment. Besides the Aryan cult, he had also imbued them with the idea of a 'Crusade Against Bolshevism', in which, (they all believed as I came to) Britain would join.

Today Adenauer is forgotten. Gorbachev has many admirers amongst the young in Western Germany and that strange romanticism of the Thirties has been rekindled. Young Germans are beginning to see themselves as the forerunners of a new 'European Peace' that will exorcise the guilt of the older generation. German leaders are instinctively once more tapping that dangerous romantic appetite. Although today it is leading towards a 'Crusade For Peace', should a new Führer appear with different ideas, that crusade could quite quickly turn again to Deutschland uber Alles.

The Soviet/German Axis

In practical terms Gorbachev's twin policies are aimed at the Findlandisation of the Central and Eastern European countryside. These, he hopes, could be bound together with West Germany and the Soviet

Union in some sort of geo-political framework. All would be free to choose their own (probably) quasi-socialist governments and would be subject only to some mutually agreed restraint on military spending and foreign alliances. The lessons of a demilitarised and therefore prosperous Japan with its obedient labour force, have not been lost on Bonn or Moscow. Any such arrangement would clearly be a giant step towards the economic rehabilitation of the Soviet Union, aided by a united and industrially sophisticated Germany.

France

One defeat and two partial or total occupations by Germany have left their mark. The average older Frenchman still fears *Les Boches* and the idea of *La Revanche* is not forgotten. Also very many of the older generation have never forgiven Britain for fighting on in 1940. So de Gaulle's philosophy of the Soviets as an ally, in a Europe from 'The Atlantic to the Urals' (though what happens beyond the Urals is never stated) is still part of an entirely cynical French foreign policy.

'France is true to herself only when she stands in the front rank: only great enterprises can neutralize the poison of disunity her people carry in their veins.'

Those words represent an eternal truth in the modern French character. And this is understood by Mitterand as it was by de Gaulle when he wrote them in his *War Memoirs*. The idea that the Gauls and the Teutons might stop fighting and resurrect, under French suzerainity the Europe of Charlemagne, has always been evident in the numerically considerable *monarchiste* element of French society.

The Developing Franco-German-Soviet Axis

As West Germany is now so obviously wooing the Soviets, France has to resume the initiative which de Gaulle started and which has moved only in fits and starts since 1964. The Soviets have never been drawn to de Gaulle's European Europe (to the Urals). But Gorbachev sees it as some sort of umbrella, under which France and the Soviet Union may 'cosy up' to each other.

Some kind of reunification between the two Germanies and the liquidation of NATO and the Warsaw Pact, leading to the withdrawal of American and British troops from Western Europe and the Soviet occupying forces from Eastern Europe, have long been matters near the top of the Franco-Soviet agenda. Europe, as the French see it, should be sustained by two pillars of comparable strength: a nuclear armed USSR to the East and a Franco-German Alliance (with France alone possessing nuclear weapons) to the West. This equal structural relationship, almost partnership, is also likely to appeal to the romantic streak in the German young; whilst the French fear of *Les Boches* would be considerably diminished by the possession of nuclear arms.

A View of Britain

Sadly our allies in Western Europe no longer recall Britain as their saviour of 1944–45. Some see us as lukewarm to the EEC; France sees us as resisting a united Ireland (after all de Gaulle, on his State visit to Dublin proposed a toast to *L'Irlande tout entier*.) The majority of the supermarket drunks in Calais are British, as are the football hooligans of the Eighties. We refuse to learn or speak other European languages. Sadly *Perfide Albion* has few friends on the Continent.

The Drive for a United States of Europe

It seems that Gorbachev, together with increasingly powerful elements in West and East Germany, and in France in the shape of M. Rocard, are in unholy concert with Jacques Delors (President of the EEC Commission and, reportedly, a rather incompetent French Minister of Finance who was shuffled off to Brussels). Together, with some Britons who have 'gone native', they are now beginning to work towards a Federal Europe, from Moscow to the Atlantic; the worry is, where does this leave Britain?

It is at least arguable that such a concept can only lead to one of three results:

(1) The Soviet Union will be such a permanent drain on the resources of Western Europe that the EEC will never become one of the three industrial power houses of the twenty-first century. (The other two would be America and a Sino-Japanese economic alliance.)

(2) As Gorbachev is hoping, the Soviet Union will become so strong that finally all Europe, including Britain, France and Germany will be Finlandised.

(3) In the working towards (2) the old enmity between the Slavs and the Teutons or the Teutons and the Gauls, will surface once more; and there will be war.

Britain has only two choices, short of 'going it alone'. She can mobilise Italy, Spain, Portugal and the Netherlands in her support and try to remain, economically and militarily in the European '1st Division' whilst working for a *Europe des Patries* rather than a Franco-German-Soviet and finally Soviet only, dominated Federation. Alternatively she could ask, with Ireland, to become the 52nd and 53rd States in the USA. Liverpool, after all, is less than two hours flight time further from the USA, than Honolulu.

Undoubtedly our present Government will strive for the first option. But it seems that the NATO Alliance is beginning to suffer from old age. The Brussels Treaty stationing British troops on the Continent, has only a decade to run. No American President has been able, unequivocally and satisfactorily, to answer the question as to how far Europeans can safely rely for their security on the American nuclear deterrent. The signs are on the wall, writ large, that by the end of the century or so, US and British troops will begin to leave continental Europe. For the Americans this will be a popular homecoming. Indeed it may be an essential homecoming, if the long border with Mexico from Brownsville to Tijuana, is to be more effectively sealed against drug running and Hispanic infiltration already exceeding the flood of Chinese into Hong Kong. For the British it will signal a return to a small home based standing army.

But of course you may be right and my pessimism may be misplaced. It takes about twenty years to conceive, design, build and deploy a modern warship. If we accept your thesis then, as I understand it, you visualise a Federal Europe from Moscow to the Atlantic. Each country at peace with its neighbours in some sort of post communist quasi-Marxist amity.

But if your optimism is better founded than I believe, then now is the time to consider Britain's future strategy, and the Navy's role within that strategy. It is to the latter that I turn in Part III.

(In parenthesis I think you are unwise to select Hungary as an example of what might happen in Russia. The Magyars have never been communist inclined. The Bolshevik Bela Kun was thrown out in August 1919 after only 5 months, when a *coup d'état* brought back the Archduke Joseph. But the Supreme Council in Paris (probably Lloyd George) ruled that no Hapsburg should stage a 'come-back'. After the Treaty of Trianon in 1920 Hungary was always regarded as a monarchy with a vacant throne. It took another war and the Soviet invasion of 1956 to re-impose a communist regime (by force.) The Russians are very different people. Except at the beginning of the century when the Duma started to have an influence, they are fundamentally conditioned to an autocracy and almost certainly will find it impossible to shake off the habit.)

PART III

TOWARDS A BRITISH STRATEGY FOR THE POST NATO YEARS

'Remember then that your vocation, deliberately chosen is war. War, as I have said, as a means of peace; but still war'. So read the old seamanship manual. But the profession of arms today is only rarely a vocation. 'War', wrote Mahan, 'is an exertion of violence to procure a political end . . .'

General Sir John Hackett added, with rather more relevance in today's context:

> 'War, total war, we have to avoid. Warfare, acts of organised violence between groups of men which in sum amount to less than total war, . . . we must do something about.' '. . . the main purpose of the profession of arms is not to win wars but to avoid them; that is to say, by timely warfare to lessen the risk of general war'.

> 'Back to Business in Great Waters', wrote Professor Keegan in *The Daily Telegraph* in August 1988. And, in support of this headline, 'The Falklands campaign was a painful warning that bombast cuts no ice in the effective operational area of a superior naval power. The American landing in Grenada rammed home the lesson in the Caribbean. And the international naval expedition to the Gulf has reminded the whole world that the guerilla rhetoric that struck terror in the Sixties is just so much sound and fury when its trumpeters forsake their jungles and alleyways for the high seas.'

In the circumstances described in Part II (Europe), which I regard as inevitable within two decades, Britain, despite the Channel Tunnel will still be Sir Eyre Crowe's 'island State on the ocean flank of Europe', albeit by then, a Europe to the Urals, probably under a barely concealed hegemony of the Soviet Union, with the passive adherence of Germany and France.

Crowe's statement of the basis of England's foreign policy was given in the context of, 'an Island State with vast overseas colonies and dependencies. .', and such considerations no longer apply. Nevertheless, if we take into account the views of the wise men quoted in para. 1 above and the fact that the global future seems to suggest three great industrial power blocs, much of whose trade between each other and with the rest of the world will be seaborne, certain assumptions seem valid.

Firstly piracy and terrorism are likely to have become more widespread and sophisticated. Therefore, seapower of some sort or another is likely to be needed. And in this, the Royal Navy may still be the first of schools.

Before considering what sort of seapower this would be exercised a timescale has to be established. For the next few years, whether or not Gorbachev or his like minded successors move Europe in the direction I think you seek, we and our children will live in a climate of mortal peril. Internal turmoil in the Soviet Union and in China is inevitable and this is likely to cross frontiers.

Any sort of major arms reduction, in the context of the NATO/Warsaw Pact, seems to be almost impossibly complicated. But in the light of the structural changes that are just conceivable in the EEC, always well short of the federal, but perhaps bringing Moscow into Europe (a process which may take decades to work out), some sort of political framework that could eventually give rise to arms reduction, seems faintly possible.

The trigger which should activate any firm planning on new maritime measures will be the moment when the firm planning for a reduction in US and British forces on the Continent becomes visibly imminent. Until then the following seems to merit consideration.

The Royal Navy may be (after a large gap) the third largest oceanic Navy in the world but in numbers it is the fourth, if the highly efficient and effective US Coast Guard is regarded, as it should be, as a Navy. It is arguable that the 'mission' of the USCG (which stretches far beyond that of 'guarding the coasts', for it fought in World War II, Korea and Vietnam) and its composition, both have a pattern that the three industrial 'power blocs', the Sino-Japanese, the American/Canadian, and the (extended) EEC, now perhaps slowly evolving, could emulate.

An assumption, that the gradual pattern of EEC change will coincide with the disappearance of NATO and the Warsaw Pact, leads to the possibility that the main role of home based purely national armies in Europe will become that of para-military counter-terrorist forces and perhaps EEC task forces trained to cope with natural disasters of the type Mr Hanning advocates. The problems of piracy on the High Seas, the sort of situations that Professor Keegan envisages, the enforcement of shipping and anti-pollution laws, the prevention of seaborne terrorist activities, the prevention of smuggled arms and drugs, the clearing up after major polluting accidents, ice breaking, sea rescues, weather prediction, the development of the sea bed, all these and more, would be within the capability of a powerful EEC maritime air/naval force, in the USCG pattern.

The profession of arms, General Hackett says, 'is the containment of violence; the orderly application of armed force; the management of violence'. The Standing Naval Force, Atlantic (STANAVFORLANT), the brainchild, in quite another context, of Admirals of the Fleet Sir Varyl Begg and Lord Hill-Norton, and Admiral Moorer USN and Admiral Holmes USN, now shows how well international naval contingents can work together. Here, surely, sometime in the future, if the world does not relapse into chaos meanwhile, is the pattern that the three great industrial complexes should put together from their national naval forces. Three great maritime police forces, Janowitz' Constabulary Concept, working together to contain violence in their own defined sea areas of influence.

Such a major change cannot be achieved overnight. Britain's initial plans, at least until it can be confidently determined that the Russian Bear has changed its coat, must include close operational links with the US Navy in the Atlantic. But surely Britain with a long maritime tradition could show the way to a new concept of seapower more attuned to the conditions that optimists see as likely to prevail in the future? Together with France, Portugal, Spain, The Netherlands, Italy, Belgium, and, if they wish, Norway, Sweden, Denmark and Greece, all nations with a knowledge of the sea, and the USSR with its unequalled experience of the Arctic, it should be possible to bring together a most powerful maritime influence. And this influence could be tailored to deal adequately with any oceanic crises affecting the sovereign nations of the extended EEC.

However thoughtful and helpful they may be, armies and air forces on the territories of other nations are always a source of friction and criticism. Multinational forces such as the French or Spanish Foreign Legions are regarded as a danger to their sponsoring countries, if allowed to reside on metropolitan soil. The belief, held by some, that nationalism can be eradicated is naïve. Worldwide, nationalism is on the increase but the brotherhood of the sea is a different matter. Given a degree of technical standardisation and a common aim, ships of different nations work well together in a politically and militarily neutral, though always a physically dangerous and unpredictable, environment.

Jomini and Mahan are not often read these days. It was Jomini who wrote, 'Whatever the object, the vital and paramount question is the intensity with which the spirit of the nation is absorbed in its attainment'. It was the belief that the spirit of our nation was absorbed in their endeavour that helped to inspire the deeds of those fighting men at sea, in the air and yomping across the peat bogs in the bitter chill of a Falkland winter. It also revealed that beneath all the tawdry glitter of today, our nation, as so often in the past when the chips are down, is drawn towards the imaginative use of maritime power. We should build on that enthusiasm.

In the Falklands too some of the Commanders may also have remembered Nelson's words quoted by Mahan: 'Something must be left to chance. Our only consideration, is the honour and benefit to our Country worth the risk? If so, in God's name, let us get to work.'

This also seems to me to be wise advice; and more likely to be of use in the future rather than the present unseemly attitude of burying our heads in the 'sand and putting our trust in an increasingly geriatric NATO.

So, as this troublesome world unrolls before us and our army at last comes home from the continent where, breaking with centuries of tradition it was rightly sent to deal with the prevailing crisis of the time, it is now to sea and air power that the nation must begin to look. But, as has been said:

> A navy cannot be created on the occasion of crisis. A navy cannot be improvised. It must have continuity. The young hands learn from the old hands in the practice of their arts. Tradition embodies and preserves experience and knowledge from generation to generation.'

In the belief that any EEC Navy should have at its core the Royal Navy it is necessary to consider some fundamentals. Warships that were spoken of in the Sixties are only now coming from the building yards; and in this study we are looking at least twenty years ahead, and perhaps much more.

Clearly it would be dangerous in the next couple of decades to dismantle Britain's nuclear deterrent. It is essential both as a hedge against any Soviet backsliding and also because there are other countries, less responsible, who will soon have nuclear weapons. Britain, as a world leader against terrorism, is a plum target. Apart from that, Britain, by then relieved of the increasing cost of the Army in Europe, with France, should provide the EEC Navy with its oceanic element.

Mobility is one of the prime military assets at which to aim. In the Sixties, with the help of three well known Defence Correspondents I launched the concept of a 'Constabulary Force' founded on nuclear powered mini-carriers of the Invincible type and nuclear powered tankers and support ships for the escorts. I still believe that in principle we should, as far as possible, distance ourselves from the tyranny of oil.

If Britain and France shoulder the oceanic implications of the EEC Constabulary Navy, then Italy, with the help of France and Greece and Turkey and the Soviet Union would become responsible for peace in the Mediterranean. The Soviet Union would safeguard and keep open the polar route to the Pacific while the smaller nations in the EEC might provide much of the inshore (air and sea) requirements necessary to guard against terrorist attacks on North Sea oil, to prevent or deal successfully with terrorist minelaying and finally, to confront the drugs and terrorist arms imports into Europe, now so clearly on the increase.

So, if you are right and I am wrong, then the time is ripe for a new look at the sort of seapower, and the instruments we might need to exercise it in the next century.

POLITICS

AN OPEN LETTER TO MR KINNOCK
WHILST LEADER OF THE
OPPOSITION

Several years ago it seemed to me, from his speeches, that Mr Kinnock, the Leader of the Opposition, had been inadequately briefed on the whole subject of deterrence. In what at first was a private letter to him I tried to give the full perspective and to convey my views on where he was leading his Party.

I sent a copy to a contemporary of mine who, quite unknown to me, showed it to Mr Michael Ivens, CBE, Director of Aims of Industry, and the latter telephoned me to say that he thought my analysis was so clear that he would like to publish the whole letter and distribute it widely in Parliament and outside. I felt it was unfair to do so before Mr Kinnock had had a chance openly to reply and wrote to him accordingly. But a message from his chief of staff made clear that he had no intention of doing so.

What follows is only that part of the Open Letter referring directly to the main aspects of deterrence and I have not thought it necessary to republish my more personal views as to where Mr Kinnock was leading his Party. History may well take a more favourable view than was current at the time of his efforts to confront the Militant Tendency and to reduce the powers of the Unions. I only hope that my statement on the policy of deterrence may have helped him a little, as well as others who may have read it, to clear their thoughts on this esoteric subject, at that time fully comprehended by only a few.

As it is the debate is not yet over. More and more countries are arming themselves with nuclear weapons and the means of their delivery. Always a staunch believer in Trident I sometimes wonder now, with the great pressures on the Defence Budget leading to a most dangerous reduction in

275

our overall defence capability, whether we should not have gone for smaller (and cheaper) submarines, as Lord Owen suggested. Submarines able to manoeuvre in shallower waters than Trident, and armed with US Cruise missiles, would be a less expensive means of deterring any long distance attack on the UK. However Cruise missiles can be intercepted and, at present Trident cannot. So the possibly imminent ending of liberalisation in Russia together with the emergence of the former Republics of the Soviet Union as nuclear powers in their own rights, seems fully to confirm the wisdom of the Trident option, which is both long lasting and flexible in its deterrence power.

Defensive Role

To the West in general and perhaps to some elements in the United Kingdom in particular, *détente* means an era of peace and prosperity; a sort of Utopia just around the corner if only difficult military men would stop proclaiming 'Reds under the bed'. The great Russian military research and development programme and armoury of missiles, men, aircraft and warships, Mr. Healey might say, is for an entirely explicable and historically justifiable *defensive* role against the West and against China in particular. And of course there is some truth in that. The horrendous casualties suffered by the Soviet Union in The Great Patriotic War, though almost comparable to those in Stalin's purges, are not only nearer in time but are spoken of openly. Whereas Stalin's decimation of the peasants is never referred to.

Détente in the Kremlin's eyes means a period which Brezhnev hoped would end in 1985 . . . but he was an optimist, during which by every means short of war, including subversion by 'agents of influence' in the political, religious and educational life of Western Nations the political collapse of the Western capitalist society would be engendered. This (the Kremlin hoped) would lead to 'Finlandisation' whereupon all decisions in the European West would at least be susceptible, if not at first entirely dependent, on the views of Moscow.

Détente, to me, means relaxation of tension. This is surely something for which we all hope. But, in my view, there can never be any real relaxation of tension unless (most improbably for some years yet) the Soviets abandon the communist idea of world hegemony or (I hope equally improbably) the West caves in. The only alternative method of relaxation therefore must depend on some sort of equilibrium of forces, with a durable worldwide balance to underpin it.

Surrogate Forces

The Soviets, I think, would assert that it is the global balance of forces that matters and they would argue that this balance favours the West. Most Western Europeans recognise that both the United States and the Soviets maintain large forces worldwide. For example on the Sino-Soviet Border or the Western Pacific. But the West, whilst tending to regard these as manifestations of the global interests of super-powers is also uncomfortably conscious of the wide spread of Soviet and surrogate forces in Angola, Nicaragua, Cuba, Ethiopia, the Yemen, Mozambique and Cambodia and not least Afghanistan where, through Baluchistan (where I am told active subversion is falling on fertile ground), they threaten the West's oil supply.

It is difficult to define how far these global forces relate to the US/Soviet balance. Indeed they cannot be said to be directly relevant to the NATO/Warsaw Pact balance or to the security of Europe. In Western eyes, however, the level of forces deployed by the Warsaw Pact in Eastern Europe and the ease with which these Shock Armies (to use the Soviet term) can be quickly reinforced from adjacent Soviet Military Districts, together with the large Soviet 'anti surface ship submarine fleet in being' aimed at the Atlantic reinforcement route, are regarded as a threat. This may not be a threat in the sense that any actual aggression against Western Europe is immediately contemplated. But it is a threat in the sense that such a vast preponderance of force can act as a determining factor in a political negotiation or in the management of a sudden, and probably unexpected, crisis.

Thus a military balance is indeed a factor in the security relationships of Europe. For without a reasonable military balance (military being used in the widest sense) there can be no political security or stability and little prospect of progress towards a genuine relaxation. But the relationship between military balance and political stability is not only of itself most complex, but it is also difficult to explain. Let me try.

Military capabilities exist independently of any political context. Whether or not a military capability is to be judged as a threat will depend primarily on the political context; and the more tense the political situation the more immediate the threat will seem. There follows the paradox therefore that the existence of a military balance provides the material for armed conflict. But a common perception of that military balance by both 'sides' makes the outbreak of active conflict unlikely, with the corollary that the political balance is preserved. On the other hand a palpable imbalance in military capability, may enable one *side* to support political pressure with a threat of force, before which the other *side* may believe there is no choice but to give way; with the corollary that the political equilibrium is upset, without any recourse to actual military conflict.

In terms of the Warsaw Pact and NATO all the above is perceptible and comparatively easily understood in the context of nuclear strategy and, by deployed land and air forces, in the context of what we call a continental strategy.

Russia's Maritime Strategy

Russia however, as a superpower within the Warsaw Pact, and through a command economy and by depriving her civilian sector (something only possible within a closed society) has devoted resources not only to a nuclear and a continental strategy but to a maritime strategy as well. To some extent this maritime strategy can be accounted for by Russia's concurrent preoccupation with a global strategy and her thrust to influence littoral states worldwide with her communist doctrine. But unlike the Warsaw Pact with its interior lines of communication, continental NATO and the United Kingdom must rely on supply, re-supply and reinforcement by sea. From published figures in Janes and from the International Institute for Strategic Studies it appears that the Warsaw Pact already has a considerable maritime preponderance in the Eastern Atlantic and might well be in a position to interdict NATO supply lines from the United States. Thus the Soviet maritime activity in the sea areas adjacent to Western Europe may already be said to have upset the military equilibrium.

So we are in a classic 'chicken and egg' situation. Should improved political relations precede the reduction of forces and a gradual dismantling – or *vice versa*? But this is not the end of the matter. When one *side* has a fully controlled press and an entirely closed society and an autarchic or command economy, and the other *side* a free press, a reasonably free or mixed economy and a free society, the conditions and pressures on the governments on either *side* bear little or no resemblance to each other.

All normal people in the West hope and constantly pray for some form of *détente* or – more accurately – relaxation of tension leading to disarmament and an ability to deal adequately with the *real* problems of the world. This feeling is almost certainly reciprocated by the 85% of the inhabitants of the USSR who are not members of the Communist Party as well as by a large proportion of the small 15% who are, but who relish too much the unique privileges with which membership of the party endows them, to express any such feeling. But the great divide which separates the two *sides* is, that whilst those in the West who enjoy a measure of freedom and already a much higher standard of life, believe they can discern even more inviting *uplands*, the wholly repressive society in the Soviet Union inhibits any such surge of hope amongst Russians. As it does also indeed amongst the many other nations which are part of the Soviet Union, or which are forcefully controlled satellites.

Open and Closed Societies

It is here that the Soviet *diarchy* possesses such an immense advantage over the West. The easy and attractive policy of *détente* can be constantly proclaimed by the Soviet Government *above the table*, can be picked up and parroted by a naïve Western Press and (as may seem appropriate to the Kremlin) by the Soviet and satellite press also. But the very publicity given in the West to the alleged imminence of political détente, has two significant effects. Both of these are favourable to the Soviet Union and both are entirely inimical to the future of Western society.

The public wish in the West to be defended against a very real threat which the media, the press and some politicians are (naively or unscrupulously) playing down is, quite naturally, markedly reduced.

Opportunities are created for the increased prosecution of an *under the table* attack by subversion and black propaganda and disinformation, constantly engineered against the West by the KGB.

This also creates confusion in the West when considered against the massive Soviet military R. & D. and production effort. Those in the West who are aware of this effort and who are not so dishonest that they bury their heads in the sand, proclaim the need for some sort of similar expenditure to sustain, at least, some degree of military equilibrium. But this view tends to be seen by a bemused Western public quite unnecessarily to prevent the orderly march towards the verdant uplands; with the possibility of an even higher standard of living frequently proclaimed so loudly as imminent, by naive and foolish visionaries, and even more by those who are dedicated to disruption.

Whilst to an extent mutual disarmament would be of immense advantage to the peoples of East and West this is a truth far from evident to the great mass of the Soviet people. Their standard of life is artificially debased to maintain a level which will permit the Kremlin to continue the vast military programme. Public aspirations towards any credible alternative are forcibly and ruthlessly suppressed; whilst memories of the 1941–1945 *Great Patriotic War* are still kept vividly in the public mind by the well controlled press.

To sum up. Any further military imbalance between East and West will destroy the present very tenuous sense of equilibrium and will create a political disequilibrium utterly inimical to the West.

The present societal repression in Eastern Europe, which the Soviet Union will continue to exert, will permit the enhancement of this military imbalance with a rising danger to the future for the West.

Linchpin of NATO

There can be little doubt in anyone's mind that the United Kingdom is the linchpin of NATO. This is partially as a result of our performance in 1940; of our maritime tradition; of our unique change in 1949 to a continental strategy; to Mr. Attlee and Ernest Bevin, for their nuclear policy; and to the carrying on of that nuclear deterrent by all governments since.

But the fact that Britain is the linchpin carries with it an enormous burden. Because we are the linchpin Britain is the main target for a vast subversive drive by the Soviets, to recruit agents of influence in positions of power. There is also in my view, little doubt that, in the unlikely event of hostilities, the swathe of airfields from Norfolk to Gloucestershire would be the target for the Spetznaz Brigades and many of the eight Soviet airborne divisions. The destruction or capture of these airfields would, at the very least, effectively emasculate the military reinforcement potential of NATO and thus destroy the Alliance as a credible entity.

I accept that many people are unaware of the facts that I have tried to set out; that the facts themselves are immensely difficult to enunciate understandably, and also that the background of Soviet repression, far worse than anything the Nazis ever created, is quite unbelievable to most ordinary peaceloving and freedom accustomed folk in our island. You have probably read Hearnshaw's *Survey of Socialism* giving the breakdown from bishops to peasants of the two million of Lenin's first efforts at *mass murder*, before the subsequent vast abridgement of the population which followed from famine. You will I am sure have immersed yourself in Solzhenitsyn, and thus know what goes on today in the Gulag.

Being a Socialist you must be well aware that true Socialism is but a temporary stopping place on the road to that form of Communism known as Democratic Centralism. You must also be well aware of the history of the Bolshevik Revolution. You will know of Kerensky's valiant efforts, with General Kornilov and the dynamic Savinkov, together with the moderate Russian Social Democratic Labour Party, in a courageous Duma, with a large anti-Bolshevik majority, to introduce liberal policies after the Czar's abdication. And you will know how the German attacks from outside broke the front and the subversion by V.I. Ulianov (alias Lenin), from inside, blew up the rear. And you will know also, I expect, how thanks to Lenin and Trotsky, and All Russian Democratic Congress and the All Russian Congress of the Soviets, still talking; still protesting, still with a substantial majority in the Duma, were brushed into the wilderness. So the old Russian Social Democratic Labour Party became the *Russian Communist Party* and then, as we have it today, the *Communist Party of the Soviet Union.*

AN INDICTMENT OF THE MAASTRICHT TREATY

As with many other people the idiocies of the Maastricht Treaty and the dictates of M. Delors (as I understood them) had been, for some months generating a head of steam I found it difficult to contain.

A comment by our local butcher that the local abattoir, under EC orders, now had to employ a vet to be in attendance for most of 21 days in each month at an hourly cost of £46, and the bright lights of the French fishing fleet as they caught our cod off the north coast of Cornwall, while our own boats were made to stay in harbour, finally caused my safety valves to lift.

After the 1992 Election in which the Conservative Party was returned with a remarkable proportion of the vote but with a majority of only 21, I became increasingly disturbed at the implications for the United Kingdom of the Maastricht treaty. This worry was accentuated by the impossibility of obtaining a copy due to the Government's apparent refusal to distribute any information on a matter so fraught with problems for all of us I finally overcame this by joining the Bruges Group of 'Euro-sceptics' and was thus enabled to purchase an authorised copy. Second only to this worry was the 'Options for Change' exercise, apparently reducing our defence capability in an age of increasing discord, because of a lack of funds deriving from political incompetence equalled only by that being currently displayed in our negotiations with China over Hong Kong.

Reading the Maastricht Treaty it seemed to confirm my worst fears and these were accentuated by the Government's emphasis on 'Party Unity' as opposed to our nation's interest, and its refusal of a referendum on what must be the most momentous change in the ordering of our national life since 1066; while attempting to force the ratification through Parliament by heavy handed if not wholly improper 'whipping procedures'.

I concede that nearly half a century in the Royal Navy, two years working amongst the then just freed Nations of Western Europe, three years in the USA and five years as Director General of Intelligence at the MOD has fortified my inclination to look outwards to the rest of the world. There lie (in my view) the greatest markets of the future despite the present appalling poverty of most of them. I was brought up, as were all my generation, to believe that the insertion of the adjective 'Great' before Britain was accomplished by our ability to import raw materials, to manufacture them by our own energy sources into goods which could be sold abroad, and to export such goods in our own well built merchant ships protected from piracy (once more today on the increase) by the Royal Navy. I am, in fact like so many others, one of Mr Waldegrave's 'flat-earthers', and proud of it

Now the emphasis is on 'service' industries, transport, retail, advertising, nursing, teaching, financial management, delivery, whereby more and more brain power leads inevitably to greater productivity and longer individual product life of those consumer durables to be exported (we are told) mainly to European customers, whose similar 'service' industries are already incestuously competing with each other in an increasingly sated market. As a result there will be general and accelerating unemployment and, even discounting the immigration into Western Europe from less prosperous countries, the breakdown of moral cohesion in British and European society.

It was Hitler's aim to turn the continent, including the UK, into one single economic system consistent with political and economic servitude to Germany. That seems to be the future for the European Community. And it is impossible to live in any part of the UK without daily meeting new restrictions (at present emanating from Brussels rather than Berlin) which are rigidly enforced by petty officials who, in the conquered countries in World War II, would probably have been dubbed as German collaborators.

The letter that follows therefore went to the Prime Minister, the Chairman of the Conservative Party and the Chief Whip.

A LETTER TO PRIME MINISTER JOHN MAJOR. March 1993.

Vice Admiral Sir Louis Le Bailly, K.B.E., C.B., O.B.E., D.L.F.I.Mech. E., M.I.Mar.E., F.Inst.Pet.

Garlands House,
St Tudy,
Bodmin,
Cornwall.PL30 3NN.

The Rt . Hon. John Major MP,
Prime Minister

I have long been a Conservative supporter and voted for you at the last election and I think it was due mainly to my wife that many others down here did so also. Nevertheless Mr Tyler (Lib-Dem) took over from Gerry Neale and more and more this is the trend in North Cornwall. I fear your Chancellor's budget has done nothing for those who are fighting their way up but still have a long way to go. Motor car salesmen still seem able to go to the Seychelles or Kenya for their holidays. But the owners of 'old bangers' liable to expensive annual MOTs, who cannot afford new cars but must have 'wheels' to get to work, are heavily penalised by the petrol and excise tax.

Patience is Needed

It has always seemed to me, who with my wife endured the last war in the Royal Navy, that the EEC, a free trade area, developing perhaps into some sort of co-operative entity consisting of countries with widely different traditions, constitutions and language but, over many perhaps 50–100 years, learning to work together, was a worthwhile aim conducive to peace. A peace which twice in my lifetime has been destroyed by German aggrandisement. Patience is what the West lacks today. Egged on by 'groups' and self-seekers (such as Delors) and the USA there is always a striving for 'quick fixes'. You must carry the nation with you; and we do not move fast.

May I remind you of the old saying:

> Faced with the Gordian knot,
> Cut it if you dare,
> Undo it, if you can,
> If you can do neither don't despair
> The rope will rot.

Past History and Lack of Government Information

I spent 1946–48 chairing an International Committee establishing common specifications and nomenclature for petroleum fuels, lubricants and greases for what is now NATO. So I am by no means averse to bringing Europe together and even in this relatively minor project, covering only France, Belgium, Holland, Denmark, Norway, Luxembourg, Italy, USA and Canada (but not of course at that time Germany) I vividly experienced the problems of language and usage in even such a comparatively small international negotiation, especially with the French and Belgians.

After you had negotiated the Maastricht Treaty I fear the Government committed a fundamental error in not acquainting the British Public with what it meant over and beyond the bounds set by the Single European Act, about which most are singularly ignorant anyway, and the Treaty of Rome. It took me several months to acquire a copy of Maastricht and certainly not a single sponsored Government publication about the Treaty has ever found its way to this area. There was a general wish (now greatly reduced, largely due to M. Delors' attitude) to tie Britain, albeit loosely and *slowly* into some sort of European organisation which, optimists believed, would gradually obviate the risk of the several appalling wars Germany has forced on our Continent in the last 115 years. That one can understand.

Available Options

Your rhetoric has now brought matters to a head and I see only the following options facing our Nation:

(1) To ratify the Treaty of Maastricht and to accept the complete destruction of our native Parliamentary institutions and the marginalising or destruction of the vital third constitutional leg, namely the Crown; while submitting ourselves to a nine Nation legislature, whose representatives belong to countries which have reached depths of corruption that we have

not yet plumbed; have a recent history of dictatorship (Germany and Italy, Portugal, Spain and Greece) or revolution (Germany, France, Italy, Spain, Portugal and Greece). And dictatorship or revolution in all these countries are both still too near the surface for our safety. In the face of all this your Government seems set on lumbering us with an international Parliament where we have but 16% of the voting power against the 84% held by these historically unstable Nations.

(2) As we are nearer Washington DC than Hawaii and many of the other states of the Union, another option would be to negotiate our way back into the nation (the USA) which sprang from our loins and accept more or less the same penalties, albeit with a more reasonable and agreeable and less centralised and bureaucratically controlled substitute Constitution than that implicit in (1) above.

(3) The third option is to see ourselves as we really are. A small island state on the ocean flank of Europe which has shed its Empire with the very minimum of residual colonial hostility, which has stood against tyranny when others succumbed, which still enjoys a legacy (perhaps a reducing legacy) of worldwide respect for its democractic institutions, for its skilled diplomacy and for the conduct and effectiveness of its armed forces and for the concept of Commonwealth. An island whose survival as an independent community still ultimately depends on the import of raw materials, their manufacture into saleable goods and the export of such goods, but whose survival as an independent community would be in the greatest peril if we accepted either Options (1) or (2).

The Thatcher Years

There is much talk (put about by the Opposition parties and even perhaps some of your adherents) of the damage done by the Thatcher years. I would not agree and would assert that the net credit side of the policies pursued between 1979 and 1991 outweighed the many mistakes that were (certainly and inevitably) made. I think history will show that she and her government, but primarily Mrs Thatcher herself, placed a barrier across the slope down which, like the Gadarene Swine, our nation was heading. But a barrier has to be strong and its artificers skilled if it is to be kept in repair. Not surprisingly the initial structure she was building needed continuous shoring up. Instead, through incompetent economic policies and our entry into the ERM, which I believe you master-minded, it has been breached and so the path to the cliff edge is once more open. Furthermore the destruction of our manufacturing industries and their total (rather than partial and minimal) displacement by service industries, an overall economic policy driven forward over the years by successive Conservative governments always more prone to the unhealthy influence of the City of London than the Labour Party (who too have erred in this respect), has added further pressure on Mrs Thatcher's barrier, now in danger of complete collapse.

Thoughts on the Three Options

Under Policy Option (1) above, as I read it the Maastricht Treaty will:
(a) Usurp our Law enacted in 1932 that no British Parliament may bind its successors. The Treaty omits any mechanism for such secession. Rather it provides unlimited fines by the European Court for non-compliance and includes a Clause that the Treaty is concluded for an UNLIMITED PERIOD.
(b) The Treaty authorises an external and unelected power (the Commission) to impose personal taxation which may even be retrospective.
(c) The Treaty permits nationals or other EEC countries to stand in municipal elections in defiance of the 1700 Act of Settlement precluding all such candidates unless they are native or naturalised citizens.
(d) By a majority vote (which thus leaves NO power of veto by the UK) the Treaty authorises the calling up of citizens of the UK for service in the armed forces of the EU, again in defiance of the Act of Settlement which ensured that no such law could be enforced without the specific consent of the British Parliament.
(e) Ratification of the Treaty would put HM The Queen in breach of her Coronation Oath (and therefore the Coronation Oath Act passed by Parliament in 1953) which binds her to her oath for her entire reign.

The Coronation Oath

Like all other MPs you have sworn to *be faithful and bear true allegiance* to Her present Majesty. I find it difficult to conceive, how in all honour, you can ask your Party to support a Treaty which puts her in clear breach of her Coronation Oath. At the very best you are stretching the words *faithful* and *true allegiance* to their ultimate, and (I would hold) well beyond the limit of their usually understood meaning.

Germany

Germany is in a bad way now but always shows (as she did after Weimar) an astonishing ability quickly to revive, as those of us saw the state of the country in the late Forties are well aware. May I remind you of a letter from Leo Amery to General Smuts in the Forties, he wrote: 'I think we make a great mistake if we underrate the attractiveness of Hitler's 'New Order' for most of Europe. The conception of Europe as a single economic system does offer a great deal, even if these advantages have to be paid for by a measure of economic as well as political servitude to Germany.' I would say *plus ça change, plus c'est la même chose.*

Impact of the Brussels Bureaucracy

The idiosyncracies which daily occur as the Brussels bureaucracy imposes its will have led to a calamitous distaste for Tory rule. These idiosyncracies are joyfully emulated and inflicted on our citizens by your administration. As an example we in North Cornwall, nightly, are able to see the lights of the French fishing fleet just off our shores while our boats under a Gummer/Curry MAFF diktat have to remain in harbour. If this already too long letter was not to become longer I could list the unnecessary impositions on our farmers and retailers which is resulting in a complete collapse of the Tory vote. The other two Parties are even worse; but this is not generally understood. To those who know a little of the facts, your socialist and liberal-democratic parliamentary colleagues have long sought a Socialist International and if the Treaty is ratified it seems to me they will have it. To revert to Mrs Thatcher's barrier, it will no longer be there and I fear you and (in several respects) your remarkably lack lustre cabinet will be held to blame. The word 'Betrayal' is now quite often heard in this, what once was, 'Toryland'.

Option 2. Union with the United States

Option 2 above has never been studied, though often spoken of. When that great US Ambassador David Bruce said at a Pilgrim's Dinner, 'The human and material resources of the United States, Great Britain, the old Commonwealth countries of Canada, Australia and New Zealand constitute the supreme power block in history. Other combinations, may outnumber us, but none approach us in faithfulness in international conduct, in sincere devotion to peace through justice, in excellence in those attributes that distinguish civilisation from barbarism,' he was surely stating a truth on which Britain and the USA, as a last resort, might well wish to build.

Option 3. The Source of National Wealth. Labour, Not Capital Intensive Industries.

So that leaves Option 3. We have to accept that the City of London only reached its peak of international acclaim not through its well lubricated consumption of alcohol or the activities of the Freemasons (from which the Lord Mayor is always drawn) but through the sweat of the British labourer in manufacturing industry (I include farming and fishing) which produced the exports in which the City traded and profited. We also have to accept (and the City, like Parliament, with few if any qualified engineers will find it hard to do so) that *capital intensive* technology, much of it still in its infancy or the early development stage applied to the service industries, and the consequential abandonment of more *labour intensive* manufacturing has landed us (and many other like minded countries with equally stupid policies) into accelerating unemployment. The scientist's dreams which so often hypnotize politicians have too often been accepted in lieu of the views of more down to earth engineers (of which there are few left in Parliament now Nick Ridley has left us) whose mission, so well expressed in the Charter of the Institution of Civil Engineers, reads as follows: 'To direct the great services of power in nature for the use and convenience of man.' Unhappily 'the convenience of man' is not always what the scientist in his search for knowledge comprehends. So politicians and governments, ignorant of what technology can do or just might do given good luck, are misled by the scientists into assuming instant success; and unemployment on the scale in this country and in the rest of Europe, which you are so set on joining, is the clear result. In the words of the old proverb, 'We have fallen into a well through gazing at the stars.'

The Abrogation of our Historic Maritime Heritage

To give some examples. It was our nineteenth century built shipyards which helped to win the Battle of the Atlantic in two world wars and by their post World War II efforts restored much of the world's tonnage. But the sophisticated developments by which ships can now be built more economically, born of great engineering endeavour but unsuited to slipways on the river banks of the Clyde, Tyne and Tees, could never be put into practice in the UK because, in the following years the money needed completely to revamp the industry was squandered on *even* more advanced technology, such as the (largely useless) Concorde. Shipbuilding, even with new technology a fairly labour intensive industry, was discarded and deemed a 'Third world activity,' just hammering iron! Three facts confirm the price of forgetting our maritime heritage: poorly built and badly engined third world built tankers are wearing out too quickly and either disappearing altogether or needlessly breaking down and polluting our shores; 270 new super-tankers are needed in the next 5 years, of 115 cruise liners recently listed in the newspapers only 2 were built in Britain, and our shipbuilding industry, still essentially labour intensive, under financially stingy Conservative and (later) Labour policies, has disappeared. I blame Macmillan who wrenched sponsorship of the industry from the Admiralty who had for so long and so successfully looked after it. It was he as Chancellor, despite his experience as an MP for Stockton on Tees, who denied the funds to fulfill the potential of the new maritime engineering college at Plymouth, conceived under a Labour Government not only for Naval improvement but to bring a new look to our great shipbuilding, shipping and fishing industries. It is true that Macmillan approved the naval establishment element of the great project. And the triumphant success of his act was demonstrated in the Falklands, where our Fleet kept the seas in action for 120 days as opposed to the 8 days in 30 capability the Royal Navy offered Admiral Chester Nimitz USN in the Battle of the Pacific. But an Establishment whose potential for the enhancement of our shipbuilding industry, our merchant marine, our fishing industry and the harvesting of the sea and sea bed was, by his action and a lack of Treasury vision, denied the Nation. Now that that potential is once more being fostered by a bonding with Plymouth University, it is a Conservative Government that is yet again failing to understand the relationship of naval maritime technology on those once profitable industries, by threatening, on bogus but specious arguments, to break the bond with Plymouth University, by removing the Establishment to the RMCS at Shrivenham or some other university while, at the same time, putting back some 70 years those relationships between naval deck and engineer officers fostered by Manadon, that contributed so much to the Falklands success.

The Destruction of our Coal Industry

It is even more depressing when the problems of the coal industry are addressed. I do not for one moment condone the Scargill agitation. But like many others of my generation I have seen Yorkshire, Northumberland, Durham and Derbyshire miners in battle and no more patriotic men can be found to lead if only there is good leadership and if only the facts are carefully explained to them. There has been a lack of leadership by management in the coal industry. This has shown signs of great improvement lately just as your policies are closing our one source of national energy *for ever*, unless new pits are dug again. You forget that the 'few' who won the Battle of Britain had Spitfires fuelled with high octane petrol made from coal and that Germany fought the war on oil from coal.

Nuclear Proliferation. Future Scarcity of Oil

You are aware that several countries in the Middle East either have or soon will have the atom bomb. I told the JIC 20 years ago that the Law of Colonial Ingratitude would soon start to operate in the Soviet Union and its satellite Empire and that we should enter an age of discord and conflict; and that Islamic Fundamentalism would spread from Pakistan to Morocco and in doing so our petroleum energy sources would either be destroyed or curtailed or grossly up-priced. North Sea Oil supplies will last a few years yet and gas even longer, though its main use should be as a feedstock for fertilisers rather than uneconomic production of electricity. But in this age of discord, where a rising sea level, wind and weather, sabotage or accident, are all certainties likely to interfere with the residual supplies, oil from this source cannot be relied on. Yet you have closed some coal pits for ever. Gasification of coal or coal into oil have never had the millions spent on research that they should have and when the supply of oil from overseas ceases partially or altogether, we shall be so short of energy that farmers (for instance), who use 10 Joules (units of fossil fuel energy) for every Joule of edible energy they produce, will have to have more labour on the land from which (it is said) 10,000 a year are leaving to join your dole queues, despite the land Gummer is 'putting aside'.

No Overall Security Strategy. 'Party' Instead of 'National' Loyalty

As Corelli Barnett wrote recently we appear to have no overall strategy or vision for the future. If you have, then presumably electoral considerations prevent you from publicising them. 'Charters' have become laughing stocks. Incidentally by stressing 'Party Loyalty' as Fowler and others do and as the other two Parties do, you are grossly underestimating the loyalty to our COUNTRY (regardless of Party) held not only by the native born but even by many of the polyglot population who now inhabit it.

Longer Life Consumer Durables and Population Explosion Argues for a World Market Rather Than an Incestuous European Strategy

This letter started as an indictment of your Maastricht Treaty. Cars, washing machines, consumer durables are becoming MORE durable as good engineering has given them longer life and therefore less need of replacement. So the market in an already sated Europe will soon diminish. By looking predominantly to Europe Parliament is showing a lack of vision and it is a tragedy that will hit our children and grandchildren that the Conservative Party also is hypnotised by this false Utopia. It is the wide world where the markets are increasing at the rate of 200 people per *minute* needing to be fed, and some of these with access to the media have hopes and desires that are virtually limitless. There is our destiny. Somehow we must inspire them, as we once so well did, into ways of feeding themselves. And somehow we have to help modestly to fulfil at least some of their aspirations. Only by this sort of strategy, if your clever but unimaginative 'Think-Tanks' could for a while lift their eyes from Europe, could the UK begin to achieve fuller employment. I do not advocate a return to a trading *Empire*. But sometimes I wonder if Her Majesty (and David Bruce in part, already quoted) are the only people to recognise the true potential of today's Commonwealth, if it could only consummate the sum of goodwill which exists. Why is it, one has to ask, that France can send *médecins du monde* or *médecins sans frontières* to the death spots of the world? Why is it that we so little support the thousands of young, able and willing to help the starving multitudes, rather than waste their time in stolen car racing or hooliganism? Only the few who somehow can raise their £2000 seem to have the chance which the majority so often crave.

The Need for Wider Vision and Stronger Leadership

In the face of the profound changes and vexations so apparently intractable, a lesser breed might well have disintegrated or lost the will to survive proudly. But our people have an indomitable physical and moral strength, a hard, stubborn strain of realism, untouched by defeatism, a genius for innovation, an adaptability to emergencies – but they have to be led on a path they recognise and understand – or they will dig in their toes. Today I fear there is a lack of leadership in any recognisable direction except Europe and the growing distrust of that goal, which I share, is daily becoming more apparent. Our people are the travellers and the traders. We are literally the neighbours of every country accessible by sea. You must look well beyond Europe rather than ape the incestuous policies of France and Germany, if you really wish to sustain our Constitution and the authority of Parliament, to restore UK employment and our Nation's moral cohesion.

EPILOGUE

EPILOGUE, MAY 1993

Most people in my generation remember exactly where they were when they heard of the Japanese attack on Pearl Harbour. What was not apparent to most of us was that by this action Japan not only brought about a declaration of war, but also electrified the whole psychology of the American Nation; and created a unity of outrage and purpose in the wider field of international conflict which continues to this day.

In fact Japan broke America loose from its own history and Jeffersonian tradition of isolation from Europe which had driven the early settlers westwards across the Atlantic away from revolutions, conflicts and starvation. Pearl Harbour was the start of half a century of American global engagement against the threat of Nazi fascism in a Hot War, and Soviet communism in a Hot War in Vietnam and a Cold War world wide. But whether this philosophy will continue is a matter for great concern. In the recent Presidential race one candidate, speaking without doubt for many of his fellow citizens said:

> We cannot forever defend wealthy nations that refuse to defend themselves; we cannot permit endless transfusions of the life-blood of American capitalism into the mendicant countries and economic corpses of socialism without bleeding to death.

Congress predominantly occupied with 'pork barrel' politics and isolationist by inclination, has recently turned down Secretary Baker's request to increase the US contribution to the United Nations.

Since this Anthology started to be brought together the world has changed and it may change again before publication. Nazism has (almost) disappeared and, it may just be, communism too (as the US Ambassador recently put it) 'in it's own spiritual gangrene'. Though I rather doubt it. Now we have to ask ourselves where does this leave the world? What has been called the PAX BALLISTICA, that era when the two great super-powers faced each other in a balance of terror called *Mutual Assured Destruction* has now ended. Will it bring peace? Fifty years from Pearl Harbour to Minsk. China on the verge of an industrial revolution which will multiply atmospheric pollution a hundredfold. What next for our own UK and indeed for the whole world? If after five decades the now single super-power across the Atlantic divests itself of its world role where shall we all end up?

As I see it there are certain priorities which the British Government must set out to achieve and certain actions which they would do well to reverse.

Unemployment will never be solved unless the country reverts in some degree to its older and more labour intensive manufacturing industries. Amongst them I would regard as especially important shipbuilding and shipping. As I wrote in my letter to the Prime Minister, of the 115 Cruise Liners now plying their trade only 2 were built in Britain and, in the next five years, something like 300 super-tankers have got to be built somewhere. Why not in the UK?

Our UK coal reserves are immense, the world oil reserves much less so and it is a waste of gas to turn it into electricity. Gas is more useful as feedstock for all the chemicals and fertilisers which will be needed to feed the world population expanding at the rate of 200 per minute. To 'Care and Maintenance' some of our coal mines might perhaps be justifiable. To fill them in so that they will have to be dug again is not. The Battle of Britain was won on high octane petrol derived from our coal; Germany fought the war on oil from coal and South Africa has partially existed on this process during Apartheid. As with shipbuilding a more enlightened energy policy would help greatly towards solving the unemployment problem.

The oceans and the ocean bed have to be developed and harvested if chronic worldwide starvation is to be in any way reduced. The current neglect of our once thriving fishing industry is on a par in terms of idiocy with our energy policy. Has no one in the Government heard of Fish Protein Concentrate (FPC) which did so much to keep starvation at bay in the Soviet Union in the last few years?

Maastricht has been a mess; and by the time this Anthology is published the Treaty will either have been ratified or not. I hope not. The dreams of a Federal Europe are rightly dead. The fact is that technology has got out of control. Well meaning scientists and so called liberally educated administrators are largely responsible. In his recent book *The Essential Anatomy of Britain* Anthony Sampson has updated Professor Freddie Garner's great Redwood Lecture in 1951 on 'The Training of a Technologist' when the former writes:

> It is hard to resist the fundamental social explanation of the failures of British engineers: they are the victims of a class rift running through the educational system with a deep bias against practical skills; which in turn leads into a wider rift between politicians and administrators on one side, and engineers and technologists on the other . . . And the cost of the rift is revealed in the lack of vision and planning for the future, compared to the bold projects of the continent

Whether the present chaos in our educational system, often caused by teachers out of touch with Sampson and Garner's fundamental truths so well expressed in the Charter of the Institution of Civil Engineers (The engineer's task is to 'direct the great services of power in nature for the use and convenience of Man') will ever be resolved in time for our Nation to recover, is anyone's guess. Signs are not hopeful. We seem anxious to emulate the Gadarene Swine.

Whether the great super-power confrontation is over or not it is difficult to determine. By the time this Anthology is published Yeltsin may or may not be in power. If he is then just possibly some order may evolve in the present chaos of the recent Soviet Empire. If he is unseated that chaos will be worse and, in either case, the danger from nuclear weapons stolen by or sold to Third World Countries, will be acute.

Due to British Treasury and political incompetence the UK is once more on the financial rocks. And once more it is those thrown on the unemployment scrap heap and the Armed Services who suffer most. I have spent my life in the Royal Navy so I presume only to comment on what is happening to it. Twice in my lifetime the Germans have built fine fleets. But they missed the essential lessons of seapower. As Paul McGuire has written:

> Admiralty is the understanding of the uses of seapower. It must be fed from the blood and marrow of a people accustomed to the sea; . . . it is shaped by skill and wisdom enduring and enlarged from generation of seamen and statesmen who understand the sea . . .

> A navy cannot be created on the occasion of crisis. A navy cannot
> be improvised. It must have continuity. The young hands learn
> from the old hands in the active practice of their arts.

There seems to be no British statesmen today who understand the broad
needs of seapower. The Navy has been brought to its lowest ebb since the
Treaty of Amiens 190 years ago. And unhappily this is just at the moment
when the oceans, holding the only answer to the world's future, will
certainly become areas of conflict. Sadly too, the Navy Board who,
through their active life have enjoyed unprecedented standards of ship
availability and weapon effectiveness, (inherited from the wise decisions
of their Fisher trained war experienced predecessors who embraced new
technology and created a naval technological university to train all naval
officers in its mysteries), have failed to persuade their political masters
that it was those decisions taken just 25 years before the battle which
ultimately assured victory in the Falklands; and which therefore should on
no account be abrogated. It is ironic (or worse) that just when the Government is talking of the value and importance of directed and disciplined
education it should insist on the closure of the Royal Naval Engineering
College, the one engineering institution which many leaders of industry
and academe hold to be probably the country's finest exemplar.

Hope is a virtue. Despair a sin. *Peccavi*. But it's all been great fun!